ORDERED TOPOLOGICAL
VECTOR SPACES

Harper's Series in Modern Mathematics

I. N. Herstein and Gian-Carlo Rota,
Editors

Ordered

Topological

Vector

Spaces

Anthony L. Peressini

Department of Mathematics
University of Illinois

Harper & Row

Publishers
New York, Evanston, and London

Ordered Topological Vector Spaces

Library of Congress Catalog Card Number: 67-12554

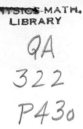
To My Wife

Contents

Preface

This book has evolved from mimeographed lecture notes prepared by the author for use in seminars conducted at the University of Illinois. These lectures were attended by some of my colleagues on the faculty and also by a number of graduate students who had just completed an introductory course in functional analysis. In order to make these seminars as useful as possible for the latter group, the lectures were presented at a rather pedestrian pace with more attention being given to technical details and to the discussion of examples than would be customary in seminars attended exclusively by individuals with some research experience in functional analysis. Since this detailed style of presentation seemed to be well received by the students and since the relaxed pace did not seem to evoke any serious objections from the faculty members in attendance, I decided to retain these features in the manuscript that I prepared for publication. For this reason, this book should be quite accessible to any student who is acquainted with the basic theory of topological vector spaces. For example, a one-semester introductory course in functional analysis based on portions of texts such as Kelley-Namioka [1], Robertson and Robertson [1], or Schaefer [1] should provide a suitable background for a prospective reader.

No attempt has been made to present an encyclopedic account of the subject of ordered topological vector spaces in this book; the choice of topics considered was dictated by the author's own interests in the field. Nevertheless, the reader of this book should become sufficiently familiar with the basic techniques in this area to enable him to read papers in the literature that deal with aspects of the subject not covered here. Suggestions for further related reading have been included at the end of most sections of each chapter.

I wish to express my gratitude to the many students and colleagues who provided critical remarks and encouragement during the preparation of this text. In particular, I benefited much from the many suggestions and comments of Professor Helmut H. Schaefer, whose beautiful lectures first awakened my interest in functional analysis and in the subject matter of this book. I am also very grateful to Professor Donald R. Sherbert for his critical reading of the manuscript, to Professor Eliot C. Weinberg for several very informative discussions, and to the staff of Harper & Row for their assistance. Finally, I wish to thank my wife, to whom this book is dedicated, for her competent typing of the manuscript and for her patience, understanding, and encouragement during the entire project.

ANTHONY L. PERESSINI

Urbana, Illinois
February 1, 1967

ORDERED TOPOLOGICAL
VECTOR SPACES

Chapter One

Ordered Vector Spaces

A real vector space equipped with an order structure that is "compatible" with its linear structure is called an ordered vector space. The present chapter is devoted to a study of the interplay of these two structures with particular emphasis on the algebraic properties of vector spaces endowed with a lattice order, that is, vector lattices. Since most of the concrete ordered vector spaces that arise in analysis have one or more natural topological structures that must be considered, the basic objective of this chapter is to set the stage for the study of ordered topological vector spaces that will be undertaken in the succeeding chapters.

The basic definitions and lattice theoretic formulae are collected at the beginning of the first section. In particular, it is shown that the

1

order relation is completely determined by certain geometric properties of the set of non-negative elements referred to as the cone in the ordered vector space. This material is followed by a discussion of a number of examples that will be used to illustrate and motivate the subsequent theory. Section 2 begins a study of some of the classes of linear mappings and linear functionals that arise in a natural way when the underlying vector space is ordered. The collection of all positive linear mappings, that is, linear mappings that leave the cone of the ordered vector space invariant, and the related class of order bounded linear mappings are studied in some detail.

Ordered vector spaces in which the cone has a base play a significant role in the uniqueness theory for Choquet integral representations and the spectral theory of positive operators. The investigation of the algebraic properties of cones with bases is carried out in Section 3 and culminates in the Choquet-Kendall theorem characterizing the bases corresponding to lattice structures as linearly compact simplexes. Topological aspects of the theory of cones with bases will be discussed in Section 4 of Chapter 4.

In Section 4, we consider the basic properties of lattice ideals and bands in a vector lattice; the principal result of this section is the theorem of Riesz on band decompositions in order complete vector lattices. The final section of the chapter studies two types of convergence determined by the order structure of a vector lattice, as well as the corresponding notions of "continuity" for linear mappings determined by these convergence concepts. The connection between these modes of order convergence and topological convergence will be established in Section 2 of Chapter 4.

§1. BASIC DEFINITIONS AND LATTICE-THEORETIC FORMULAE; EXAMPLES

Throughout the following exposition, we shall restrict our attention to vector spaces over the real field R.

An **ordered vector space** is a real vector space E equipped with a transitive, reflexive, antisymmetric relation $\leq$ satisfying the following conditions:

(O$_1$) If x, y, z are elements of E and $x \leq y$, then $x + z \leq y + z$.

(O$_2$) If x, y are elements of E and α is a positive real number, then $x \leq y$ implies $\alpha x \leq \alpha y$.

The notation $y \geq x$ often will be used in place of $x \leq y$. If $x \leq y$ and $x \neq y$, we shall write $x < y$.

The **positive cone** (or simply the **cone**) K in an ordered vector space E is defined by $K = \{x \in E : x \geq \theta\}$, where θ denotes the zero element in E. The cone K has the following " geometric " properties:

(C$_1$) $K + K \subset K$.

(C$_2$) $\alpha K \subset K$ for each positive real number α.

(C$_3$) $K \cap (-K) = \{\theta\}$.

In particular, it follows from (C$_1$) and (C$_2$) that K is a convex set in E. On the other hand, if K is a subset of a real vector space E satisfying (C$_1$), (C$_2$), and (C$_3$), then

$$x \leq y \quad \text{if } y - x \in K$$

defines an order relation $\leq$ on E with respect to which E is an ordered vector space with positive cone K. Thus, for a given real vector space E, there is a canonical one-to-one correspondence between the collection of order relations with properties (O$_1$) and (O$_2$) and the collection of all subsets of E with properties (C$_1$), (C$_2$), and (C$_3$). It is convenient to introduce a term to describe a subset of E containing θ and satisfying (C$_1$) and (C$_2$); we shall call such a set a **wedge**.

Suppose that E is an ordered vector space. If x, y are elements of E and $x \leq y$, then the set $[x, y] = \{z \in E : x \leq z \leq y\}$ is the **order interval between x and y**. A subset B of E is **order bounded** if there exist x, y in E such that $B \subset [x, y]$. A subset D of E is **majorized** (resp. **minorized**) if there is an element z in E such that $z \geq d$ (resp. $z \leq d$) for all $d \in D$. If every pair x, y of elements of a subset D is majorized (minorized) in D, then D is **directed** ($\leq$) [resp. **directed** ($\geq$)]. If D is a subset of E that is directed ($\leq$) [directed ($\geq$)] and $x \in D$, the set $S_x = \{y \in D : y \geq x\}$ [resp. $S_x = \{y \in D : y \leq x\}$] is the **section of D determined by x**. The class $\{S_x : x \in D\}$ is a filter base on E for a filter $\mathfrak{F}(D)$ called the **filter of sections of D**.

Suppose that K is the positive cone in an ordered vector space E. K **generates** E if E is the linear subspace spanned by K, that is, $E = K - K$. Observe that K generates E if and only if E is directed ($\leq$). An element $e \in E$ is an **order unit** if for each $x \in E$ there is an $\alpha > 0$ such that $x \leq \alpha e$. The positive cone K in E generates E if E contains an order unit. E is **almost Archimedean** if $-\alpha y \leq x \leq \alpha y$ for some $y \in K$, and all real numbers $\alpha > 0$ implies $x = \theta$. E is **Archimedean** if $x \leq \theta$ whenever $\alpha x \leq b$ for some $b \in K$ and all $\alpha > 0$. Clearly, every Archimedean ordered vector space is almost Archimedean.

If B is a subset of an ordered vector space E and if $x \in E$ has the following properties:

(a) $x \geq b$ for all $b \in B$,
(b) $z \geq x$ whenever $z \geq b$ for all $b \in B$,

then x is called the **supremum** of B and we write $x = \sup(B)$. The **infimum** of B, written $\inf(B)$, is defined dually, that is, by replacing $\geq$ by $\leq$ in (a) and (b). If the supremum $\sup\{x, y\} = x \vee y$ and the infimum $\inf\{x, y\} = x \wedge y$ of every pair $\{x, y\}$ of elements of E exist, then E is a **vector lattice**. Since $x \vee y = -\{(-x) \wedge (-y)\}$, E is a vector lattice if the supremum (or infimum) of every pair of elements of E exists. If E is a vector lattice and $x \in E$, we define

$$x^+ = \sup\{x, \theta\} \qquad x^- = (-x)^+ \qquad |x| = \sup\{x, -x\}.$$

x^+ and x^- are called the **positive part** and **negative part**, respectively, of the element x, while $|x|$ is referred to as the **absolute value** of x.

If E is a vector lattice, the following identities are direct consequences of (O_1) and (O_2):

$$z - (x \vee y) = (z - x) \wedge (z - y). \tag{1}$$

$$z + (x \vee y) = (z + x) \vee (z + y); \quad z + (x \wedge y) = (z + x) \wedge (z + y). \tag{2}$$

$$\alpha(x \vee y) = (\alpha x) \vee (\alpha y); \qquad \alpha(x \wedge y) = (\alpha x) \wedge (\alpha y) \tag{3}$$

for all positive real numbers α.

If we replace z by $x + y$ in (1), we obtain the identity

$$x + y = x \vee y + x \wedge y. \tag{4}$$

More generally,

$$x + y = x \vee z + y \wedge w \quad \text{whenever } x + y = z + w. \tag{5}$$

For if $x + y = z + w$, then $x \cup z + y \cap w = x \cup (x + y - w) + y \cap w = x + \{\theta \cup (y - w)\} + y \cap w = x + w \cup y - w + y \cap w = x - w + y + w = x + y$. In particular, if y is taken to be θ in (4), the following important decomposition results:

$$x = x^+ - x^-. \tag{6}$$

Since the elements x^+, x^- are obviously in the positive cone K of E, it follows from (6) that the cone in a vector lattice E always generates E. From the first identity in (3) we conclude that $|\alpha x| = |\alpha| \, |x|$ for all real numbers α, while the first identity in (2) implies that $x + |x| = (2x)^+ = 2x^+$. In view of (6), this in turn implies the following decomposition formula for the absolute value:

$$|x| = x^+ + x^-. \tag{7}$$

It is now clear that

$$x^+ = \tfrac{1}{2}(|x| + x); \qquad x^- = \tfrac{1}{2}(|x| - x). \tag{8}$$

The following assertions are easily verified:

$$x \le y \quad \text{if and only if } x^+ \le y^+ \ \text{ and } x^- \ge y^-. \tag{9}$$

$$|x| \le y \quad \text{if and only if } -y \le x \le y. \tag{10}$$

One immediate consequence of (10) is that every almost Archimedean vector lattice is Archimedean.

If x and y are elements of a vector lattice E, then x and y are **disjoint**, written $x \perp y$, if $|x| \cap |y| = \theta$. Equation (4) shows that

$$x \perp y \quad \text{if and only if } |x| \cup |y| = |x| + |y|. \tag{11}$$

Since $|x| \cup |y| = |x| + (|y| - |x|)^+ = |x| + \tfrac{1}{2}\{||y| - |x|| + |y| - |x|\} = \tfrac{1}{2}\{||y| - |x|| + |y| + |x|\}$ by (2) and (8), it follows from (11) that

$$x \perp y \quad \text{if and only if } ||y| - |x|| = |y| + |x|. \tag{12}$$

Note that (12), (7), and (6) imply that $x^+ \perp x^-$ for any element x in a vector lattice E. On the other hand, if $x = y - z$, where $y \ge \theta$, $z \ge \theta$, $y \perp z$, then $y + z = |y - z| = |x| = x^+ + x^-$ by (12) and (7); moreover, $y \ge x^+$ and $z \ge x^-$, since $y \ge x$ and $z \ge -x$. Therefore $y = x^+ + x^- - z \le x^+ + x^- - x^- = x^+$ and, similarly, $z \le x^-$, that is, $y = x^+$ and $z = x^-$. We conclude that $x = x^+ - x^-$ is the only decomposition of an element x in a vector lattice E as the difference of two disjoint elements of the cone in E.

1.1 Proposition. A vector lattice E is distributive, that is,

$$x \cup (y \cap z) = (x \cup y) \cap (x \cup z);$$
$$x \cap (y \cup z) = (x \cap y) \cup (x \cap z) \quad \text{for all } x, y, z \text{ in } E. \tag{13}$$

Proof. Since $x \cup (y \cap z) \leq (x \cup y) \cap (x \cup z)$, it follows that $\theta \leq \{(x \cup y) \cap (x \cup z)\} - \{x \cup (y \cap z)\} = (x \cup y) \cap (x \cup z) + \{(-x) \cap ((-y) \cup (-z))\} = \{[\theta \cap \{(x - y) \cup (x - z)\}] \cup [(y - x) \cap \{\theta \cup (y - z)\}]\} \cap \{[\theta \cap \{(x - y) \cup (x - z)\}] \cup [(z - x) \cap \{(z - y) \cup \theta\}]\} \leq ((y - z)^{+}) \cap ((z - y)^{+}) = \theta$. Hence, $x \cup (y \cap z) = (x \cup y) \cap (x \cup z)$. The second equation in (13) follows from the first since $(x \cap y) \cup (x \cap z) = [(x \cap y) \cup x] \cap [(x \cap y) \cup z] = x \cap \{(z \cup x) \cap (z \cup y)\} = \{x \cap (z \cup x)\} \cap \{z \cup y\} = x \cap \{y \cup z\}$.

A number of useful lattice theoretic inequalities are summarized in the following result.

1.2 Proposition. If x, y, z are elements of a vector lattice E, then:

$$|x + y| \leq |x| + |y|. \tag{14}$$
$$||x| - |y|| \leq |x - y|. \tag{15}$$
$$|(x \cup z) - (y \cup z)| \leq |x - y|. \tag{16}$$
$$|x^{+} - y^{+}| \leq |x - y|; \quad |x^{-} - y^{-}| \leq |x - y|. \tag{17}$$
$$(x + y)^{+} \leq x^{+} + y^{+}; \quad (x + y)^{-} \leq x^{-} + y^{-}. \tag{18}$$
$$(x + y) \cap z \leq x \cap z + y \cap z \text{ if } x, y, z \text{ are in the cone.} \tag{19}$$

Proof. Since $|x| \geq x$, $|x| \geq -x$ and $|y| \geq y$, $|y| \geq -y$, it follows that $|x| + |y| \geq x + y$ and $|x| + |y| \geq -(x + y)$, which implies (14). The relation $|x| = |(x - y) + y| \leq |x - y| + |y|$, together with symmetry, yield (15).

To prove (16), we first observe that $|s - t| = (s - t) \cup \theta - (s - t) \cap \theta = (s \cup t) - t - (s \cap t) + t = (s \cup t) - (s \cap t)$ for all s, t in E. Applying this identity to both sides of (16), we obtain

$$|(x \cup z) - (y \cup z)| = (x \cup z) \cup (y \cup z) - (x \cup z) \cap (y \cup z) = (x \cup y) \cup z$$
$$- (x \cap y) \cup z \quad \text{and} \quad |x - y| = x \cup y - x \cap y.$$

Therefore, it is sufficient to prove (16) under the additional hypothesis that $x \geq y$; otherwise x and y can be replaced by $x \cup y$ and $x \cap y$, respectively. In that case, choose $w \geq \theta$ so that $x = y + w$. Then $x \cup z = (y + w) \cup z = w + (y \cup (z - w)) \leq w + y \cup z$, hence, $x \cup z - y \cup z \leq w = x - y$. This completes the proof of (16).

The first inequality in (17) is obtained by setting $z = \theta$ in (16). The second inequality in (17) follows from the first since $x^- = (-x)^+$. (18) is an immediate consequence of (8) and (14).

Finally, if x, y, z are elements of the cone in E and $u = (x + y) \cap z$, then $u \leq x + y$ and $u \leq z \leq x + z$, since $x \geq \theta$. Therefore, $u \leq (x + y) \cap (x + z) = x + (y \cap z)$. On the other hand, $u \leq z + (y \cap z)$, since $y \cap z \geq \theta$. Hence,

$$u \leq (x + y \cap z) \cap (z + y \cap z) = x \cap z + y \cap z,$$

which completes the proof of the proposition.

1.3   Decomposition Lemma.   If $\{x_i : i = 1, 2, \ldots, n\}$ and $\{y_j : j = 1, \ldots, m\}$ are finite subsets of the positive cone K in a vector lattice E, and if

$$\sum_{i=1}^{n} x_i = \sum_{j=1}^{m} y_j,$$

then there exists a finite subset $\{z_{ij} : i = 1, \ldots, n; j = 1, \ldots, m\}$ of K such that

$$x_i = \sum_{j=1}^{m} z_{ij} \qquad i = 1, \ldots, n$$

$$y_j = \sum_{i=1}^{n} z_{ij} \qquad j = 1, \ldots, m.$$

Proof.   It is sufficient to prove the result for $m = n = 2$. Hence, suppose that $x_1 + x_2 = y_1 + y_2$ where $x_i \in K$, $y_i \in K$ $(i = 1, 2)$. Define $z_{11} = x_1 \cap y_1, z_{12} = x_1 - z_{11}, z_{21} = y_1 - z_{11}$, then z_{11}, z_{12}, z_{21} are in K. Moreover, $z_{12} \cap z_{21} = \theta$ and $z_{12} + x_2 = z_{21} + y_2$. Therefore, if we define $z_{22} = x_2 - z_{21} = y_2 - z_{12}$, it is only necessary to show that $z_{22} \in K$. But $z_{21} \leq z_{12} + x_2$ since $y_2 \in K$; hence,

$$z_{21} = z_{21} \cap (z_{12} + x_2) \leq z_{21} \cap z_{12} + z_{21} \cap x_2$$

by (19). Since $z_{12} \cap z_{21} = \theta$, it follows that $z_{21} \leq z_{21} \cap x_2$; that is, $z_{22} = x_2 - z_{21} \geq \theta$ which completes the proof.

1.4   Corollary.   If x, y, z are elements of a vector lattice E such that $\theta \leq z \leq x + y$, there exist x_1, y_1 in E such that $\theta \leq x_1 \leq x$, $\theta \leq y_1 \leq y$, $z = x_1 + y_1$.

The conclusion of (1.4) may be reformulated as follows:

$$[\theta, x] + [\theta, y] = [\theta, x + y] \quad \text{for all } x \geq \theta, y \geq \theta. \tag{D}$$

Thus, every vector lattice satisfies (D); however, as we shall see in our discussion of the examples at the end of this section, not every ordered vector space for which (D) holds is a vector lattice $\big(\text{see } (1.7)\big)$. In view of the fact that a number of significant results and constructions in the theory depend only on this property and not on the presence of a richer lattice structure, it seems worthwhile to emphasize this fact by referring to ordered vector spaces with property (D) as spaces with the **decomposition property**.

A subset B of an ordered vector space E is **order complete** if every directed ($\leq$) subset D of B that is majorized in E has a supremum that belongs to B. Of course, if B is a symmetric set (that is, if $-x \in B$ whenever $x \in B$), then B is an order complete subset of E if and only if every directed ($\geq$) subset D of B that is minorized in E has an infimum in B. In particular, if E itself is order complete, we say that E is an **order complete vector space**. Observe that an order complete vector space E is a vector lattice if and only if the cone in E is generating. An order complete vector space that is also a vector lattice is referred to as an **order complete vector lattice**. If D is a subset of a vector lattice E and D is majorized by an element z of E, the set D' of all suprema of finite subsets of D is directed ($\leq$) and majorized by z. Therefore, if E is an order complete vector lattice, and if B is a majorized (resp. minorized) subset of E, then $\sup(B)$ $\big(\text{resp. } \inf(B)\big)$ exists in E. A vector lattice is σ-**order complete** if the supremum of every countable majorized subset of E exists in E (or, equivalently, if the infimum of every countable minorized subset of E exists in E). It is an easy matter to verify that order complete vector spaces and σ-order complete vector lattices are always Archimedean.

If E is an ordered vector space with positive cone K and if M is a linear subspace of E, then M is an ordered vector space for the order determined by the cone $K \cap M$. If φ is the canonical map of E onto the quotient space E/M, then $\varphi(K)$ is a wedge in E/M; however, as we shall see in our discussion of the examples at the end of this section, $\varphi(K)$ is not necessarily a cone in E/M (see (1.7)).

If $\{E_\alpha : \alpha \in A\}$ is an arbitrary family of ordered vector spaces and K_α is the positive cone in E_α for each $\alpha \in A$, then the product space $\prod_{\alpha \in A} E_\alpha$ is an ordered vector space for the order generated by the cone $K = \prod_{\alpha \in A} K_\alpha$. Similarly, the direct sum $\bigoplus_{\alpha \in A} E_\alpha$† is an ordered vector space for the cone $K = \bigoplus_{\alpha \in A} K_\alpha$; in fact, the order structure determined by this cone is identical to that induced by $\prod_{\alpha \in A} E_\alpha$ on the linear subspace $\bigoplus_{\alpha \in A} E_\alpha$. These order structures on subspaces, quotients, products, and direct sums of ordered vector spaces will be referred to as the **canonical order structures**, and, unless a statement is made to the contrary, it will always be assumed that these spaces are ordered in this way. Observe that the decomposition property as well as the properties of being a vector lattice, σ-order complete vector lattice, and order complete vector lattice are preserved in the formation of products and direct sums.

The remainder of this section will be devoted to a detailed discussion of a number of examples of ordered vector spaces.

1.5 Example. Consider n-dimensional Euclidean space R^n equipped with the order structure determined by the cone $K = \{x = (x_k) \in R^n : x_k \geq 0 \text{ for } k = 1, \ldots, n\}$. Ordered in this way, R^n is precisely the product of n copies of the real line R in its usual order; hence, R^n is an order complete vector lattice. R^n contains order units; for example, $e = (1, 1, \ldots, 1)$ is an order unit in R^n.

The cones in R^n that generate vector lattice structures are characterized by the following result:

Proposition. R^n is a vector lattice with respect to the order generated by a cone K if and only if there are n linearly independent vectors

---

† Recall that the direct sum of a family $\{B_\alpha : \alpha \in A\}$ of sets is the subset B of $\prod_{\alpha \in A} B_\alpha$ consisting of those $x = (x_\alpha) \in \prod_{\alpha \in A} B_\alpha$ such that $x_\alpha = \theta$ for all $\alpha \in A$ outside some finite subset of A depending on x.

$v^{(k)}(k = 1, \ldots, n)$ such that

$$K = \left\{ x = (x_j) \in R^n : v^{(k)}(x) = \sum_{j=1}^n x_j v_j^{(k)} \geq 0; \quad k = 1, \ldots, n \right\}.$$

Though a direct proof could be given here, we prefer to derive this result as a simple consequence of the Choquet-Kendall Theorem in Section 3 of this chapter.

1.6 Example. The vector space ω of all sequences $x = (x_n)$ of real numbers ordered by the positive cone $K = \{x = (x_n) \in \omega : x_n \geq 0$ for all $n\}$ is an order complete vector lattice since it is the product of countably many copies of the real line R in its usual order. However, unlike R^n in the corresponding order, ω does not contain an order unit.

The linear subspace φ of ω consisting of the sequences $x = (x_n)$ such that $x_n = 0$ for all but a finite number of choices for n, is also an order complete vector lattice. This follows immediately from the fact that φ is the direct sum of countably many copies of the real line R in its usual order. φ does not contain order units.

A **sequence space** is a linear subspace λ of ω such that λ contains φ. The **Köthe dual** $\lambda^\times$ of a sequence space λ is defined as follows:

$$\lambda^\times = \left\{ u = (u_n) \in \omega : \sum_{n=1}^\infty |x_n u_n| < + \infty \quad \text{for all } x = (x_n) \in \lambda \right\}.$$

$\lambda^\times$ is a sequence space and $\lambda^{\times\times} = (\lambda^\times)^\times$ always contains λ. If $\lambda = \lambda^{\times\times}$, the sequence space λ is called **perfect**.

We shall now list a number of examples of sequence spaces together with their Köthe duals:

a. $\lambda = \omega, \lambda^\times = \varphi.$

b. $\lambda = \varphi, \lambda^\times = \omega.$

c. $\lambda = \ell^p = \left\{ x \in \omega : \sum_{n=1}^\infty |x_n|^p < + \infty \right\} (1 < p < +\infty),$

$\lambda^\times = \ell^q$ where $\dfrac{1}{p} + \dfrac{1}{q} = 1.$

d. $\lambda = \ell^1 = \left\{ x \in \omega : \sum_{n=1}^{\infty} |x_n| < +\infty \right\}$,

$\quad \lambda^{\times} = \ell^{\infty} = \left\{ x \in \omega : \sup_n \{|x_n|\} < +\infty \right\}$.

e. $\lambda = \ell^{\infty}, \lambda^{\times} = \ell^1$.

f. $\lambda = (c) = \left\{ x \in \omega : \lim_n x_n \text{ exists} \right\}, \lambda^{\times} = \ell^1$.

g. $\lambda = (c_0) = \left\{ x \in \omega : \lim_n x_n = 0 \right\}, \lambda^{\times} = \ell^1$.

h. $\lambda = \pi_{\infty} = \left\{ x \in \omega : \limsup \sqrt[n]{|x_n|} = 0 \right\}$,

$\quad \lambda^{\times} = \rho_0 = \left\{ x \in \omega : \limsup \sqrt[n]{|x_n|} < +\infty \right\}$,

i. $\lambda = \rho_0, \lambda^{\times} = \pi_{\infty}$.

j. $\lambda = \pi_r = \left\{ x \in \omega : \limsup \sqrt[n]{|x_n|} \le \frac{1}{r} \right\}$,

$\quad \lambda^{\times} = \rho_{1/r} = \left\{ x \in \omega : \limsup \sqrt[n]{|x_n|} < r \right\}$.

k. $\lambda = \rho_r (r > 0), \lambda^{\times} = \pi_{1/r}$.

See §30 in Köthe [1], Chapter 10 in Cooke [1], and Toeplitz [1] for verifications of the statements in the above list. In all cases, the proofs are rather straightforward. It is clear from the contents of this list that the study of sequence spaces and their Köthe duals provides a suitable framework for a systematic treatment of the standard Banach sequence spaces and their corresponding spaces of continuous linear functionals. In addition, this study has been useful in connection with certain problems in other areas of analysis, for example, summability theory (see, for example, Cooke [1] and Zeller [1]), complex function theory (see Toeplitz [1]), and the theory of nuclear spaces (see Pietsch [1]; Komura-Koshi [1]).

If λ is a sequence space, then λ and $\lambda^{\times}$ are in duality (in the sense of Bourbaki [1], Köthe [1], or Schaefer [1]) with respect to the bilinear functional

$$\langle x, u \rangle = \sum_{n=1}^{\infty} x_n u_n \qquad x \in \lambda, u \in \lambda^{\times}.$$

An excellent account of the topological and algebraic properties of the dual system $\langle \lambda, \lambda^\times \rangle$ can be found in §30 of Köthe [1]. We will have occasion to make use of a number of results from this theory in our subsequent discussion of the order structure of sequence spaces.

Since a sequence space λ is a linear subspace of the order complete vector lattice ω, λ is an ordered vector space for the canonical subspace ordering. The positive cone K in λ is

$$K = \{x \in \lambda : x_n \geq 0 \quad \text{for all } n\}.$$

All of the sequence spaces listed above are vector lattices; all but (c) are order complete vector lattices. The element $e = (e_n)$ defined by $e_n = 1$ for all n is an order unit in (c) and ℓ^∞; none of the remaining sequence spaces listed contain order units. All of the sequence spaces mentioned in the list are Archimedean. The simple verifications of the preceding assertions will be left to the reader.

Unless it is specifically stated to the contrary, we will always assume that sequence spaces are ordered in the manner described in the preceding paragraph. However, as an example of an interesting order structure on a sequence space that differs from the order induced by ω, we mention the order in ℓ^2 determined by the so-called Lorentzian cone

$$H = \left\{ x \in \ell^2 : x_1 \geq 0; \; x_1^2 - \sum_{n=2}^{\infty} x_n^2 \geq 0 \right\}.$$

With respect to this order, ℓ^2 is not a vector lattice but it does contain an order unit. The reader can find an interesting application of the Lorentzian order structure to a problem in spectral theory in Krein-Rutman [1].

In 1951, Dieudonné [1] extended the theory of sequence spaces, developed primarily by Köthe, to spaces of locally integrable functions on a locally compact, σ-compact measure space. We shall now outline this generalization with particular emphasis on the order structure of these spaces. Suppose that X is a locally compact, σ-compact Hausdorff space and that μ is a non-negative Radon measure on X. A real-valued μ-measurable function f on X is **locally integrable** if

$$\int_C |f|\, d\mu < +\infty$$

for each compact subset C of X. Two locally integrable functions f and g are **equivalent** if

$$\int_C |f - g|\, d\mu = 0$$

for each compact subset C of X. This defines an equivalence relation on the class of all locally integrable functions on X, and the collection Ω of all equivalence classes with respect to this equivalence relation is a vector space. For the sake of convenience, we shall often refer to elements of Ω as functions with the understanding that the reference is actually to the equivalence classes of the functions in question.

For a given subset A of Ω, we define Λ and $\Lambda^\times$ to be the following linear subspaces of Ω:

$$\Lambda = \left\{ f \in \Omega : \int_X |fg|\, d\mu < +\infty \quad \text{for all } g \in A \right\}$$

$$\Lambda^\times = \left\{ h \in \Omega : \int_X |fh|\, d\mu < +\infty \quad \text{for all } f \in \Lambda \right\}$$

Λ is called a **Köthe function space** and $\Lambda^\times$ is referred to as the **Köthe dual** of Λ. In view of the manner in which $\Lambda^\times$ is defined, it is clear that $\Lambda^{\times\times} = (\Lambda^\times)^\times$ coincides with Λ. The vector spaces Λ and $\Lambda^\times$ are placed in duality by the bilinear form

$$\langle f, g \rangle = \int_X fg\, d\mu \qquad f \in \Lambda, g \in \Lambda^\times.$$

If $f \in \Omega$, we define $f \geq \theta$ to mean $f(x) \geq 0$ for all x in the complement of a set N such that $\mu(N) = 0$. Then Ω is a vector lattice which is clearly σ-order complete. In fact, it will be shown later that Ω is actually order complete. If Λ is a Köthe function space, then Λ is a vector lattice for the canonical subspace order induced by Ω. Moreover, it is clear that if $f \in \Omega$, $g \in \Lambda$, and $|f| \leq |g|$, then $f \in \Lambda$. Therefore, a Köthe function space is necessarily order complete.

Suppose that Φ is the linear subspace of Ω consisting of all bounded, measurable functions with compact support in X. It is clear that $\Omega^\times$ contains Φ; on the other hand, one can show that any element of Ω that is not in Φ cannot be in $\Omega^\times$; hence, $\Omega^\times = \Phi$. In particular, if X is compact, then $\Omega = L^1_\mu(X)$ and $\Phi = L^\infty(X)$.

If, in the definition of Köthe function spaces, we take the subset A of Ω to be $L_\mu^q(X)$ for $q > 1$, then $\Lambda = L_\mu^p(X)$ where $\dfrac{1}{p} + \dfrac{1}{q} = 1$; moreover, $\Lambda^\times = L_\mu^q(X)$. Thus, the Lebesgue spaces and their standard dual spaces comprise dual systems of the type $\langle \Lambda, \Lambda^\times \rangle$.

1.7 Examples. The vector space R^X of all real-valued functions on a set X is an order complete vector lattice for the order structure generated by the cone

$$K = \{f \in R^X : f(t) \geq 0 \quad \text{for all } t \in X\}.$$

R^X contains an order unit if and only if X is a finite set.

The linear subspace $B(X)$ of all bounded functions in R^X is an order complete vector lattice for the canonical subspace order, though $B(X)$ is not an order complete subset of R^X. $B(X)$ contains order units; in fact, the function identically equal to one on X is an order unit in $B(X)$.

If X is a topological space, the linear subspace $C(X)$ of all continuous functions on X is a vector lattice for the order structure induced by R^X. Nevertheless, for suitable choices of X, it is possible to construct linear subspaces M of $C(X)$ such that M has the decomposition property but M is not a vector lattice for the canonical subspace order structure. Namioka (see (8.10 in [1]) has constructed an example of this sort as follows: Suppose that X is the interval $[0, 2]$ of the real line and that

$$M = \{f \in C[0, 2] : f(1) = f(0) + f(2)\}.$$

It is clear that M contains functions that are positive throughout $[0, 2]$, that is, M contains order units. In particular, the cone in M is generating. However, the algebraic relation imposed on the values at 0, 1, 2 of functions in M precludes the existence of the positive part f^+ for certain $f \in M$ (e.g., $f(x) = x - 1$). Therefore, M is not a vector lattice.

Suppose that f_1, f_2 are functions in M that are non-negative on $[0, 2]$ and that $h \in M$ satisfies $\theta \leq h \leq f_1 + f_2$. The functions h_1, h_2 in $C[0, 2]$ defined by

$$h_1 = h \cap f_1, \qquad h_2 = h - h_1$$

obviously satisfy the relations

$$\theta \le h_1 \le f_1, \qquad \theta \le h_2 \le f_2, \qquad h = h_1 + h_2$$

in $C[0, 2]$. Although h_1, h_2 need not be in M, it is possible to modify h_1, h_2 to obtain functions h'_1, h'_2 in M such that

$$\theta \le h'_1 \le f_1, \qquad \theta \le h'_2 \le f_2, \qquad h = h'_1 + h'_2. \qquad (*)$$

In fact, if $a = h_1(0) + h_1(2)$, then $a \le \min \{f_1(1), h(1)\} = h_1(1)$. Since $h(0) - h_1(0) = h_2(0) \le f_2(0)$ and $h(2) - h_1(2) = h_2(2) \le f_2(2)$, it follows that

$$h_2(1) + \{h_1(1) - a\} \le f_2(1).$$

If k is the piecewise linear function defined on $[0, 2]$ by joining the points $(0, 0)$, $(1, h_1(1) - a)$, $(2, 0)$ with line segments and if k_0 is the infimum in $C[0, 2]$ of the functions $k, f_2 - h_2, h_1$, then

$$k_0(0) = 0, \qquad k_0(1) = h_1(1) - a, \qquad k_0(2) = 0, \qquad \text{and } k_0 \ge \theta.$$

Define $h'_1 = h_1 - k_0$, $h'_2 = h_2 + k_0$, then a straightforward computation shows that h'_1, h'_2 are elements of M and that $(*)$ is satisfied. Therefore, M has the decomposition property.

A very simple example of a linear subspace N of an ordered vector space E ordered by a cone K with the property that the canonical image of K in the quotient space E/N is a wedge but not a cone is provided by the subspace N of constant functions in $C[0, 2]$. In this case, the canonical image of the cone coincides with E/N since E/N can be represented by the space of all real-valued, continuous functions on $[0, 2]$ that vanish at 0.

In general, $C(X)$ is not a σ-order complete vector lattice; for example, if X is a closed interval $[a, b]$ on the real line and $a < b$, then it is a simple matter to verify that $C[a, b]$ is not σ-order complete. On the other hand, if X is the set N of natural numbers in the discrete topology, then $C(N)$ is order complete (and hence σ-order complete) since $C(N)$ can be identified with the space ω of all sequences of real numbers (see (1.6)). These two examples provide a fair indication of the general situation as we shall now see.

Recall that a topological space X is **extremally disconnected** if the closure of every open set is open.

Proposition. If X is an extremally disconnected topological space, then $C(X)$ is order complete. If X is completely regular and $C(X)$ is order complete, then X is extremally disconnected.

Proof. Suppose that X is extremally disconnected. To prove that $C(X)$ is order complete, it is sufficient to show that every collection $\{f_\alpha : \alpha \in A\}$ of non-negative functions in $C(X)$ has an infimum. For each $\alpha \in A$ and each positive real number r, define

$$G_{\alpha r} = \{x \in X : f_\alpha(x) < r\}.$$

Then $G_{\alpha r}$ is open; hence,

$$G_r = \bigcup_{\alpha \in A} G_{\alpha r}$$

is also open for each $r > 0$. But X is extremally disconnected; hence, the closure $\bar{G}_r$ of G_r is open for each $r > 0$. Moreover, $X = \bigcup_{r>0} \bar{G}_r$, Therefore, for each $x \in X$, either there is an $r > 0$ such that

$$x \in \bar{G}_{r+\varepsilon} \qquad x \notin \bar{G}_{r-\varepsilon}$$

for each $\varepsilon > 0$, or else

$$x \in \bigcap_{r>0} \bar{G}_r$$

Define a function g on X as follows:

$$g(x) = \begin{cases} r & \text{if } x \in \bar{G}_{r+\varepsilon}, x \notin \bar{G}_{r-\varepsilon} \quad \text{for each } \varepsilon > 0 \\ 0 & \text{if } x \in \bigcap_{r>0} \bar{G}_r \end{cases}$$

Since

$$E_r = \{x \in X : g(x) < r\} = \bigcup_{\varepsilon>0} \bar{G}_{r-\varepsilon}$$

and

$$F_r = \{x \in X : g(x) \le r\} = \bigcap_{\varepsilon>0} \bar{G}_{r+\varepsilon},$$

it follows that E_r is open (since X is extremally disconnected) and F_r is closed. Therefore, if (r_1, r_2) is any open interval on the positive real axis, the set

$$g^{-1}(r_1, r_2) = E_{r_2} - F_{r_1}$$

is open in X. It follows that g is a continuous function on X.

For any fixed $\alpha \in A$ and each $r > 0$, the set E_r contains

$$\{x \in X : f_\alpha(x) < r - \varepsilon\}$$

for each $\varepsilon > 0$. Therefore, $g \leq f_\alpha$ for each $\alpha \in A$. If $h \in C(X)$ and $h \leq f_\alpha$ for each $\alpha \in A$, then

$$\{x \in X : h(x) < r - \varepsilon\} \supset G_{r-\varepsilon}$$

for all $r > 0$, $\varepsilon > 0$. Consequently, for all $r > 0$, $\varepsilon > 0$,

$$\{x \in X : h(x) \leq r - \varepsilon\} \supset \bar{G}_{r-\varepsilon}$$

since h is continuous. It follows that

$$\{x \in X : h(x) < r\} \supset \bigcup_{\varepsilon > 0} \bar{G}_{r-\varepsilon} = \{x \in X : g(x) < r\}$$

for each $r > 0$; hence, $h \leq g$. We conclude that $g = \inf\{f_\alpha : \alpha \in A\}$, that is, $C(X)$ is order complete.

Now suppose that X is completely regular and that $C(X)$ is order complete. If G is a nonempty open set in X, then for each $y \in G$ there is an $f_y \in C(X)$ with range in $[0, 1]$ such that $f_y(y) = 0$ and $f_y(x) = 1$ for $x \notin G$. If $g = \inf\{f_y : y \in G\}$, then g vanishes on G. Hence, g must also vanish on the closure $\bar{G}$ of G since g is continuous. If $x \notin \bar{G}$, there is an $h_x \in C(X)$ with range in $[0, 1]$ such that $h_x(y) = 0$ for $y \in \bar{G}$ and $h_x(x) = 1$. But then $h_x \leq f_y$ for all $y \in G$, so that $g(x) = 1$. Since g is continuous, the complement of $\bar{G}$ is closed, that is, $\bar{G}$ is open. Therefore, X is extremally disconnected.

1.8 Example. Suppose that H is a real Hilbert space and that $\mathscr{L}(H)$ is the collection of all continuous linear operators on H. If A and B are self-adjoint elements of $\mathscr{L}(H)$, define $A \geq B$ to mean

$$(Ax, x) \geq (Bx, x)$$

for all $x \in H$. With respect to this order relation, $\mathscr{L}(H)$ is an ordered vector space with positive cone

$$K = \{A \in \mathscr{L}(H) : A \text{ is self-adjoint and } A \geq 0\}.$$

It is clear that K is not a generating cone; in fact, the linear hull of K is precisely the set $\mathscr{S}$ of self-adjoint operators on H. Although $\mathscr{L}(H)$ does not contain order units, the identity operator I is an order unit in the linear subspace $\mathscr{S}$ for the order structure induced by $\mathscr{L}(H)$. For if $A \in \mathscr{S}$, then

$$(Ax, x) \leq \|Ax\| \, \|x\| \leq \|A\| \, \|x\|^2 = (\|A\| \, Ix, x)$$

for all $x \in H$. It is clear that $\mathscr{L}(H)$ and $\mathscr{S}$ are Archimedean ordered vector spaces.

1.9 Notes. Though we have restricted our attention to vector spaces over the real field in this exposition, it is sometimes useful to consider ordered vector spaces over the complex scalar field or to "complexify" real ordered vector spaces. For instance, such considerations have been employed in order to make use of the powerful techniques of complex function theory for the investigation of the spectral properties of positive operators. We refer the reader to, for example, Ando [2], Bonsall [4], Karlin [1], and Schaefer [3], [8] for details concerning these matters. Section 6 of Schaefer [3] presents a basis for a systematic account of ordered topological vector spaces over the complex field.

Mullins [1] studied the order structure of Köthe function spaces over measure spaces more general than those considered in (1.6); in particular, he obtained necessary and sufficient conditions in terms of the structure of the underlying measure space for Ω to be order complete.

In addition to providing another example quite different from that in (1.7) of a space with the decomposition property that is not a vector lattice, Schaefer obtained a sufficient condition for a space with the decomposition property to be a vector lattice (see Section 13 in [4]).

The proposition in (1.7) relating the order completeness of $C(X)$ to the topological nature of X is due to Nakano [1]. Necessary and sufficient conditions for the σ-order completeness of $C(X)$ can be found in Gillman-Jerison [1] (p. 51), Ito [1], and Nakano [1]. Also, see Stone [1], [2] for related results.

An order relation can be introduced in an arbitrary B*-algebra by the cone of positive, self-adjoint elements as in (1.8). It turns out that commutativity of the algebra is intimately related to the decomposition property and the lattice properties of the resulting order.

For details, see Curtis [1], Fukamiya-Misonou-Takeda [1], Kadison [2], Sherman [1], and Topping [1].

§2. LINEAR MAPPINGS ON ORDERED VECTOR SPACES

We shall begin this section by introducing some important classes of linear mappings on an ordered vector space.

2.1 Definitions. Suppose that E_1 and E_2 are ordered vector spaces with positive cones K_1 and K_2, respectively. A linear mapping T of E_1 into E_2 is:

a. **positive** if $T(K_1) \subset K_2$, that is, $Tx \geq \theta$ whenever $x \geq 0$,

b. **strictly positive** if $Tx > \theta$ whenever $x > \theta$,

c. **order bounded** if T maps each order bounded set in E_1 into an order bounded set in E_2.

It is clear that every strictly positive linear mapping is positive and that every positive linear mapping is order bounded.

2.2 Examples. a. Suppose that R^n and R^m are finite dimensional Euclidean spaces ordered by their respective cones of points with non-negative coordinates (see (1.5)). If (t_{ij}) is the matrix of a linear mapping T of R^n into R^m with respect to the bases of "unit vectors" $e^{(k)} = (\delta_{ik})$ (where δ_{ik} denotes the Kronecker delta), then it is easy to show that T is positive if and only if $t_{ij} \geq 0$ for all i, j. Moreover, a positive linear mapping T is strictly positive if and only if each column of T contains at least one positive entry. Every linear mapping of R^n into R^m is order bounded since each such mapping is the difference of two positive linear mappings.

b. If λ and μ are sequence spaces (see (1.6)) and if $T = (t_{ij})$ is an infinite matrix, then T is a **matrix transformation** of λ into μ if

(MT-1) For each $x = (x_j) \in \lambda$, the series $\sum\limits_{j=1}^{\infty} t_{ij} x_j$ converges absolutely for each i.

(MT-2) For each $x = (x_j) \in \lambda$, the sequence $y = (y_i)$ defined by $y_i = \sum\limits_{j=1}^{\infty} t_{ij} x_j$ is an element of μ.

If T is a matrix transformation of λ into μ, the mapping $y = Tx$ defined by (MT-2) is clearly linear. On the other hand, if A is a linear mapping of λ into μ and if there exists a matrix transformation T of λ into μ such that $Tx - Ax$ for all $x \in \lambda$, then A is **represented** by the matrix transformation T. Since $\lambda \subset \varphi$, the matrix transformation T representing A is unique if it exists.

Our interest in linear mappings that can be represented by matrix transformations is justified by the following result which is essentially due to Köthe and Toeplitz [1]. (Also see (6.2,II) and (6.4,VII) in Cooke [2]).

Proposition. Suppose that λ and μ are sequence spaces and that $y \in \lambda$ whenever $y \in \omega$ and $|y_1| \leq |x_i|$ $(i = 1, 2, \ldots)$ for some $x \in \lambda$. If A is a linear mapping of λ into μ, the following assertions are equivalent:

a. A is continuous for the weak topologies $\sigma(\lambda, \lambda^\times)$ and $\sigma(\mu, \mu^\times)$.
b. A is sequentially continuous for $\sigma(\lambda, \lambda^\times)$ and $\sigma(\mu, \mu^\times)$ (that is, $\{Ax^{(n)}\}$ converges for $\sigma(\mu, \mu^\times)$ to $Ax^{(0)}$ whenever $\{x^{(n)}\}$ is a sequence in λ that converges to $x^{(0)} \in \lambda$ for $\sigma(\lambda, \lambda^\times)$).
c. A can be represented by a matrix transformation $T = (t_{ij})$ of λ into μ.

If we order λ and μ by their respective cones of sequences with non-negative components, and if A is a linear mapping of λ into μ that can be represented by a matrix transformation $T = (t_{ij})$, then a straightforward verification shows that A is a positive linear mapping of λ into μ if and only if $t_{ij} \geq 0$ for all i, j. Similarly, a positive linear mapping A is strictly positive if and only if each column of T contains at least one positive entry. In Section 3 of Chapter 4, we shall exhibit an example of a linear mapping on ℓ^2 that is represented by a matrix transformation but is not order bounded.

The collection $K(E_1, E_2)$ of all positive linear mappings of an ordered vector space E_1 into an ordered vector space E_2 is a wedge in the vector space of all linear mappings of E_1 into E_2. Moreover, if the cone K_1 in E_1 is generating, the wedge $K(E_1, E_2)$ is actually a cone.

Suppose that E_1, E_2 are ordered vector spaces, that E_1 has the decomposition property, and that the cone K_1 in E_1 is generating. If T is a linear mapping of E_1 into E_2 such that the supremum of the set $\{Ty : \theta \leq y \leq x\}$ exists for each $x \in K_1$, the mapping T^+ of K_1 into E_2 defined by

$$T^+x = \sup \{Ty : \theta \leq y \leq x\} \tag{1}$$

is clearly positively homogeneous, that is, $T^+(\alpha x) = \alpha T^+(x)$ for all $\alpha \geq 0$. Since E_1 has the decomposition property, $T^+(x + y) = T^+(x) + T^+(y)$ for all x, y in K_1, that is, T^+ is additive on K_1. The mapping T^+ can be extended to all of E_1 as follows: For each $x \in E_1$, we define $T^+x = T^+x_1 - T^+x_2$ where $x = x_1 - x_2$ with x_1, x_2 in K_1. Since T^+ is additive on K_1, T^+x does not depend on the particular choice of x_1, x_2 in K_1 such that $x = x_1 - x_2$. Moreover, T^+ is a linear mapping of E_1 into E_2 which is easily seen to be the supremum of T and 0. Since $T = T^+ - (T^+ - T)$, it follows that T is the difference of two positive linear mappings of E_1 into E_2. Therefore, T is necessarily an order bounded linear mapping. On the other hand, if E_2 is an order complete vector lattice and T is an order bounded linear mapping of E_1 into E_2, the supremum of the set $\{Ty : \theta \leq y \leq x\}$ exists for each $x \in K_1$. Therefore, the supremum of T and 0 exists.

Now suppose that $\{T_\alpha : \alpha \in A\}$ is a family of linear mappings of E_1 into E_2 such that the supremum of the set

$$\left\{ \sum_{i=1}^{n} T_{\alpha_i} x_i : x_i \in K_1 ; \sum_{i=1}^{n} x_i = x ; \alpha_i \in A \right\} \tag{*}$$

exists for each $x \in K_1$. For each $x \in K_1$, we define Sx as follows:

$$Sx = \sup \left\{ \sum_{i=1}^{n} T_{\alpha_i} x_i : x_i \in K_1 ; \sum_{i=1}^{n} x_i = x, \alpha_i \in A \right\}. \tag{2}$$

It is clear that S is a positively homogeneous mapping of K_1 into E_2. Moreover, if E_1 is a vector lattice, a straightforward application of (1.3) yields the conclusion that S is additive on K_1. S can be extended uniquely to a linear mapping (again denoted by S) of E_1 into E_2 just as in the case of T^+; moreover, S is the supremum of $\{T_\alpha : \alpha \in A\}$. Observe that the supremum of the set (*) exists for each $x \in K_1$

whenever $\{T_\alpha : \alpha \in A\}$ is majorized by a linear mapping T_0 and E_2 is order complete. Combining this with the results of the preceding paragraph, we conclude the following result concerning the order structure of the vector space $L^b(E_1, E_2)$ of all order bounded linear mappings of E_1 into E_2.

2.3 Proposition. If E_1 is a vector lattice and E_2 is an order complete vector lattice, the vector space $L^b(E_1, E_2)$ of order bounded linear mappings of E_1 into E_2, ordered by the cone $K(E_1, E_2)$ of positive linear mappings, is an order complete vector lattice.

Let us now refine our conclusions concerning the lattice structure of $L^b(E_1, E_2)$ when E_1 is a space with the decomposition property ordered by a generating cone K_1 and E_2 is an order complete vector lattice. The definition of T^+ given by (1) yields the following formulae for the lattice operations in $L^b(E_1, E_2)$ for $x \geq \theta$:

$$(T_1 \cup T_2)(x) = \sup \{T_1(y) + T_2(z) : y, z \text{ in } K_1 ; y + z = x\}. \quad (3)$$

$$(T_1 \cap T_2)(x) = \inf \{T_1(y) + T_2(z) : y, z \text{ in } K_1 ; y + z = x\}. \quad (4)$$

If we set $T_1 = -T_2$ in (3) we obtain the following formula for the absolute value in $L^b(E_1, E_2)$ for $x \geq \theta$:

$$|T|(x) = \sup \{T(y - z) : y, z \text{ in } K_1 ; y + z = x\}. \quad (5)$$

If E_1 is a vector lattice and $x = y + z$ where $y \in K_1$, $z \in K_1$, then $-x \leq y - z \leq x$, that is, $|y - z| \leq x$. Therefore

$$|T|(x) \leq \sup \{Tw : |w| \leq x\}$$

for $x \geq \theta$. On the other hand, if $|w| \leq x$, then $Tw = T(w^+ - w^-) \leq |T|(|w|) \leq |T|(x)$; hence,

$$|T|(x) = \sup \{Tw : |w| \leq x\} \quad (6)$$

for $x \geq \theta$. In particular,

$$|Tx| \leq |T| \, |x| \quad (7)$$

for any $x \in E_1$. Another useful formula for $|T|$ can be derived from (2): For each $x \geq \theta$,

$$|T|(x) = \sup \left\{ \sum_{i=1}^n |Tx_i| : x = \sum_{i=1}^n x_i ; x_i \in K_1 \quad \text{for all } i \right\}. \quad (8)$$

To verify (8), we first observe that if $T_1 \geq T$ and $T_1 \geq -T$ for some $T_1 \in L^b(E_1, E_2)$, then

$$\sum_{i=1}^{n} |Tx_i| \leq \sum_{i=1}^{n} T_1 x_i = T_1 x$$

for any representation of x of the form $x = \sum_{i=1}^{\infty} x_i$, where $x_i \in K_1$ for all i. On the other hand, (2) implies that

$$|T|(x) = \sup \left\{ \sum_{i=1}^{n} (\pm Tx_i) : x = \sum_{i=1}^{n} x_i \, ; \, x_i \in K_1 \quad \text{for all } i \right\}$$

$$\leq \sup \left\{ \sum_{i=1}^{n} |Tx_i| : x = \sum_{i=1}^{n} x_i \, ; \, x_i \in K_1 \quad \text{for all } i \right\};$$

hence, formula (8) is valid. Similar computations show that

$$T^+ x = \sup \left\{ \sum_{i=1}^{n} (Tx_i)^+ : x = \sum_{i=1}^{n} x_i \, ; \, x_i \in K_1 \quad \text{for all } i \right\}$$

$$T^- x = \sup \left\{ \sum_{i=1}^{n} (Tx_i)^- : x = \sum_{i=1}^{n} x_i \, ; \, x_i \in K_1 \quad \text{for all } i \right\}$$

(9)

for each $x \geq \theta$ in E_1.

It should be noted that if T is a linear mapping of E_1 into E_2 such that the suprema in any of the formulae (3), (5), (6), (8), or (9) exist for each $x \geq \theta$, then $T \in L^b(E_1, E_2)$.

If $\mathscr{A} = \{T_\alpha : \alpha \in A\}$ is a directed ($\leq$), majorized subset of $L^b(E_1, E_2)$, then the definition of the supremum of $\mathscr{A}$ given by (2) takes the simple form

$$(\sup \mathscr{A})(x) = \sup \{Tx : T \in \mathscr{A}\} \tag{10}$$

for $x \geq \theta$.

If E_2 is the order complete vector lattice R of real numbers in its usual order, the mapping S defined on K_1 by (10) can be shown to be additive and positively homogeneous in K_1 if E_1 has the decomposition property and $E_1 = K_1 - K_1$, since the supremum involved is a monotone limit. If we combine this observation with our earlier conclusions concerning T^+, we obtain the following result:

2.4 Proposition (Riesz). If E is an ordered vector space with the decomposition property and a generating cone, the vector space of all order bounded linear functionals on E, ordered by the cone of positive linear functionals, is an order complete vector lattice.

The vector space $L^b(E, R)$ of all order bounded linear functionals on an ordered vector space E will be denoted by E^b, while the symbol K^* will be used to denote the wedge $K(E, R)$. The linear hull E^+ of K^* in E^b, that is, $E^+ = K^* - K^*$ will be referred to as the **order dual** of E. If E is an ordered vector space with the decomposition property and a generating cone, (2.4) implies that E^+ coincides with the order complete vector lattice E^b.

2.5 Example. Recall that a Radon measure on a compact Hausdorff space X is any continuous linear functional on the space $C(X)$ of continuous real valued functions on X, equipped with the supremum norm:
$$\|f\| = \sup \{|f(t)| : t \in X\}$$
(see N. Bourbaki [2]). If $C(X)$ is ordered by the cone of non-negative functions on X $\big($see (1.7)$\big)$ the unit ball in $C(X)$ is just the order interval $[-1, 1]$ where 1 denotes the function that is identically equal to one on X. Therefore, since 1 is an order unit, a linear functional on $C(X)$ is continuous if and only if it is order bounded. Thus, the order dual of $C(X)$ coincides with the space $\mathscr{M}(X)$ of Radon measures on X; in particular, the space $\mathscr{M}(X)$ is an order complete vector lattice.

2.6 Notes. Many of the basic concepts and constructions in this section were introduced for function spaces by Riesz [1], [2]. Kantorovich (e.g. [1], [3], [4]) not only generalized Riesz's work to essentially the level presented here but also developed much of the fundamental theory for other interesting classes of linear mappings determined by the order structure of the underlying vector spaces. We shall discuss a portion of this work in Section 5 of this chapter.

§3. CONES WITH BASES; THE CHOQUET-KENDALL THEOREM

We shall begin this section with a number of simple observations concerning ordered vector spaces in which the positive cone possesses a base. After the convenient equivalence in (3.6) has been established, we shall discuss a number of examples, and then proceed to the important Choquet-Kendall Theorem which characterizes lattice orderings on vector spaces in terms of algebraic properties of bases. The section closes with an outline of an application of this characterization to the uniqueness theory for Choquet integral representations.

3.1 Definition. Suppose that E is a vector space ordered by a cone K and that $K \neq \{\theta\}$. A nonempty convex subset B of K is a **base** for K if each nonzero element $x \in K$ has a unique representation of the form $x = \lambda b$ for $\lambda > 0$, $b \in B$.

Since a base B for a cone is necessarily a convex set, it is clear that $\theta \notin B$.

3.2 Proposition. A nonempty convex subset B of a vector space E is a base for a cone K in E if and only if $K = \bigcup\{\lambda B : \lambda \geq 0\}$ and the smallest linear manifold in E containing B does not contain θ.

Proof. If B is a base for K, it is clear that $K = \bigcup\{\lambda B : \lambda \geq 0\}$. The smallest linear manifold containing B is $L = \{\mu b + (1 - \mu)b' : b \in B, b' \in B, \mu \in R\}$. Therefore, if $\theta \in L$, there are $\mu_0 > 1$ and b_0, b'_0 in B such that $\mu_0 b_0 = (\mu_0 - 1)b'_0$. But this contradicts the uniqueness property for base representations; hence, $\theta \notin L$.

On the other hand, if B satisfies the stated condition and if $\lambda b = \lambda' b'$ for b, b' in B and positive real numbers λ, λ', then

$$\theta = \frac{1}{\lambda - \lambda'} \{\lambda b - \lambda' b'\} \in L$$

if $\lambda \neq \lambda'$. It follows that $\lambda = \lambda'$ and hence $b = b'$; consequently, B is a base for K.

As we shall see, the following corollary to (3.2) is a very useful technical device in the theory of cones with bases.

3.3 Corollary. If B is a base for the cone K in an ordered vector space E and if $\sum_{i=1}^{n} \lambda_i b_i = \theta$ for $b_i \in B$, $\lambda_i \in R$ ($i = 1, 2, \ldots, n$), then $\sum_{i=1}^{n} \lambda_i = 0$.

Proof. If L is the smallest linear manifold containing B and if $\lambda = \sum_{i=1}^{n} \lambda_i \neq 0$, then $\theta = \frac{1}{\lambda} \sum_{i=1}^{n} \lambda_i b_i$ is contained in L. Hence, in view of (3.2), it must be true that $\sum_{i=1}^{n} \lambda_i = 0$.

3.4 Corollary. If B is a base for the cone K in an ordered vector space E and if $\lambda b \leq \lambda' b'$ (resp. $\lambda b < \lambda' b'$) for b, b' in B and λ, λ' in R, then $\lambda \leq \lambda'$ (resp. $\lambda < \lambda'$).

Proof. Since $\lambda b \leq \lambda' b'$, there exist $b'' \in B$ and $\lambda'' \geq 0$ such that $\lambda b + \lambda'' b'' = \lambda' b'$. It follows from (3.3) that $\lambda' = \lambda + \lambda''$; hence, $\lambda \leq \lambda'$. If $\lambda b < \lambda' b'$, then $\lambda'' > 0$; hence, $\lambda < \lambda'$.

3.5 Corollary. If B is a base for the cone K in an ordered vector space E and if $n x_0 \leq y_0$ for x_0, y_0 in K and each positive integer n, then $x_0 = \theta$. If E is a vector lattice, then E is Archimedean.

Proof. Choose b, b' in B and non-negative real numbers λ, λ' such that $x_0 = \lambda b$, $y_0 = \lambda' b'$, then $n \lambda b \leq \lambda' b'$ for each positive integer n. (3.4) implies that $n \lambda \leq \lambda'$ for each n; hence, $\lambda = 0$, that is, $x_0 = \theta$. If E is a vector lattice and $\lambda x \leq y$ for some $y \in K$ and all $\lambda > 0$, then $\lambda x^+ \leq y$ for all $\lambda > 0$. Therefore $x^+ = \theta$, that is, $x = -x^- \leq \theta$. It follows that E is an Archimedean vector lattice.

We shall now establish a useful connection between strictly positive linear functionals and bases.

3.6 Proposition. A subset B of a vector space ordered by a cone K is a base for K if and only if there is a strictly positive linear functional h on E such that $h^{-1}(1) \cap K = B$.

Proof. If h is a strictly positive linear functional on E, the linear manifold $h^{-1}(1)$ contains $h^{-1}(1) \cap K$, $\theta \notin h^{-1}(1)$, and $K = \bigcup \{\lambda h^{-1}(1) \cap K : \lambda \geq 0\}$. Therefore $h^{-1}(1) \cap K$ is a base for K by (3.2).

Conversely, if B is a base for K, a routine application of Zorn's lemma yields the existence of a linear manifold L_0 which is maximal (with respect to inclusion) in the class of all linear manifolds in E containing B but not θ. It is an easy matter to verify that L_0 is a hyperplane; hence, $L_0 = h^{-1}(1)$ for some linear functional h on E. Since $h(b) = 1$ for each b in the base B, it follows that h is a strictly positive linear functional and that $B = h^{-1}(1) \cap K$.

Observe that if the cone K in E generates E, it is not necessary to apply Zorn's lemma in the above proof since the smallest linear manifold containing B is a hyperplane.

3.7 Examples. a. If λ is a sequence space (see (1.6)), the linear functional

$$\psi_u(x) = \langle x, u \rangle \qquad (x \in \lambda)$$

determined by $u \in \lambda^\times$ is strictly positive if and only if $u_i > 0$ for all i. It follows, for example, that the positive cones in $\ell^p(1 \leq p \leq +\infty)$, (c), (c_0), φ all have bases. On the other hand, the positive cone in ω does not have a base since φ actually represents the order dual of ω, that is, every linear functional in ω^+ is representable as a ψ_u for an appropriate choice of u in φ.

b. If $B[a, b]$ is the order complete vector lattice of bounded, real valued functions on the interval $[a, b]$ $(a \neq b)$ (see (1.7)), the positive cone $K = \{f \in B[a, b] : f(t) \geq 0 \text{ for all } t \in [a, b]\}$ does not have a base. In fact, suppose ψ is any positive linear functional on $B[a, b]$ and 1_x is the characteristic function of the singleton $\{x\}$ for $x \in [a, b]$. Then, for each positive integer n, there are at most a finite number p of points $x_i \in [a, b]$ such that $\psi(1_{x_i}) > 1/n$, since

$$\frac{p}{n} \leq \psi\left(\sum_{i=1}^{p} 1_{x_i}\right) \leq \psi(1)$$

(where 1 denotes the characteristic function of $[a, b]$). It follows that $\{x \in [a, b] : \psi(1_x) > 0\}$ is at most a countable set; hence, ψ is not strictly positive. Consequently, (3.6) implies that K does not have a base.

c. Suppose that E is an ordered vector space with an order unit e such that the order dual E^+ of E is nontrivial, that is, $E^+ \neq \{\theta\}$. If K^* is the cone of positive linear functionals on E, the set

$$B = \{f \in K^* : f(e) = 1\}$$

is clearly a base for K^*. In particular, the set of positive Radon measures of total mass 1 on a compact Hausdorff space X is a base for the cone of positive Radon measures on X (see (2.5)).

d. Suppose that B is a compact, convex set in a locally convex space E. We shall also assume that B is contained in a closed hyperplane H such that $\theta \notin H$. (Note that if this latter condition is not satisfied, we may consider the compact, convex subset $B' = B \times \{1\}$ of the closed hyperplane $H' = E \times \{1\}$ in the vector space $E' = E \times R$ equipped with the product topology.) Then the set $K = \bigcup\{\lambda B : \lambda \geq 0\}$ is a cone in E with base B. As we shall see at the end of this section, the order structure determined by K plays a significant role in the uniqueness theory for Choquet integral representations of the points of B.

The following simple result provides a characterization of the vector lattices among all ordered vector spaces in terms of the "geometric" structure of the cone.

3.8 Proposition. If E is a vector space ordered by a cone K, the following assertions are equivalent:

a. E is a vector lattice.
b.   For each pair x, y of elements of E, there exists an element z of E such that $(x + K) \cap (y + K) = z + K$.
c.   For each element x of E, there is an element z of E such that $(x + K) \cap K = z + K$.

Proof. This result follows immediately from the following simple observation: For any $u \in E$, $u + K$ coincides with the set of all $v \in E$ such that $v \geq u$.

If the cone in an ordered vector space has a base, it is natural to ask if a characterization of vector lattices similar to (3.8) can be given in terms of geometric properties of the base. As we shall see presently, such a characterization is possible, though it lies much deeper in the theory than (3.8).

3.9 Definition. A convex, nonempty subset A of a vector space E is a **simplex** if, for all x, y in E and all non-negative real numbers α, β, the set $(x + \alpha A) \cap (y + \beta A)$ is either empty or of the form $z + \gamma A$ for an appropriate choice of $z \in E$ and $\gamma \geq 0$. A convex subset A of E is **linearly compact** if $A \cap L$ is either empty or a closed bounded interval in L for each one dimensional manifold L in E (when L is regarded as a copy of the real line R in E).

A routine argument shows that this definition of simplex agrees with the usual definition for bounded subsets of Euclidean n-dimensional space R^n. Moreover, a convex subset of R^n is linearly compact if and only if it is compact for the Euclidean topology (see (B) and (3) in Klee [1] for a proof of this assertion).

The following technical lemma will be needed for the proof of our main result.

3.10 Lemma. Suppose that E is a vector space ordered by a generating cone K, that $\dim(E) > 1$ and that B is a base for K such that B is a linearly compact simplex. If x, y, z are elements of E and α, β, γ are non-negative real numbers such that

$$(z + \gamma B) = (x + \alpha B) \cap (y + \beta B), \text{ then } x \le z, y \le z, \gamma \le \alpha, \gamma \le \beta.$$

Proof. As a consequence of the hypotheses that K generates E and the dimension of E is greater than one, it is true that B contains more than one element. If $\alpha = 0$, it follows that $\gamma = 0$ and $z = x = y + \beta b$ for some $b \in B$; hence, we can also assume that $\alpha > 0$, Let $b_1 \in B$, then $(B - b_1)$ is a convex, nonempty, linearly compact set containing θ. If $w = (z - x) + (\gamma - \alpha)b_1$ and if $b \in B$, then $w + \gamma(b - b_1) = (z + \gamma b) - x - \alpha b_1 \in \alpha(B - b_1)$; consequently,

$$w + \gamma(B - b_1) \subset \alpha(B - b_1). \tag{1}$$

An easy induction argument based on (1) shows that

$$w + \frac{\gamma}{\alpha} w + \cdots + \frac{\gamma^{n-1}}{\alpha^{n-1}} w + \frac{\gamma^n}{\alpha^n} \{\alpha(B - b_1)\} \subset \alpha(B - b_1). \tag{2}$$

Suppose, contrary to a part of our assertion, that $\gamma > \alpha$. Since $\theta \in (B - b_1)$ and $\alpha(B - b_1)$ is linearly compact, it follows that $w = \theta$. But then $\frac{\gamma^n}{\alpha^n} \{\alpha(B - b_1)\} \subset \alpha(B - b_1)$, which contradicts the fact that $\alpha(B - b_1)$ is linearly compact since $\alpha(B - b_1) \neq \{\theta\}$. Therefore, $\gamma \le \alpha$.

If $\gamma = \alpha$ then $w = \theta$ by (2); hence, $z = x$. If $\gamma < \alpha$, then (2) and the fact that $\alpha(B - b_1)$ is linearly compact imply that $\dfrac{w}{1 - \gamma/\alpha} \in \alpha(B - b_1)$; consequently, $x \le z$. The same argument may be used to show that $\gamma \le \beta$ and $y \le z$; hence, the proof of the lemma is complete.

We shall now establish the main result of this section.

3.11 Proposition (*Choquet-Kendall*). If E is a vector space ordered by a generating cone K with a base B, then E is a vector lattice if and only if B is a linearly compact simplex.

Proof. Suppose that E is a vector lattice and that $(x + \alpha B) \cap (y + \beta B)$ is not empty for some x, y in E and non-negative real numbers α, β. Without loss in generality, we can assume that $y = \theta$ and $\beta = 1$. If $z = x + \alpha b_1 = b_2$ for b_1, b_2 in B, then $z = x^+ + (\alpha b_1) \cap b_2$ by Equation (5) in Section 1. Choose $\gamma \ge 0$, $b_3 \in B$ so that $(\alpha b_1) \cap b_2 = \gamma b_3$; then

$$x^+ = b_2 - \gamma b_3, \qquad x^- = \alpha b_1 - \gamma b_3. \tag{1}$$

We shall now show that $(x^+ + \gamma B) = (x + \alpha B) \cap B$. If $b \in B$, then $x^- + \gamma b = \rho b_4$ for an appropriate choice of $\rho \ge 0$ and $b_4 \in B$. In view of (1), $x^+ + \gamma b = x + (\alpha b_1 - \gamma b_3 + \gamma b)$; hence, $\rho = \alpha$ by (3.3). Similarly, $x^+ + \gamma b = b_2 - \gamma b_3 + \gamma b = \rho' b_5$ for a suitable choice of $\rho' \ge 0$ and $b_5 \in B$; hence, $\rho' = 1$. Therefore, $x^+ + \gamma b \in (x + \alpha B) \cap B$. On the other hand, if $w \in (x + \alpha B) \cap B$, then $w = x + \alpha b = b'$ for a suitable choice of b, b' in B. As before, we can write

$$w = x^+ + (\alpha b) \cap b' = x^+ + \tau b'',$$

where $\tau \ge 0$ and $b'' \in B$. Then

$$x^+ = b' - \tau b'' \qquad x^- = \alpha b - \tau b'',$$

and, since $b' = b_2 - \gamma b_3 + \tau b''$, it follows that $\gamma = \tau$; consequently, $w \in (x^+ + \gamma B)$. Thus, $(x^+ + \gamma B) = (x + \alpha B) \cap B$, that is, B is a simplex.

If we suppose that B is not linearly compact, then there is a one-dimensional linear manifold L in E such that either

(a) $L \cap B$ contains a "half line" $L' = \{b_1 + \lambda c : \lambda \ge 0\}$ where $c \ne \theta$; or,

(b) $L \cap B$ is a bounded, non-closed interval in L.

In case (a), we note that $c \notin K$. (For if $c = \mu b$ for $\mu > 0$ and $b \in B$, then $b_1 + \mu b - b' = \theta$ for some $b' \in B$. Therefore, $\mu = 0$ by (3.3) contrary to the definition of μ.) Consequently, if $z = c \cap (2c)$, then $z < c$. However, $c - \tau b_1 \leq c$ and $c - \tau b_1 \leq 2c$ for all $\tau > 0$ since $2c - (c - \tau b_1) = \tau(b_1 + c/\tau) \in \tau L'$. It would follow that $\theta \leq c - z \leq \tau b_1$ for all $\tau > 0$; hence, $c = z$ by (3.5), contrary to our previous conclusion. Therefore, the situation described in (a) cannot occur. To show that (b) is also impossible, suppose, for example, that $L \cap B$ contains a segment of the form $\{\lambda b_1 + (1 - \lambda)c : 0 < \lambda \leq 1\}$ where $c \notin B$. If $c \in K$, then $c = \mu b$ for some $\mu > 0$ and $b \in B$. But then

$$c = \mu b = 2\left(\frac{c + b_1}{2}\right) - b_1 ,$$

which implies that $\mu = 1$, contrary to the fact that $c \notin B$; consequently, $c \notin K$. Now $(1 - \rho)c + \rho b_1 \in B$ for all ρ such that $0 < \rho < 1$; hence, $c + \tau b_1 \in K$ for all $\tau > 0$. It follows that $c - \tau b_1 < 2c$ for all $\tau > 0$. Just as before, we are led to the contradictory conclusions $c = c \cap (2c)$ and $c \notin K$. Therefore B is linearly compact.

Conversely, suppose that the base B for K is a linearly compact simplex. If x and y are given elements of E, there exists a $z \in E$ such that $x \leq z$ and $y \leq z$ since the cone is generating. Therefore, there exist b_1, b_2 in B and non-negative real numbers α, β with $z = x + \alpha b_1 = y + \beta b_2$. The fact that B is a simplex implies that there exist an $a \in E$ and $\gamma \geq 0$ such that $(x + \alpha B) \cap (y + \beta B) = a + \gamma B$. It is clear that $a \leq z$ and (3.10) implies that $x \leq a$ and $y \leq a$. We shall prove that a is the supremum of x and y.

Choose b_3, b_4 in B and non-negative real numbers α', β' such that $x + \alpha' b_3 = y + \beta' b_4 = a$. Since B is a simplex, there exist $a' \in E$ and $\gamma' \geq 0$ such that $(x + \alpha' B) \cap (y + \beta' B) = a' + \gamma' B$. It is clear that $a' \leq a$; moreover, if $b \in B$, then, by (3.3),

$$a + \gamma b = x + (\alpha' b_3 + \gamma b) = x + (\alpha' + \gamma)b_3'$$

for a suitable choice of $b_3' \in B$. Since $a + \gamma b \in (x + \alpha B)$, there exists a $b_3'' \in B$ such that $a + \gamma b = x + \alpha b_3''$; hence, $\alpha' + \gamma = \alpha$ by (3.3).

Similarly, $\beta' + \gamma = \beta$; therefore, $a' + (\gamma' + \gamma)B = (a' + \gamma'B) + \gamma B \subset (x + \alpha'B + \gamma B) \cap (y + \beta'B + \gamma B) = (x + \alpha B) \cap (y + \beta B) = a + \gamma B$. We conclude that

$$\left(a' + (\gamma' + \gamma)B\right) \cap (a + \gamma B) = a' + (\gamma' + \gamma)B,$$

therefore, $a \le a'$ and $\gamma \ge \gamma' + \gamma$ by (3.10). This implies that

$$(x + \alpha'B) \cap (y + \beta'B) = \{a\}$$

If we had started with any other upper bound z^* for x and y, the preceding procedure would yield an element $a^* \in E$ and non-negative real numbers α^*, β^* such that $x \le a^* \le z^*, y \le a^* \le z^*$, and

$$(x + \alpha^*B) \cap (y + \beta^*B) = \{a^*\}$$

If we choose b_3^*, b_4^* in B and non-negative real numbers α^*, β^* such that $a^* = x + \alpha^* b_3^* = y + \beta^* b_4^*$, then $\alpha' b_3 - \alpha^* b_3^* = \beta' b_4 - \beta^* b_4^*$. Hence, $\beta' - \beta^* = \alpha' - \alpha^* = \delta$, and we can assume that $\delta \ge 0$ without loss in generality. Note that

$$a^* + \delta B \subset (x + \alpha^*B + \delta B) \cap (y + \beta^*B + \delta B)$$

$$= (x + \alpha'B) \cap (y + \beta'B) = \{a\},$$

hence, either E is one-dimensional (in which case E is surely a vector lattice) or $\delta = 0$. But if $\delta = 0$, it follows that $a = a^*$. We conclude that a does not depend on the choice of the upper bound z for x and y; consequently, a is the supremum of x and y. This establishes the fact that E is a vector lattice and the proof of the proposition is complete.

Observe that the proposition in (1.5) is a simple application of the Choquet-Kendall Theorem to finite-dimensional ordered vector spaces. The following result, which is also an immediate consequence of (3.11), will be useful in our discussion of integral representations.

3.12 Corollary. If B is a compact convex set in a locally convex space and if B is contained in a closed hyperplane H such that $\theta \notin H$, then the cone $K = \bigcup \{\alpha B : \alpha \ge 0\}$ determines a lattice order on $K - K$ if and only if B is a simplex.

The following example shows that (3.11) is a proper extension of (3.12).

3.13   Example.   If $B = \{f \in C[a, b] : f(x) \geq 0$ for all $x \in [a, b]$ and $\int_a^b f(x)\, dx = 1\}$, then B is a base for the cone K of non-negative functions in the space $C[a, b]$ of real-valued, continuous functions on the closed interval $[a, b]$ since the linear functional F defined by

$$F(f) = \int_a^b f(x)\, dx,$$

is strictly positive (see (3.6)). For any $f \in B$, there exists a $g \in C[a, b]$ such that $g \neq \theta$ and $f \pm g \in B$. Therefore, B does not have any extreme points; hence, B is not compact in any locally convex topology on $C[a, b]$ by the Krein-Milman Theorem. However, since $C[a, b]$ is a vector lattice for the order structure generated by K, B is a linearly compact simplex.

3.14   Example.   We shall now present a brief outline of the theory of Choquet integral representations and the relation of this theory to the material presented in this section. If B is a compact convex set in a locally convex space E and if μ is a probability measure on B (that is, μ is a non-negative, regular, Borel measure on B such that $\mu(B) = 1$; equivalently, by the Riesz Representation Theorem, μ is a positive Radon measure on B of total mass 1), then a point $x \in E$ is the **barycenter** of μ if

$$f(x) = \int_B f\, d\mu$$

for each continuous linear functional f on E.

The Krein-Milman Theorem can be restated in the following measure theoretic form: Every point of a compact set B in a locally convex space E is the barycenter of a probability measure μ supported by the closure of the set Ext (B) of extreme points of B, that is, $\mu(B \sim \overline{\text{Ext}\,(B)}) = 0$. Now it is often true that B coincides with the closure of Ext (B); for example, this is true if B is rotund, and Klee [2] has shown the " most " convex compact sets are rotund. In such cases, the preceding reformulation of the Krein-Milman Theorem is of no interest since each point x of B is obviously the barycenter of the point mass ε_x concentrated at x. However, a fundamental theorem due to Choquet [1] shows that each point of a compact, convex, metrizable set B is the barycenter of a probability measure supported by the set Ext (B). In view of the fact that the set Ext (B) need not even be a Borel set for arbitrary compact convex sets B (see Bishop-de Leeuw [1], page 327 for an interesting example) it is not possible to extend this result directly to the non-metrizable case. Nevertheless, Bishop and de Leeuw [1] have shown that the conclusion of the Choquet theorem holds if the phrase "μ is supported by Ext (B)" is taken to mean that μ vanishes on each Baire set in B disjoint from Ext (B). This result is established by introducing the following order relation $\leq'$ on the set of non-negative regular Borel measures on B: $\mu_1 \leq' \mu_2$ if $\mu_1(f) \leq \mu_2(f)$ for each convex, continuous function f on B. (Recall that f is convex if $f(\alpha x + (1 - \alpha)y) \leq \alpha f(x) + (1 - \alpha)f(y)$ for all x, y in B and all $\alpha \in R$ such that $0 \leq \alpha \leq 1$). A measure μ which is maximal with respect to the order relation $\leq'$ is called a **maximal measure**. A Zorn's lemma argument shows that for any non-negative, regular Borel measure μ, there exists a maximal measure μ_1 such that $\mu \leq' \mu_1$; moreover, μ and μ_1 have the same barycenter since each continuous linear functional on E is convex on B. Since it can be shown that a maximal measure vanishes on each Baire set disjoint from Ext (B), every point x of B is the barycenter of a probability measure μ supported by Ext (B); namely, a maximal measure μ such that $\varepsilon_x \leq' \mu$.

It is not generally true that, for each element x of a compact, convex set B, there is a unique probability measure supported by Ext (B) with x as its barycenter. In fact, if B is a subset of R^n with a finite number of extreme points, then each point of B is the barycenter of a unique probability measure μ supported by Ext (B) if and only if B is a simplex. This finite dimensional result is quite indicative of the general situation. For if B is a compact convex subset of a locally convex space E and if B is contained in a closed hyperplane H such that $\theta \notin H$ (see (3.7)), then, by making use of (3.12), one can show that every point of B is the barycenter of a unique maximal probability measure supported by Ext (B) if and only if B is a simplex. Moreover, if B is metrizable, the preceding uniqueness criterion may be sharpened by deleting the word "maximal" and adding that μ vanishes on $(B \sim \text{Ext}(B))$ since the maximality of μ is equivalent to the statement that μ is supported by Ext (B). In the course of the proof of this uniqueness theorem, (3.12) is used to conclude that the base of maximal probability measures on B for the cone of all maximal measures on B is actually a simplex. The function φ that associates with each maximal probability measure on B its barycenter in B is an affine mapping (that is, φ and $-\varphi$ are convex functions) of this base onto B. Consequently, if φ is one-to-one, that is, if each x in B is the barycenter of a unique maximal probability measure on B, it follows that B is a simplex.

In addition to the fundamental papers of Choquet and Bishop-de-Leeuw cited above, we refer the reader to Phelps [1] for a very readable and systematic account of the theory outlined here.

3.15 Notes. The notion of a simplex was employed by Clarkson [1] to obtain a characterization of the continuous function spaces among all Banach spaces. (3.11) was established by Kendall [1], but the special case (3.12) of (3.11) was proved earlier by Choquet [1].

§4. LATTICE IDEALS; BANDS

This section is devoted to the study of two types of linear subspaces of a vector lattice that are "well behaved" with respect to direct sum decompositions and quotient space formations.

4.1 Definitions. A subset B of a vector lattice E is **solid** if $y \in B$ whenever $x \in B$ and $|y| \leq |x|$. A linear subspace M of E is a **lattice ideal** if M is a solid subset of E. If E is an order complete vector lattice and if M is a lattice ideal in E, then M is a **band** in E if M contains the supremum of every subset of M that is majorized *in* E.

Every lattice ideal M in a vector lattice E is a **sublattice** of E; that is, for any x, y in M, the supremum and infimum of x and y in E lie in M. Moreover, if E is an order complete vector lattice and if M is a lattice ideal in E, then M is an order complete vector lattice for the subspace order structure, and the suprema and infima of subsets of M coincide with the corresponding suprema and infima in E.

4.2 Examples. a. The most significant examples of solid sets aside from lattice ideals and bands are provided by the multiples of the unit ball in the classical Banach spaces $L^p[a, b](p \geq 1)$, $C(X)$, $\ell^p(p \geq 1)$, (c), (c_0) etc. when these spaces are equipped with their usual "pointwise" order structure (see (1.6), (1.7)). (c) is a sublattice of ℓ^∞ and ω, but (c) is not a lattice ideal in either of these spaces. The following result provides a characterization of order complete sequence spaces in terms of lattice ideals.

Proposition. If a sequence space λ is a vector lattice, then λ is order complete if and only if λ is a lattice ideal in ω.

Proof. Suppose that λ is order complete, that $x \in \lambda$, and that $|y| \leq |x|$. Since $|x| \in \lambda$, the elements $y^{(n)}$ defined by

$$y_i^{(n)} = \begin{cases} |x_i| & \text{if } i \neq n \\ y_n & \text{if } i = n \end{cases}$$

are also in λ and $y^{(n)} \geq -|x|$ for all n. Therefore, the set $\{y^{(n)} : n = 1, 2, \ldots\}$ has an infimum in λ and a straightforward argument shows that this infimum is y. Therefore, λ is a lattice ideal in ω. On the other hand, if λ is a lattice ideal in ω, then λ is order complete since ω is order complete (see the remark following (4.1)).

It is clear that (c_0) is a lattice ideal in ℓ^∞ and ω, but it is not a band in either of these spaces. Indeed, if $x^{(n)}$ is the element of (c_0) defined by

$$x_i^{(n)} = \begin{cases} 0 & \text{if } i \text{ is even or if } i \geq 2n \\ 1 & \text{if } i \text{ is odd and if } i < 2n \end{cases}$$

then the set $\{x^{(n)}\}$ has a supremum $x^{(0)}$ in ℓ^∞ or ω defined by

$$x_i^{(0)} = \begin{cases} 0 & \text{if } i \text{ is even} \\ 1 & \text{if } i \text{ is odd} \end{cases}$$

but $x^{(0)} \notin (c_0)$

b. Consider the space $C(X)$ of continuous real valued functions on a compact Hausdorff space X equipped with the norm

$$\|f\| = \sup \{|f(t)| : t \in X\}$$

and the order structure discussed in (1.7). The closed lattice ideals in $C(X)$ coincide with the closed algebraic ideals when $C(X)$ is regarded as a Banach algebra. For it is well known that the closed algebraic ideals in $C(X)$ are precisely the sets

$$I_F = \{f \in C(X) : f(x) = 0 \quad \text{for all } x \in F\}$$

where F is an arbitrary closed subset of X. It is clear that each such I_F is a lattice ideal in $C(X)$. On the other hand, if I is a norm closed lattice ideal in $C(X)$ and if $f \in I$, $g \in C(X)$, then $|fg| \leq \|g\| \, |f|$; hence, I is a norm closed algebraic ideal. The latter argument also shows that every lattice ideal in $C(X)$ is an algebraic ideal. The converse is not true in general; for example, if X is the closed interval $[-1, 1]$ of the real line and if I is the algebraic ideal generated by $f(x) = x$, then

$$I = \{h \in C[-1, 1] : h(x) = xg(x) \quad \text{for some } g \in C[-1, 1]\}$$

and $|f| \notin I$.

c. If X is a set and $B(X)$ is the order complete vector lattice of all real-valued, bounded functions on the set X (see (1.7)), then, for each subset Y of X, the set $M_Y = \{f \in B(X) : f(y) = 0 \text{ for all } y \in Y\}$ is a band in $B(X)$.

If M is a linear subspace of a vector space E ordered by a cone K, the image $\dot{K} = \varphi(K)$ of K under the canonical quotient mapping $\varphi : E \to E/M = \dot{E}$ is a wedge in $\dot{E}$. However, as we have seen in (1.7), $\dot{K}$ is not a cone in general, even if E is a vector lattice and M is a sublattice of E. The next result shows that a much better order-theoretic correspondence between E and $\dot{E}$ is valid if M is a lattice ideal.

4.3 Proposition. If E is a vector lattice and M is a lattice ideal in E, the quotient space $\dot{E} = E/M$ is a vector lattice for the order structure determined by the canonical image $\dot{K}$ in $\dot{E}$ of the cone K in E.

Proof. Suppose that $\dot{x} \in \dot{K} \cap (-\dot{K})$; then there exist x_1, x_2 in K such that $\dot{x} = \varphi(x_1) = -\varphi(x_2)$ where φ is canonical mapping of E onto $\dot{E}$. This implies that $\varphi(x_1 + x_2) = \dot{\theta}$, that is, $x_1 + x_2 \in M$. Therefore, since $\theta \leq x_1 \leq x_1 + x_2$ and M is a lattice ideal in E, it follows that $x_1 \in M$. We conclude that $\dot{x} = \dot{\theta}$; hence, $\dot{K}$ is a cone in $\dot{E}$.

If $\dot{x} \in \dot{E}$ and $x \in \dot{x}$, it is clear that $\varphi(x^+) \geq \dot{x}$ and $\varphi(x^+) \geq \dot{\theta}$. On the other hand, if $\dot{z} \geq \dot{x}$ and $\dot{z} \geq \dot{\theta}$, there exist z_1, z_2 in $\dot{z}$ and x_1 in $\dot{x}$ such that $z_1 \geq x_1$ and $z_2 \geq \theta$. But then $z_1 \stackrel{\cup}{} z_2 \geq \theta$, $(z_1 \stackrel{\cup}{} z_2) \geq x_1$ and, since $(z_1 \stackrel{\cup}{} z_2) - z_1 = \theta \stackrel{\cup}{} (z_2 - z_1) \in M$, it follows that $z_1 \stackrel{\cup}{} z_2 \in \dot{z}$. Since $|x_1^+ - x^+| \leq |x_1 - x|$ and M is a lattice ideal in E, we conclude that $\varphi(x^+) = \varphi(x_1{}^+)$; hence, $\dot{z} \geq \varphi(x^+)$. Therefore, $\varphi(x^+) =$ sup $\{\dot{x}, \dot{\theta}\}$, that is, $\dot{E}$ is a vector lattice.

In Section 1, we defined two elements x, y of a vector lattice E to be disjoint (written $x \perp y$) if $|x| \cap |y| = \theta$. If A is a subset of E, the set of all elements y of E such that $y \perp x$ for each $x \in A$ will be denoted by $A^\perp$. For example, if A is a subset of $C(X)$ and $I(A)$ is the closed ideal in $C(X)$ generated by A, then $I(A) = I_F$, where F is the intersection of the null sets of the elements of A $\big($see $(4.2)(b)\big)$ and $A^\perp = I_G$ where G is the closure of the complement of F in X.

4.4 Proposition. If A is a subset of a vector lattice E, the set $A^\perp$ is a lattice ideal in E and $A^\perp$ contains sup (B) for any subset B of $A^\perp$ for which sup (B) exists in E.

Proof. The fact that $A^\perp$ is a linear subspace of E follows from the relation $|\alpha x| = |\alpha| |x|$ and Equation (19) in Section 1. Since $|x| \leq |y|$ and $y \perp z$ clearly imply that $x \perp z$, it follows that $A^\perp$ is a lattice ideal in E. Finally, suppose B is a subset of $A^\perp$ that has a supremum $b \in E$. Without loss in generality, we can assume that B is a subset of the cone in E. If $y \in B$, then, in view of Equation (11) of Section 1, $|x| \vee y = |x| + y$ for all $x \in A$. But then $|x| \vee b = |x| \vee$ sup $(B) =$ sup $\{|x| \vee y : y \in B\} =$ sup $\{|x| + y : y \in B\} = |x| + b$; hence, $b \perp x$. Therefore, $b \in A^\perp$.

We shall see that the strong direct sum decomposition introduced in the following definition is characteristic of direct sums of bands in order complete vector lattices.

4.5 Definition. If E is an ordered vector space and E is the direct sum of two linear subspaces M and N of E, then E is the **order direct sum** of M and N if $x \geq \theta$ and $x = x_1 + x_2$ where $x_1 \in M$, $x_2 \in N$ imply $x_1 \geq \theta$, $x_2 \geq \theta$; that is, the projections $P_M : E \to M$ and $P_N : E \to N$ are positive linear mappings.

4.6 Proposition. If E is a vector lattice and M is a linear subspace of E such that $E = M + M^\perp$, then $M = (M^\perp)^\perp$ and E is the order direct sum of M and $M^\perp$.

Proof. Since $M \cap M^\perp = \{\theta\}$, it follows that E is the direct sum of M and $M^\perp$. Clearly, $M \subset (M^\perp)^\perp$; if $z \in (M^\perp)^\perp$ but $z \notin M$, choose the unique $x \in M$, $\theta \neq y \in M^{\perp}$ such that $z = x + y$. For any $w \in M^{\perp}$ it is true that $\theta = |z| \cap |w| = |x + y| \cap |w| \geq ||x| - |y|| \cap |w| = (|x| + |y|) \cap |w| \geq |x - y| \cap |w|$ since $x \perp y$ (see Equation (12) of Section 1); hence, $x - y \in (M^{\perp})^{\perp}$. In view of the fact that $x + y \in (M^{\perp})^{\perp}$, it follows that $y \in (M^{\perp})^{\perp}$. This contradicts the definition of y; hence, it must be true that $M = (M^{\perp})^{\perp}$.

If $z \in E$ and $z = x + y$, where $x \in M$ and $y \in M^{\perp}$, then $|z| = |x + y| \leq |x| + |y|$. On the other hand, $|z| = |x + y| \geq ||x| - |y|| = |x| + |y|$ since $x \perp y$; hence,

(1) If $z = x + y$, $x \in M$, $y \in M^{\perp}$, then $|z| = |x| + |y|$.

In particular, E is the order direct sum of M and $M^{\perp}$.

In addition to (1), the following relations also hold:

(2) If $z = x + y$, where $x \in M$, $y \in M^{\perp}$, then $z^{+} = x^{+} + y^{+}$ and $z^{-} = x^{-} + y^{-}$.

(This result is easily verified by making use of (1) above and Equation (8) of Section 1).

If E is an order complete vector lattice, then E itself is obviously a band in E, and the intersection of any family of bands in E is again a band in E. Therefore, for any subset A of E, there is a " smallest " band $M(A)$ containing A; namely, the intersection of the family of all bands in E that contain A. We shall refer to $M(A)$ as the **band generated by A.**

The following fundamental result establishes the basic relation between bands and order direct sums in order complete vector lattices.

4.7 Proposition (Riesz [1]). If A is a subset of an order complete vector lattice E, then $A^{\perp}$ and $(A^{\perp})^{\perp}$ are bands, E is the order direct sum of $A^{\perp}$ and $(A^{\perp})^{\perp}$, and $(A^{\perp})^{\perp}$ is the band generated by A. If E is the order direct sum of two linear subspaces M and N, then M and N are bands in E and $N = M^{\perp}$.

Proof. The fact that $A^{\perp}$ and $(A^{\perp})^{\perp}$ are bands in E is an immediate consequence of (4.4). If $z \geq \theta$ and $y = \sup \{[\theta, z] \cap A^{\perp}\}$, then $y \leq z$ so that $z = y + w$, where $w \geq \theta$. Since $A^{\perp}$ is a band in E, we know that

$y \in A^\perp$; hence, in view of (4.6) and the fact that the cone is generating, we can conclude that E is the order direct sum of $A^\perp$ and $(A^\perp)^\perp$ if we show that $w \in (A^\perp)^\perp$. If $\theta \leq u \in A^\perp$ and $v = u \cap w$, then $v \in A^\perp$, since $\theta \leq v \leq u \in A^\perp$; moreover, $v \leq z - y$. For all $s \in A^\perp \cap [\theta, z]$, it is true that $s \leq y$ by definition of y; hence, $v + s \leq v + y \leq z$ for all such s. Therefore,

$$v + y = \sup \{v + s : s \in A^\perp \cap [\theta, z]\} \leq y;$$

hence $v \leq \theta$. We conclude that $w \in (A^\perp)^\perp$; hence, E is the order direct sum of $A^\perp$ and $(A^\perp)^\perp$.

If M is the band in E generated by A, then by replacing $A^\perp$ by M and $(A^\perp)^\perp$ by $M^\perp$ in the last paragraph, we can conclude that $E = M + M^\perp$. Since $M \supset A$, it follows that $M^\perp \subset A^\perp$. Also, $(A^\perp)^\perp$ is a band in E containing A; hence $(A^\perp)^\perp \supset M$. From these inclusions, we can conclude that $M = (A^\perp)^\perp$ and $M^\perp = A^\perp$.

Now suppose that E is the order direct sum of two linear subspaces M and N. If $z \in E$, there exist z_1, w_1 in M and z_2, w_2 in N such that

$$z = z_1 + z_2, \qquad |z| = w_1 + w_2.$$

Since $|z| \geq z$ and $|z| \geq -z$, it follows that $w_1 \geq |z_1|$ and $w_2 \geq |z_2|$. Therefore, $|z| = |z_1 + z_2| \leq |z_1| + |z_2| \leq w_1 + w_2 = |z|$; hence, $w_1 = |z_1|$ and $w_2 = |z_2|$. By making use of Equation (8) in Section 1, we can now conclude that

$$z^+ = z_1^+ + z_2^+, \qquad z^- = z_1^- + z_2^-.$$

Moreover, if $y \in E$ and $y = y_1 + y_2$, where $y_1 \in M$ and $y_2 \in N$, then

$$z \cup y = z_1 \cup y_1 + z_2 \cup y_2,$$

$$z \cap y = z_1 \cap y_1 + z_2 \cap y_2.$$

Therefore, if $z \in M$ and $y \in N$, we obtain $|z| \cap |y| = \theta$; hence, $N \subset M^\perp$. Just as in the first paragraph of the proof of (4.6), we can conclude that $N = M^\perp$. The assertion now follows from (4.6) and the first statement in (4.7).

4.8 Corollary. If M is a band in an order complete vector lattice, then $M = (M^\perp)^\perp$.

The following simple results provide some additional information concerning the structure of bands in order complete vector lattices.

4.9 Proposition. Suppose that A is a subset of an order complete vector lattice with positive cone K. If

$$M_1 = \left\{ x \in K : x \le \sum_{i=1}^{n} |x_i| \, ; \, x_i \in A \right\},$$

$$M_2 = \{ y \in K : y = \sup (C) \quad \text{where } C \subset M_1 \text{ is majorized in } E \},$$

then $M_2 = M(A) \cap K$ where $M(A)$ is the band in E generated by A.

Proof. Clearly $A \cap K \subset M_1 \subset M_2 \subset M(A)$; hence, $A^{\perp} \supset M_1^{\perp} \supset M_2^{\perp} \supset M(A)^{\perp} = A^{\perp}$. (The last equality follows from (4.7).) Therefore, E is the order direct sum of $M_1^{\perp}$ and $M(A)$ by (4.7). If $\theta \le z \in E$ and $y = \sup \{ [\theta, z] \cap M_1 \}$, then $y \in M_2$. Define $w = z - y \ge \theta$, then $w \in M_1^{\perp}$ (see the first part of the proof of (4.7)). Therefore, y is the component of z in $M(A)$, that is, $M_2 = M(A) \cap K$.

4.10 Corollary. If u is an element of an order complete vector lattice E and $M(u)$ is the band in E generated by u, then the component in $M(u)$ of an element $z \ge \theta$ is $\sup \{ n |u| \cap z : n = 1, 2, \ldots \}$.

Proof. This follows immediately from the definition of the component y of z in the proof of (4.9).

4.11 Proposition. If u and v are disjoint elements of an order complete vector lattice E, then every element of the band $M(u)$ generated by u is disjoint from every element of the band $M(v)$ generated by v.

Proof. Since $u \in M(v)^{\perp}$ and $M(v)^{\perp}$ is a band, it follows that $M(u) \subset M(v)^{\perp}$. Therefore, if $x \in M(u)$ and $y \in M(v)$, it follows that $x \perp y$.

The following example includes a simple application of the preceding results.

4.12 Example. Suppose that Σ is a field of subsets of a set S and that $ba(S, \Sigma)$ is the vector space of all real-valued, bounded, additive set functions defined on Σ. The set

$$K = \{ \mu \in ba(S, \Sigma) : \mu(E) \ge 0 \quad \text{for all } E \in \Sigma \}$$

is clearly a cone in $ba(S, \Sigma)$ and the Jordan Decomposition Theorem implies that this cone generates a lattice order on $ba(S, \Sigma)$. Moreover, if $\{\mu_\alpha : \alpha \in D\}$ is a directed ($\leq$) subset of $ba(S, \Sigma)$ that is majorized by $\mu_0 \in ba(S, \Sigma)$, then

$$\mu(E) = \sup \{\mu_\alpha(E) : \alpha \in D\} \qquad (E \in \Sigma) \qquad (*)$$

defines a set function on Σ which is additive since each μ_α is additive. Moreover, $\mu(E) \leq \mu_0(E)$ for all $E \in \Sigma$; hence, $\mu \in ba(S, \Sigma)$, and it is clear that μ is the supremum of $\{\mu_\alpha : \alpha \in D\}$ in $ba(S, \Sigma)$. Therefore, $ba(S, \Sigma)$ is an order complete vector lattice.

The linear subspace $ca(S, \Sigma)$ of $ba(S, \Sigma)$ consisting of the countably additive set functions in $ba(S, \Sigma)$ is a band in $ba(S, \Sigma)$. For if $\{\mu_\alpha : \alpha \in D\}$ is a directed ($\leq$) subset of the vector lattice $ca(S, \Sigma)$ that is majorized by $\mu_0 \in ba(S, \Sigma)$, and if $\{E_n\}$ is an increasing sequence of sets in Σ such that $\bigcup_{n=1}^{\infty} E_n = E \in \Sigma$, then the bounded additive set function μ defined by $(*)$ is actually countably additive, since

$$\sup_n \mu(E_n) = \sup_n \sup_{\alpha \in D} \mu_\alpha(E_n) = \sup_{\alpha \in D} \sup_n \mu_\alpha(E_n) = \sup_{\alpha \in D} \mu_\alpha(E) = \mu(E).$$

Therefore, $\mu \in ca(S, \Sigma)$, that is, $ca(S, \Sigma)$ is a band in $ba(S, \Sigma)$.

In view of (4.7), each $\mu \in ba(S, \Sigma)$ such that $\mu \geq \theta$ can be written in the form $\mu = \mu_1 + \mu_2$, where $\theta \leq \mu_1 \in ca(S, \Sigma)$, $\theta \leq \mu_2$, and $\mu_2 \perp \nu$ for all $\nu \in ca(S, \Sigma)$. Now the last restriction is equivalent to the assertion that $\nu = \theta$ whenever $\theta \leq \nu \leq \mu_2$ and $\nu \in ca(S, \Sigma)$; an additive set function μ_2 with this latter property is called **purely finitely additive**. Therefore, we have established the following result which is due to Yosida and Hewitt [1]:

Proposition. Every non-negative, bounded, additive set function on (S, Σ) can be decomposed into the sum of a non-negative measure μ_1 on (S, Σ) and a purely finitely additive, non-negative set function μ_2 on (S, Σ).

4.13 Notes. A number of authors (for example, see Aubert [1], Bonsall [1], [2], [5], Kadison [1], Kist [2], Maltese [1] and Veksler [1]) have studied the properties of certain linear subspaces of ordered vector spaces called order ideals with a view toward obtaining a theory parallel to the ideal theory in Banach algebras. (A linear subspace M of an ordered vector space E is an **order ideal** if the order interval $[x, y]$ is contained in M whenever x, y are elements of M. Clearly, if E is a vector lattice, then every lattice ideal in E is an order ideal and every sublattice of E that is an order ideal is also a lattice ideal.)

The notion of a band was first studied by Riesz [1], [2] for function spaces in connection with certain linear functional decompositions motivated by integration theory. Bauer [2], Gordon and Lorch [1], Gordon [1], [3], Swong [1] and Yosida-Hewitt [1], considerably extended Riesz's line of investigation. The papers by Gordon and Gordon-Lorch investigate bands from the point of view of projections rather than from the standpoint of the order direct sum decompositions used by Riesz and Bauer. Systematic and extensive treatments of the theory of bands can be found in Kantorovitch-Vulih-Pinsker [1] (where they are referred to as components) and Nakano [2], [4] (where they are called normal manifolds).

§5. CONVERGENCE IN VECTOR LATTICES

When a vector space is equipped with a lattice ordering, certain "natural" notions of convergence can be defined in terms of the resulting order structure. This section is devoted to a study of the two types of convergence of this sort that seem to be the most significant in the theory of ordered vector spaces. In Section 2 of Chapter 4, we shall relate these convergence concepts to certain topological structures that can be imposed on the space.

5.1 Definitions. A net $\{y_\alpha : \alpha \in I\}$ in a vector lattice E **decreases** (resp. **increases**) to $y_0 \in E$ if $y_0 = \inf \{y_\alpha : \alpha \in I\}$ and $y_\alpha \geq y_\beta$ whenever $\beta \geq \alpha$ (resp. $y_0 = \sup \{y_\alpha : \alpha \in I\}$ and $y_\alpha \leq y_\beta$ whenever $\beta \geq \alpha$). A net $\{x_\alpha : \alpha \in I\}$ in E **order converges** to $x_0 \in E$ if:

a. $\{x_\alpha : \alpha \in I\}$ is an order bounded subset of E.
b.   There is a net $\{y_\alpha : \alpha \in I\}$ that decreases to θ such that $|x_\alpha - x_0| \leq y_\alpha$ for all $\alpha \in I$.

Obviously, a net $\{y_\alpha : \alpha \in I\}$ in E that is order bounded and either increases or decreases to an element $y_0 \in E$ also order converges to y_0.

If $\{x_n\}$ is a sequence in a σ-order complete vector lattice E, then it is an easy matter to verify that $\{x_n\}$ order converges to $x_0 \in E$ if and only if

$$\inf_n \left(\sup_{k \geq n} x_k \right) = x_0 = \sup_n \left(\inf_{k \geq n} x_k \right). \tag{1}$$

Similarly, if $\{x_\alpha : \alpha \in I\}$ is an order bounded net in an order complete vector lattice E, then $\{x_\alpha : \alpha \in I\}$ order converges to $x_0 \in E$ if and only if

$$\inf_{\alpha \in I} \left(\sup_{\beta \geq \alpha} x_\beta \right) = x_0 = \sup_{\alpha \in I} \left(\inf_{\beta \geq \alpha} x_\beta \right). \tag{1'}$$

5.2   Examples.   a. Suppose that λ is a sequence space ordered by the cone of elements in λ with non-negative components (see (1.6)). If A is a subset of λ that has a supremum $x^{(0)}$ in λ, a straightforward argument shows that $x_n^{(0)} = \sup \{a_n : a = (a_n) \in A\}$; that is, if the supremum of a set in λ exists, it coincides with the coordinate supremum of the set. Of course, a similar remark holds for infima in λ. By making use of these facts, one can easily show that a net $\{x^{(\alpha)} : \alpha \in I\}$ in λ order converges to $x^{(0)} \in \lambda$ if and only if it is order bounded and for each integer n,

$$\lim_\alpha x_n^{(\alpha)} = x_n^{(0)}.$$

b. Suppose that (S, Σ, μ) is a σ-finite measure space consisting of a set S, a σ-field Σ of subsets of S, and a measure μ on (S, Σ). Define $M(S, \Sigma, \mu)$ to be the vector space of all real-valued functions measurable with respect Σ, two such functions regarded as identical if they agree μ-almost everywhere on S. The fact that $M(S, \Sigma, \mu)$ is a σ-order complete vector lattice for the order generated by the cone

$$K = \{f \in M(S, \Sigma, \mu) : f(x) \geq 0 \quad \mu\text{-almost everywhere}\}$$

is a consequence of the elementary properties of measurable functions. If E is a lattice ideal in $M(S, \Sigma, \mu)$, then E is σ-order complete; in fact, the suprema and infima of subsets of E coincide with the corresponding suprema and infima in $M(S, \Sigma, \mu)$. By making use of the characterization of order convergence given by Equation (1) above, we conclude that a sequence $\{f_n\}$ in E order converges to $f_0 \in E$ if and only if $|f_n| \leq g$ for some $g \in E$ and $\{f_n\}$ converges to f_0 μ-almost everywhere. In particular, order convergence coincides with bounded, μ-almost everywhere convergence for sequences in $M(S, \Sigma, \mu)$, $L^\infty(S, \Sigma, \mu)$, and $L^p(S, \Sigma, \mu)(p \geq 1)$.

One of the fundamental properties of sequential convergence with respect to a topology is embodied in the following easily verified statement: A sequence $\{x_n\}$ converges to a point x_0 if and only if every subsequence of $\{x_n\}$ has a subsequence that converges to x_0. We shall refer to this property of convergence as the **star property**. Unfortunately, order convergence does not always have the star property. For example, if we consider the space $M(S, \Sigma, \mu)$ discussed in (5.2)(b), we have already noted that order convergence for order bounded sequences coincides with almost everywhere convergence. However, if $\{f_n\}$ is an order bounded sequence in $M(S, \Sigma, \mu)$, then, if (S, Σ, μ) is a finite measure space, a standard measure theoretic argument shows that the almost everywhere convergence to $f_0 \in M(S, \Sigma, \mu)$ of some subsequence of each subsequence of $\{f_n\}$ is equivalent to the statement that $\{f_n\}$ converges to f_0 in measure. Since convergence in measure does not imply convergence almost everywhere even when the sequence in question is order bounded and the measure space is finite, we conclude that order convergence does not have the star property. Two conclusions can be drawn from the preceding considerations: First of all, order convergence cannot be identical with convergence with respect to a topology in general. Secondly, the weaker type of convergence defined by requiring the order convergence of some subsequence of each subsequence of a given sequence is an interesting object of study since it describes convergence in measure in $M(S, \Sigma, \mu)$. With this latter point in mind, we introduce the following definition.

5.3 Definition. A sequence $\{x_n\}$ in a vector lattice E **order ∗-converges** to $x_0 \in E$ if every subsequence of $\{x_n\}$ contains a subsequence that order converges to x_0.

It is clear that if $\{x_n\}$ order converges to x_0 then $\{x_n\}$ order ∗-converges to x_0.

If we define the operator $A \to \bar{A}$ on the class of all subsets of a vector lattice E by

$$\bar{A} = \{x \in E : \{x_n\} \quad \text{order *-converges to } x \text{ for some } \{x_n\} \subset A\},$$

it is not true in general that a topological closure operator is obtained. Before we present an example to substantiate this remark, we first note that

$$\bar{A} = \{x \in E : \{x_n\} \quad \text{order converges to } x \text{ for some } \{x_n\} \subset A\}.$$

5.4   Example.   Consider the subset $A = \{x^{(m,n)} : m, n = 1, 2, 3, \ldots\}$ of the order complete vector latticed ℓ^{∞} of bounded sequences of real numbers $\big($see (1.6), (5.2)(a)$\big)$ defined by

$$x_k^{(n,m)} = \begin{cases} \dfrac{1}{n} & \text{if } k = 1 \\ n & \text{if } k \geq m + 1 \qquad m, n = 1, 2, \ldots \\ 0 & \text{otherwise} \end{cases}$$

For fixed n, $\{x^{(n,m)}\}$ order converges to $x^{(n)}$ where

$$x_k^{(n)} = \begin{cases} \dfrac{1}{n} & \text{if } k = 1 \\ 0 & \text{otherwise} \end{cases}$$

Therefore, $x^{(n)} \in \bar{A}$ for each n; hence, $\theta \in \bar{A}$ since $\{x^{(n)}\}$ clearly order converges to θ. However, no sequence (or net) in A can order converge to θ since order convergence coincides with pointwise convergence and order boundedness in ℓ^{∞} $\big($see (5.2)(a)$\big)$. Therefore, $\bar{A} \neq \bar{\bar{A}}$, that is, $\bar{A}$ is not the closure of A for any topology on ℓ^{∞}.

The following definition introduces a class of vector lattices for which the operator $A \to \bar{A}$ defined above does turn out to be a topological closure operator. The conditions imposed in this definition are not always easy to check in specific spaces. However, we shall establish a very useful sufficient condition for this property in Section 2 of Chapter 4; this result will make it clear that, for example, the L^p spaces for $1 \leq p < +\infty$ are in this class under very light restrictions on the underlying measure space. That result must be delayed until then since it involves relations between order and topology that we have yet to discuss.

5.5 Definition. A vector lattice E has the **diagonal property** if, whenever $\{x^{(n,m)} : n, m = 1, 2, \ldots\} \subset E$ and

a. $\{x^{(n,m)}\}$ order converges to $x^{(n)} \in E$ for each n,
b. $\{x^{(n)}\}$ order converges to $x^{(0)} \in E$,

then there is a strictly increasing sequence $\{m_n : n = 1, 2, \ldots\}$ of positive integers such that $\{x^{(n,m_n)}\}$ order converges to $x^{(0)}$.

5.6 Proposition. If E is a vector lattice with the diagonal property, the set mapping $A \to \bar{A}$ defined for subsets A of E by
$$\bar{A} = \{x \in E : \{x_n\} \text{ order converges to } x \text{ for some } \{x_n\} \subset A\}$$
is a closure operator on E. If $\mathfrak{X}$ is the unique topology on E determined by this closure operator, a sequence $\{x_n\}$ in E converges for $\mathfrak{X}$ to $x_0 \in E$ if and only if $\{x_n\}$ order $*$-converges to x_0.

Proof. Since E has the diagonal property, it is an easy matter to verify that $\bar{\bar{A}} = \bar{A}$ for any subset A of E. The remaining Kuratowski axioms for a closure operator are clearly satisfied. Therefore, there is a unique topology $\mathfrak{X}$ on E for which the $\mathfrak{X}$-closure of any set A coincides with $\bar{A}$.

Suppose that $\{x_n\}$ is not order $*$-convergent to x, then there is a subsequence $\{x_{n_k}\}$ of $\{x_n\}$ such that no subsequence of $\{x_{n_k}\}$ order converges to x, that is, $x \notin \bar{A}$ where $A = \{x_{n_k} : k = 1, 2, \ldots\}$. Therefore, the complement V of $\bar{A}$ is a neighborhood of x and $x_{n_k} \notin V$ for all k. Hence, $\{x_n\}$ does not converge to x for the topology $\mathfrak{X}$.

Conversely, if $\{x_n\}$ is not $\mathfrak{X}$-convergent to x, there is an open neighborhood V of x and a subsequence $\{x_{n_k}\}$ of $\{x_n\}$ such that $x_{n_k} \notin V$ for all k. The limit of any subsequence of $\{x_{n_k}\}$ that order converges must be in the complement of V by definition of the closure operator determining $\mathfrak{X}$; hence, no subsequence of $\{x_{n_k}\}$ order converges to x. Thus, order $*$-convergence coincides with $\mathfrak{X}$-convergence for sequences in E.

We shall now turn our attention to a second type of convergence that is determined by the order structure of a vector lattice.

5.7 Definitions. A sequence $\{x_n\}$ in a vector lattice E is **relatively uniformly convergent** to $x_0 \in E$ if there exist an element $u \in E$ and sequence $\{\lambda_n\}$ of real numbers decreasing to 0 such that

$$|x_n - x_0| \leq \lambda_n u \qquad n = 1, 2, 3, \ldots$$

A sequence $\{x_n\} \subset E$ is **relatively uniformly *-convergent** to $x_0 \in E$ if every subsequence of $\{x_n\}$ contains a subsequence that is relatively uniformly convergent to x_0.

In Section 2 of Chapter 4, we shall identify relative uniform *-convergence with an important type of topological convergence. In particular, it will turn out that relative uniform *-convergence coincides with topological convergence in any complete, metrizable topological vector lattice. Thus, in particular, relative uniform convergence provides a useful order theoretic description of norm convergence in spaces like $C(X)$, $L^p(S, \Sigma, \mu)$, etc.

It is clear that relative uniform convergence implies order convergence in almost Archimedean vector lattices. The sequence $\{x^{(n)}\}$ in ℓ^∞ defined by

$$x_i^{(n)} = \begin{cases} 0 & \text{if } i \leq n \\ 1 & \text{if } i > n \end{cases}$$

obviously order converges to the zero element θ, yet $\{x^{(n)}\}$ does not converge relatively uniformly to θ. The following lemma will enable us to prove that order convergence implies relative uniform convergence in spaces with the diagonal property.

5.8 Lemma. If E is a σ-order complete vector lattice with the diagonal property and if $\{x_n\}$ is a sequence in E that order converges to θ, then there is an unbounded, monotone increasing sequence $\{\lambda_n\}$ of positive numbers such that $\{\lambda_n x_n\}$ order converges to θ.

Proof. Since $\{|x_n|\}$ order converges to θ, the sequence $\{w_n\}$ defined by

$$w_n = \sup\{|x_k| : k \geq n\} \qquad n = 1, 2, \ldots$$

decreases to θ. Therefore, for each positive integer k, the sequence $\{kw_n : n = 1, 2, \ldots\}$ order converges to θ. By virtue of the diagonal property, there exists a strictly increasing sequence $\{n_k\}$ of positive integers such that $\{kw_{n_k} : k = 1, 2, \ldots\}$ order converges to θ. Define $\lambda_n = k$ for $n_k \leq n < n_{k+1}$, then $\{\lambda_n w_n\}$ order converges to θ since $\{w_n\}$ is decreasing. Therefore, $\{\lambda_n x_n\}$ order converges to θ.

5.9 Proposition. If E is a σ-order complete vector lattice with the diagonal property, then order convergence is equivalent to relative uniform convergence for sequences in E.

Proof. Since every σ-order complete vector lattice is Archimedean, relative uniform convergence implies order convergence for sequences in E. On the other hand, if $\{x_n\}$ order converges to x, the preceding lemma asserts the existence of an unbounded, increasing sequence $\{\lambda_n\}$ of positive numbers such that $\{\lambda_n |x_n - x|\}$ order converges to θ. But since each order convergent sequence is necessarily order bounded, there is an element $u \in E$ such that $\lambda_n |x_n - x| \leq u$ for all n, that is, $\{x_n\}$ converges relatively uniformly to x.

5.10 Proposition. If E is a σ-order complete vector lattice with the diagonal property and if $\{y^{(k,n)}\}$ is a sequence in E that order converges to $y^{(n)} \in E$ for each positive integer n, then there is an element $y^{(0)} \in E$ such that, for any $\varepsilon > 0$ and any positive integer n, there is a positive integer $M(\varepsilon, n)$ such that

$$|y^{(k,n)} - y^{(n)}| \leq \varepsilon y^{(0)}$$

for $k \geq N(\varepsilon, n)$.

Proof. Given $\varepsilon > 0$, (5.9) asserts that there exist a sequence $\{z^{(n)}\}$ in E and a corresponding sequence $K(\varepsilon, n)$ of positive integers such that

$$|y^{(k,n)} - y^{(n)}| \leq \varepsilon z^{(n)}$$

for $k \geq K(\varepsilon, n)$. For each n, the sequence $\left\{\frac{1}{k} z^{(n)}\right\}$ order converges to θ; hence, there is an increasing sequence $\{k_n\}$ of positive integers such that $\left\{\frac{1}{k_n} z^{(n)}\right\}$ order converges to θ since E has the diagonal property. But then this latter sequence is order bounded; hence, there is a $y^{(0)} \in E$ such that $\frac{1}{k_n} z^{(n)} \leq y^{(0)}$ for each n. It is clear that $y^{(0)}$ has the property asserted in the proposition.

Each type of convergence introduced above determines a corresponding "continuity" concept for linear mappings, such a mapping being defined to be continuous if it preserves the convergence under consideration. In view of the close relation established in (5.2)(b) between order convergence and almost everywhere convergence and between order ∗-convergence and convergence in measure for certain lattices of measurable functions, it is clear that the continuity concepts associated with order convergence and order ∗-convergence are worthwhile objects of study. This is especially true since, in general, neither of these measure theoretic convergences can be identified with convergence for a topology compatible with the linear structure of the space. (We have already observed in (5.2)(b) that almost everywhere convergence is not topological in general. Though convergence in measure can be described by a metric in $M(S, \Sigma, \mu)$, scalar multiplication need not be continuous for the resulting metric topology (see, for example, Dunford-Schwartz [1], p. 102). With these considerations in mind, we introduce the following formal definitions.

5.11 *Definitions.* If E_1 and E_2 are vector lattices and T is a linear mapping of E_1 into E_2, then T is **order continuous** if the net $\{Tx_\alpha : \alpha \in I\}$ order converges to θ in E_2 whenever $\{x_\alpha : \alpha \in I\}$ is a net that order converges to θ in E_1. If, in the preceding definition, we restrict the formulation to sequences instead of arbitrary nets, we obtain weaker restrictions on T that we shall refer to as **sequential order continuity**. If T maps each sequence in E_1 that order ∗-converges to θ into a sequence that order ∗-converges to θ in E_2, then T is **sequentially order ∗-continuous**.

The collection of all order continuous (resp. sequentially order continuous; resp. sequentially order ∗-continuous) linear mappings of a vector lattice E_1 into a vector lattice E_2 will be denoted by $L^o(E_1, E_2)$ (resp. $L^{so}(E_1, E_2)$; resp. $L^{so}_*(E_1, E_2)$). It is an easy matter to verify that

$$L^o(E_1, E_2) \subset L^{so}(E_1, E_2) \subset L^{so}_*(E_1, E_2).$$

Our next task will be to relate the various types of continuity introduced in (5.11) to the notion of order boundedness discussed for linear mappings in Section 2. The restriction on an ordered vector space introduced in the following definition plays a major role in establishing this relation.

5.12 Definition. An Archimedean vector lattice E with a generating cone has the **boundedness property** if a subset B of E is order bounded whenever $\{\lambda_n x_n\}$ order converges to θ for each sequence $\{x_n\}$ in B and each sequence $\{\lambda_n\}$ of positive numbers decreasing to 0.

Of course, if B is order bounded, $\{x_n\} \subset B$ and $\{\lambda_n\}$ decreases to 0, then $\{\lambda_n x_n\}$ order converges to θ if E is Archimedean. Thus, if E has the boundedness property, the order bounded subsets of E are actually characterized by the condition stated in (5.12). Before we employ the boundedness property to relate order continuity to order boundedness for linear mappings, we shall identify some classes of spaces that enjoy this property.

5.13 Proposition. If E is an Archimedean vector lattice, each of the following conditions implies that E has the boundedness property:

a. E contains an order unit.
b. The cone K in E contains a countable subset $H = \{h_n\}$ with the following property: For each $x \in K$, there exist $h_n \in H$ and $\lambda > 0$ such that $x \le \lambda h_n$.

Proof. Since (a) obviously implies (b), we need only establish the conclusion under the assumption that (b) holds. Without loss in generality, we can assume that $h_n \le h_{n+1}$ for all n. Suppose that B is a subset of E that is not order bounded but that $\{\lambda_n x_n\}$ order converges to θ whenever $\{x_n\} \subset B$ and $\{\lambda_n\}$ decreases to 0. Then there exist $y_n \in B$ such that $y_n \notin n^2[-h_n, h_n]$ $(n = 1, 2, \ldots)$. But the sequence $\left\{\frac{1}{n} y_n\right\}$ is order bounded since it is order convergent to θ; hence, there is an integer n_0 such that

$$\frac{1}{n} y_n \in n_0[-h_{n_0}, h_{n_0}] \quad n = 1, 2, \ldots . \tag{$*$}$$

If we choose $n = n_0$ in $(*)$, we contradict the definition of y_{n_0}; hence, B must be order bounded.

It follows from (5.13) that the spaces R^n, φ, ℓ^∞, (c), $B(X)$, $C(X)$ (if X is a compact Hausdorff space), and $L^\infty(S, \Sigma, \mu)$ (if (S, Σ, μ) is a σ-finite measure space) all have the boundedness property (see (1.5)-(1.7)). A wide class of sequence spaces with the boundedness property is identified by the following result.

5.14 Proposition.   Every perfect sequence space has the boundedness property.

Proof.   If λ is a perfect sequence space, then

$$\lambda = \bigcap \{\lambda_u : u \in \lambda^\times, u \geq \theta\}$$

where each $\lambda_u = \left\{x \in \omega : \sum_{i=1}^\infty |x_i u_i| < +\infty\right\}$ is isomorphic (as a vector lattice) to ℓ^1, ω, or $\ell^1 \times \omega$ (see Köthe [1], §30, 4(3)). Since ω and ℓ^1 can easily be shown to have the boundedness property, each λ_u also has this property.

Now suppose that B is a subset of λ with the property that $\{\alpha_n x_n\}$ order converges to θ whenever $\{x_n\} \subset B$ and $\{\alpha_n\}$ decreases to 0, then B retains this property in each λ_u for $u \geq \theta$, $u \in \lambda^\times$. Therefore, there exist $y^{(u)} \geq \theta$ in λ_u such that $B \subset [-y^{(u)}, y^{(u)}]$ for each $u \geq \theta$ in $\lambda^\times$. Define y to be the infimum of $\{y^{(u)} : u \in \lambda^\times, u \geq \theta\}$ in ω, then $B \subset [-y, y]$ in ω. If we can show that $y \in \lambda$, it will follow that B is order bounded in λ. But if $u \in \lambda^\times$, $u \geq \theta$, then

$$\sum_{i=1}^\infty y_i u_i \leq \sum_{i=1}^\infty y_i^{(u)} u_i < +\infty;$$

hence, $y \in (\lambda^\times)^\times = \lambda$.

We now proceed to establish the connection between order continuous and order bounded linear mappings that we mentioned earlier.

5.15 Proposition.   If E_1 is an Archimedean vector lattice and E_2 is a vector lattice with the boundedness property, then every sequentially order continuous linear mapping of E_1 into E_2 is order bounded.

Proof.   Suppose that T is a sequentially order continuous linear mapping of E_1 into E_2 and that B is an order bounded subset of E_1.

If $\{x_n\} \subset B$ and $\{\lambda_n\}$ decreases to 0, then $\{\lambda_n x_n\}$ order converges to θ since E_1 is Archimedean. Therefore, since T is sequentially order continuous, we conclude that $\{\lambda_n T x_n\}$ order converges to θ. In view of the fact that E_2 has the boundedness property, $T(B)$ is order bounded; hence, T is an order bounded linear mapping.

It follows immediately from (5.15) that every order continuous linear mapping of an Archimedean vector lattice into a vector lattice with the boundedness property is order bounded. Under the hypotheses imposed in (5.15), it is not true that every sequentially order *-continuous linear mapping is order bounded. (We shall provide an example to substantiate this remark in Section 3 of Chapter 4.)

5.16 Proposition. If E_1 is a σ-order complete vector lattice with the diagonal property and if E_2 is an almost Archimedean vector lattice, then every order bounded linear mapping T of E_1 into E_2 is sequentially order continuous.

Proof. If $\{x_n\}$ is a sequence in E_1 that order converges to θ, then (5.8) implies that there is an unbounded, monotone increasing sequence $\{\lambda_n\}$ of positive real numbers such that $\{\lambda_n x_n\}$ order converges to θ. Since T is order bounded, there is an element y_0 in E_2 such that $|T(\lambda_n x_n)| \leq y_0$ for all n. But then $\{T(x^{(n)})\}$ order converges to θ since E_2 is almost Archimedean. Consequently, T is sequentially order continuous.

5.17 Corollary. If E is a σ-order complete vector lattice with the diagonal property, then a linear functional f on E is sequentially order continuous if and only if it is order bounded.

Proof. This result follows immediately from (5.15) and (5.16).

As we shall see, the following restriction on an ordered vector space forces the coincidence of order continuity and sequential order continuity for certain linear mappings on ordered vector spaces.

5.18 Definition. An ordered vector space E is **order separable** if every subset A of E that has a supremum in E contains a countable subset A' such that $\sup(A) = \sup(A')$.

We shall develop a useful sufficient condition for order separability in Section 2 of Chapter 4. For the time being, the following examples should help to clarify the meaning of this restriction.

5.19 Examples. a. A simple example of an order complete vector lattice that is not order separable is provided by the space $B[0, 1]$ of all bounded, real-valued functions defined on the unit interval $[0, 1]$ on the real line, ordered by the cone of functions in $B[0, 1]$ that are non-negative throughout $[0, 1]$. For example, the set A of all characteristic functions of one-point sets in $[0, 1]$ has a supremum in $B[0, 1]$ defined by

$$[\sup (A)](t) = 1 \qquad 0 \le t \le 1.$$

It is clear that no countable subset A' of A has the property that $\sup (A) = \sup (A')$.

b. Every sequence space λ is order separable. In fact, if A is a subset of λ that has a supremum $x \in \lambda$, then $x_n = \sup \{a_n : a \in A\}$ for each positive integer n $\big($see $(5.2)(a)\big)$. For each positive integer n, choose a countable set $\{a^{(n,m)} : m = 1, 2, \ldots\}$ such that

$$x_n = \sup \{a_n^{(n,m)} : m = 1, 2, \ldots\}.$$

Then $A' = \{a^{(m,n)} : m, n = 1, 2, \ldots\}$ is a countable subset of A such that $\sup (A) = \sup (A')$; hence, λ is order separable.

5.20 Proposition. If E is an order separable vector lattice, every net that decreases to θ (resp. order converges to $x_0 \in E$) contains a sequence that decreases to θ (resp. order converges to $x_0 \in E$).

Proof. First of all, suppose that $\{y_\alpha : \alpha \in I\}$ is a net that decreases to θ. Since E is order separable we can select a sequence $\{\alpha_n\} \subset I$ such that $\inf \{y_{\alpha_n} : n = 1, 2, \ldots\} = \theta$. Define $\beta_1 = \alpha_1$ and choose $\beta_2 \in I$ so that $\beta_2 \ge \beta_1$, $\beta_2 \ge \alpha_2$. After β_{n-1} has been chosen, select $\beta_n \in I$ so that $\beta_n \ge \beta_{n-1}$, $\beta_n \ge \alpha_n$. It is clear that $\{y_{\beta_n} : n = 1, 2, \ldots\}$ is a sequence that decreases to θ.

If $\{x_\alpha : \alpha \in I\}$ is a net in E that order converges to $x_0 \in E$, choose a net $\{y_\alpha : \alpha \in I\}$ in E that decreases to θ such that $|x_\alpha - x_0| \le y_\alpha$ for all $\alpha \in I$. According to the first step in the proof, there is a sequence $\{y_{\alpha_n} : \alpha_n \in I; n = 1, 2, \ldots\}$ that decreases to θ; hence, the corresponding sequence $\{x_{\alpha_n} : \alpha_n \in I; n = 1, 2, \ldots\}$ order converges to x_0.

5.21 Corollary. Every positive, sequentially order continuous linear mapping T of an order separable vector lattice E_1 into an Archimedean vector lattice E_2 is order continuous.

Proof. Suppose that T is not order continuous, then there is a net $\{y_\alpha : \alpha \in I\}$ in E_1 such that $\{y_\alpha : \alpha \in I\}$ decreases to θ, but $\{Ty_\alpha : \alpha \in I\}$ does not decrease to θ. Since T is a positive linear mapping, $\{Ty_\alpha : \alpha \in I\}$ is a monotone decreasing net. According to (5.20), there is a sequence $\{y_{\alpha_n} : \alpha_n \in I; n = 1, 2, \ldots\}$ that decreases to θ. Therefore, since T is sequentially order continuous, $\{Ty_{\alpha_n} : n = 1, 2, \ldots\}$ decreases to θ. This contradicts the statement that $\{Ty_\alpha : \alpha \in I\}$ does not decrease to θ; consequently, T must be order continuous.

We introduce the symbol E^{so} (resp. E^o) to denote the vector space of all sequentially order continuous (resp. order continuous) linear functionals on an almost Archimedean vector lattice E. According to (5.15), E^{so} is a linear subspace of the order complete vector lattice E^b of all order bounded linear functionals on E. The following result describes the relation between E^{so} and E^b more fully.

5.22 Proposition. If E is an almost Archimedean vector lattice, the space E^{so} of sequentially order continuous linear functionals on E is a band in the order complete vector lattice E^b of all order bounded linear functionals on E.

Proof. Suppose that $f \in E^{so}$ and that $|g| \leq |f|$ for some $g \in E^b$. If $\{x_n\}$ is a sequence in E that order converges to θ, choose a sequence $\{y_n\}$ that decreases to θ such that $|x_n| \leq y_n$ for all n. Since

$$|f|(y_n) = \sup \{f(z) : |z| \leq y_n\} \qquad (n = 1, 2, \ldots)$$

(see Equation (6) of Section 2), we can choose $z_n \in E$ such that $|z_n| \leq y_n$ and

$$|f|(y_n) \leq f(z_n) + \frac{1}{n} \qquad (n = 1, 2, \ldots)$$

Then

$$|g(x_n)| \leq |g|(|x_n|) \leq |f|(y_n) \leq f(z_n) + \frac{1}{n}$$

for each n; hence, $\{g(x_n)\}$ converges to 0 since f is sequentially order continuous. We conclude that E^{so} is a lattice ideal in E^b.

Now suppose that A is a directed ($\leq$) subset of the cone in E^{so} that is majorized in E^b. If $g = \sup(A)$ in E^b, then

$$g(x) = \sup\{f(x): f \in A\}$$

for $x \geq \theta$ (see Equation (10) of Section 2). If $\{y_n\}$ is a sequence in E that decreases to θ and if $\varepsilon > 0$ is given, choose $f_\varepsilon \in A$ such that

$$g(y_1) \leq f_\varepsilon(y_1) + \varepsilon.$$

Then

$$|g(y_n)| \leq f_\varepsilon(y_n) + (g - f_\varepsilon)(y_n) \leq f_\varepsilon(y_n) + \varepsilon;$$

hence, $\{g(y_n)\}$ converges to 0 since $f_\varepsilon \in E^{so}$ and ε is an arbitrary positive number. If $\{x_n\}$ is an arbitrary sequence in E that order converges to θ, choose a sequence $\{y_n\}$ that decreases to θ such that $|x_n| \leq y_n$ for all n. Then, since $|g(x_n)| \leq g(y_n)$ and $\{g(y_n)\}$ converges to 0, it follows that $\{g(x_n)\}$ converges to 0. Therefore, $g \in E^{so}$.

5.23 Corollary. If E is an order separable, almost Archimedean vector lattice, then $E^{so} = E^o$.

Proof. This result is an immediate consequence of (5.21) and (5.22).

The following result shows that λ^{so} can be identified with the Köthe dual $\lambda^\times$ for most sequence spaces λ.

5.24 Proposition. If a sequence space λ is a lattice ideal in ω, the following assertions concerning a linear functional f on λ are equivalent:

a. f is sequentially order continuous.

b.   There is a unique $u \in \lambda^\times$ such that

$$f(x) = \langle x, u \rangle = \sum_{n=1}^{\infty} x_n u_n \quad \text{for all } x \in \lambda.$$

Proof. If f is order continuous and $e^{(n)}$ is the "nth-unit vector" in λ (that is, $e_k^{(n)} = \delta_{nk}$ where δ_{nk} is the Kronecker delta), define $u_n =$

$f(e^{(n)})$. Then, if $x \in \lambda$ and $x^{(k)}$ is the element of λ defined by

$$x_n^{(k)} = \begin{cases} x_n & \text{if } k \geq n \\ 0 & \text{if } k < n \end{cases} \quad (k = 1, 2, \ldots),$$

it is clear that $\{x^{(k)}\}$ order converges to x. Since

$$f(x^{(k)}) = \sum_{n=1}^{k} x_n u_n,$$

the series $\sum_{n=1}^{\infty} x_n u_n$ converges to $f(x)$ for each $x \in \lambda$. Moreover, since λ is a lattice ideal in ω, the convergence of this series is absolute for each $x \in \lambda$. Consequently, $u = (u_n) \in \lambda^{\times}$ and $f(x) = \langle x, u \rangle$ for all $x \in \lambda$; the fact that u is the unique element of $\lambda^{\times}$ satisfying this latter equation is an immediate consequence of the fact that $e^{(n)} \in \lambda$ for all n.

On the other hand, suppose that (b) is satisfied. To show that f is sequentially order continuous, it is sufficient to prove that $|u|(y^{(n)})$ converges to 0 whenever $\{y^{(n)}\}$ is a sequence in λ that decreases to θ (see the proof of (5.22)). Now, for any positive integer N,

$$|u|(y^{(n)}) = \sum_{k=1}^{N} |u_k| y_k^{(n)} + \sum_{k=N+1}^{\infty} |u_k| y_k^{(n)}.$$

For a given $\varepsilon > 0$, choose N_1 so that

$$\sum_{k=N_1+1}^{\infty} |u_k| y_k^{(1)} < \frac{\varepsilon}{2}, \qquad (*)$$

then $(*)$ also holds when $y^{(1)}$ is replaced by any $y^{(n)}$ since $\{y^{(n)}\}$ is a monotone decreasing sequence. Moreover, the sequence $\{|u_k| y_k^{(n)}\}$ decreases to 0 for each k; hence, there is a positive integer n_0 such that

$$\sum_{k=1}^{N_1} |u_k| y_k^{(n)} < \frac{\varepsilon}{2}$$

for all $n \geq n_0$. Therefore, $\{|u|(y^{(n)})\}$ converges to 0, that is, f is sequentially order continuous.

5.25 Example. The preceding proposition shows that a linear functional on the space ℓ^{∞} of all bounded sequences of real numbers is sequentially order continuous if and only if it can be represented by an element of ℓ^1. Since it is clear that a linear functional on ℓ^∞ is continuous for the norm:

$$\|x\| = \sup_n |x_n|$$

if and only if it is order bounded, we conclude that $(\ell^\infty)^{so}$ is properly contained in $(\ell^\infty)^b$. Moreover, $(\ell^\infty)^{so} = (\ell^\infty)^o$ by (5.23) since ℓ^∞ is order separable (see (5.19)).

Notes. Order convergence was first studied by Birkhoff [1] and Kantorovitch [1], [2], while relative uniform convergence was introduced by Moore [1] and Kantorovitch [2]. Most of the results of this section were either taken from Kantorovitch [2], [3] or the author's joint paper with Sherbert [1].

We refer the reader to Birkhoff [2], Kantorovitch [2], Kantorovitch-Vulih-Pinsker [1], Lorentz [1], and Nakano [2] for further information about order-theoretic convergence.

In contrast to (5.6), DeMarr [1], [2] considered the problem of equipping a locally convex space with an order structure in such a way that convergence for the given topology of the space coincides with an order theoretic convergence.

Kantorovitch [3] and Kantorovitch-Vulih-Pinsker [1] provide much information about order continuous linear mappings including a number of representation theorems for order continuous linear mappings on specific ordered vector spaces. In (4.20) of Chapter 2, we shall characterize the order continuous linear functionals on the space of continuous functions with compact support in a locally compact, σ-compact Hausdorff space. Characterizations of these functionals for other spaces can be found in Mullins [1] and Nakamura [1].

Some applications of order convergence and order continuity to probability theory can be found in Cogburn [1].

Chapter Two

===

Ordered Topological
Vector Spaces

All of the concrete ordered vector spaces we have considered in the preceding chapter have one or more interesting topological structures associated with them. In almost all cases, the topological structures that are of interest in these spaces have the property that addition and scalar multiplication in the vector space are jointly continuous operations, that is, the spaces in question are topological vector spaces. When an ordered vector space is also a topological vector space, the resulting mixed structure is called an **ordered topological vector space**. This chapter is devoted to a systematic study of the interplay between the order and topological structures of such spaces.

The first section studies the concept of a normal cone in an ordered topological vector space in some detail. As we shall see, this concept is one of the most natural and fruitful topological restrictions on the order structure of an ordered topological vector space. Under the assumption that the cone in an ordered topological vector space is normal, it is possible to draw a number of interesting conclusions concerning the order structure of the space of continuous linear functionals, the topological convergence of monotone families, the continuity of positive linear mappings, etc. The notion of an $\mathfrak{S}$-cone in an ordered topological vector space is also introduced and the fundamental duality theorem of Schaefer relating normal cones with $\mathfrak{S}$-cones is established.

Section 2 deals with the problem of extending positive, continuous linear mappings defined on linear subspaces of ordered topological vector spaces, and with the question of determining conditions under which every positive linear mapping on an ordered topological vector space is continuous. In the third section, we establish a number of results concerning the topological convergence of monotone or directed families of elements of an ordered topological vector space.

In Section 4, we focus our attention on ordered topological vector spaces for which the underlying ordered vector space is a vector lattice. With this added order structure, a number of strong conclusions can be drawn about the order structure of the space of continuous linear functionals and about the order continuity of continuous linear mappings.

We shall assume that the reader is familiar with the theory of topological vector spaces. However, in order to avoid the confusion that may arise because of the lack of a standard vocabulary in this theory, we have summarized the basic results and definitions in the Appendix.

§1. NORMAL CONES

Since the definition of an ordered topological vector space does not require any direct relation to exist between the order and topological structures involved, it is necessary to impose further restrictions on the spaces under consideration in order to obtain a significant theory. Probably the most useful restriction of this sort is to require the cone in the ordered topological vector space to be normal with respect to the topology. This section is devoted to a detailed study of normal cones and their duality counterparts, $\mathfrak{S}$-cones. However, before we proceed to the definition of a normal cone, we need the following simple order theoretic concept:

1.1 Definitions. If A is a subset of a vector space E ordered by a cone K, the **full hull** $[A]$ of A is defined by

$$[A] = \{z \in E : x \leq z \leq y \quad \text{for } x \in A, y \in A\},$$

that is, $[A] = (A + K) \cap (A - K)$. If $A = [A]$, then A is **full**.

It is an easy matter to verify that $A \subset [A]$ and $[[A]] = [A]$ for any subset A of an ordered vector space. Also, the full hull of a convex set (resp. circled set) is convex (resp. circled).

1.2 Definition. Suppose that $E(\mathfrak{T})$ is an ordered topological vector space and that K is the positive cone in $E(\mathfrak{T})$. K is **normal** for the topology $\mathfrak{T}$ if there is a neighborhood basis of θ for $\mathfrak{T}$ consisting of full sets.

In view of the remarks preceding (1.2), it is clear that, if K is a normal cone in an ordered topological vector space $E(\mathfrak{T})$, there is a neighborhood basis $\mathscr{W}$ of θ for $\mathfrak{T}$ consisting of circled, full sets; moreover, if $\mathfrak{T}$ is a locally convex topology, we can assume that the sets in $\mathscr{W}$ are convex.

If $E(\mathfrak{T})$ is a topological vector space ordered by a cone K and if $\mathscr{W}$ is a neighborhood basis of θ for $\mathfrak{T}$, the collection $[\mathscr{W}]$ defined by

$$[\mathscr{W}] = \{[W] : W \in \mathscr{W}\}$$

is easily seen to be a neighborhood basis of θ for the finest topology $\mathfrak{T}'$ coarser than $\mathfrak{T}$ for which $E(\mathfrak{T}')$ is an ordered topological vector space with K normal for $\mathfrak{T}'$.

Although (1.2) provides a very useful technical definition for normality, a good deal more light is shed on the meaning of the concept by the equivalences established in the following result.

1.3 Proposition.   If $E(\mathfrak{T})$ is an ordered topological vector space with positive cone K, the following assertions are equivalent:

a. K is normal for $\mathfrak{T}$.

b.   There is a neighborhood basis $\mathscr{W}$ of θ for $\mathfrak{T}$ consisting of sets V for which $\theta \le x \le y \in V$ implies $x \in V$.

c.   For any two nets $\{x_\beta : \beta \in I\}$ and $\{y_\beta : \beta \in I\}$ in $E(\mathfrak{T})$, if $\theta \le x_\beta \le y_\beta$ for all $\beta \in I$ and if $\{y_\beta : \beta \in I\}$ converges to θ for $\mathfrak{T}$, then $\{x_\beta : \beta \in I\}$ converges to θ for $\mathfrak{T}$.

d.   Given a $\mathfrak{T}$-neighborhood V of θ, there is a $\mathfrak{T}$-neighborhood W of θ such that $\theta \le x \le y \in W$ implies $x \in V$.

Proof.   It is obvious that any full set containing θ has the property stated in (b); hence, (a) implies (b). Clearly, (b) implies (c). Suppose that (d) is not satisfied and that $\mathscr{W} = \{W_\beta : \beta \in I\}$ is a neighborhood basis of θ for $\mathfrak{T}$. Then there is a $\mathfrak{T}$-neighborhood V of θ with the following property: For each $\beta \in I$ there exist $y_\beta \in W_\beta$, $x_\beta \in E$ such that $\theta \le x_\beta \le y_\beta$ and $x_\beta \notin V$. The set I can be directed by defining $\beta_1 \le \beta_2$ if $W_{\beta_2} \subset W_{\beta_1}$. The net $\{y_\beta : \beta \in I\}$ then converges to θ, yet the net $\{x_\beta : \beta \in I\}$ does not converge to θ. Consequently, (c) implies (d).

To prove that (d) implies (a), suppose that (d) is satisfied and that V is a given neighborhood of θ for $\mathfrak{T}$. Choose $\mathfrak{T}$-neighborhoods V_1, V_2, V_3, of θ such that $V_1 + V_1 \subset V$, $\theta \le x \le y \in V_2$ implies $x \in V_1$, $V_2 \subset V_1$, and $V_3 - V_3 \subset V_2$. If $z \in [V_3]$, there exist $x, y \in V_3$ such that $x \le z \le y$. But then $\theta \le z - x \le y - x \in V_2$; hence, $z - x \in V_1$. Therefore, $z \in V$, that is, V contains the full $\mathfrak{T}$-neighborhood $[V_3]$ of θ which implies that K is normal for $\mathfrak{T}$.

One simple but useful consequence of the normality restriction is given in the following result.

1.4 Proposition.   If the positive cone K in an ordered topological vector space $E(\mathfrak{T})$ is normal for $\mathfrak{T}$, then every order bounded subset of E is $\mathfrak{T}$-bounded.

Proof.   If V is any full, circled neighborhood of θ for $\mathfrak{T}$ and if $[x, y]$ is a given order interval in E, choose $\lambda > 0$ so that $\lambda x \in V$, $\lambda y \in V$. Then $\lambda[x, y] \subset V$, that is, $[x, y]$ is bounded for the topology $\mathfrak{T}$.

In the examples that follow (1.8), we shall see that topologically bounded sets need not be order bounded in ordered topological vector spaces with a normal cone.

An **ordered locally convex space** is an ordered topological vector space $E(\mathfrak{T})$ equipped with a Hausdorff locally convex topology $\mathfrak{T}$.

1.5 Proposition. If $E(\mathfrak{T})$ is an ordered locally convex space with positive cone K, the following assertions are equivalent:

a. K is normal for $\mathfrak{T}$.

b. There is a family $\{p_\alpha : \alpha \in A\}$ of seminorms generating the topology $\mathfrak{T}$ such that $\theta \leq x \leq y$ implies $p_\alpha(x) \leq p_\alpha(y)$ for all $\alpha \in A$ (equivalently, $p_\alpha(z + w) \geq p_\alpha(z)$ for all z, w in K, $\alpha \in A$).

Proof. Suppose that K is normal for $\mathfrak{T}$, then, by (1.3)(b), there is a neighborhood basis $\mathscr{W} = \{W_\alpha : \alpha \in A\}$ of θ for $\mathfrak{T}$ consisting of convex, circled sets W_α such that for each $\alpha \in A$, $\theta \leq x \leq y \in W_\alpha$ implies $x \in W_\alpha$. Define p_α to be the Minkowski functional of W_α, that is, $p_\alpha(x) = \inf \{\lambda > 0 : x \in \lambda W_\alpha\}$ for each $x \in E$. Then it is easy to show that the family $\{p_\alpha : \alpha \in A\}$ has the property described in (b). On the other hand, if $\{p_\alpha : \alpha \in A\}$ is a family of seminorms satisfying (b), then the class $\mathscr{W}$ of intersections of finite collections of sets of the form

$$W_{\alpha n} = \left\{x \in E : p_\alpha(x) \leq \frac{1}{n}\right\} \qquad \alpha \in A; \quad n = 1, 2, \ldots$$

constitutes a neighborhood basis of θ for $\mathfrak{T}$ satisfying (1.3)(b). We conclude that (a) is equivalent to (b).

1.6 Corollary. The closure $\overline{K}$ of a normal cone K in an ordered locally convex space $E(\mathfrak{T})$ is a normal cone.

Proof. It is clear that $\overline{K}$ is a wedge in E. If $\{p_\alpha : \alpha \in A\}$ is a generating system of seminorms for $\mathfrak{T}$ satisfying (1.5)(b) and if $z \in \overline{K} \cap (-\overline{K})$, then $0 = p_\alpha(z + (-z)) \geq p_\alpha(z) \geq 0$ for all $\alpha \in A$; hence, $z = \theta$ since $\mathfrak{T}$ is a Hausdorff topology. Therefore, $\overline{K}$ is a cone in $E(\mathfrak{T})$. It is an easy matter to verify that $\overline{K}$ satisfies (1.5)(b); hence, $\overline{K}$ is normal in $E(\mathfrak{T})$.

1.7 Proposition. If an ordered vector space E is equipped with a norm $\| \cdot \|$ and if K is the positive cone in E, the following assertions are equivalent:

a. K is normal for the topology generated by the norm $\| \cdot \|$.

b.   There is an equivalent norm† $\| \cdot \|_1$ on E such that $0 \le x \le y$ implies $\|x\|_1 \le \|y\|_1$.

c.   There is a constant $\gamma > 0$ such that $\theta \le x \le y$ implies $\gamma \|x\| \le \|y\|$.

d.   There is a constant $\gamma > 0$ such that $\|x + y\| \ge \gamma \max \{\|x\|, \|y\|\}$ for all x, y in K.

e.   The set $\{\|x\| : \theta \le x \le y; \|y\| \le 1\}$ is bounded above.

Proof.   (*a*) is equivalent to (*b*) by virtue of (1.5). It is an easy matter to verify that (*c*), (*d*), (*e*) are equivalent statements. If $\|x\|_1$ is a norm on E satisfying (*b*), there exist constants m, M such that $m\|x\| \le \|x\|_1 \le M\|x\|$ for all $x \in E$. If $\theta \le x \le y$ then $\|y\| \ge \frac{1}{M}\|y\|_1 \ge \frac{1}{M}\|x\|_1 \ge \frac{m}{M}\|x\|$; hence, (*c*) is satisfied if we choose $\gamma = \frac{m}{M}$. On the other hand, if (*c*) holds and if $U = \{x \in E : \|x\| \le 1\}$, then $\theta \le x \le y \in \gamma U$ implies $x \in U$. Hence, K is normal for the norm topology on E by virtue of the equivalence of (*a*) and (*d*) in (1.3).

The following result shows that normality of the cone is preserved by the standard vector space constructions.

1.8   *Proposition.*   If K is a normal cone in an ordered topological vector space $E(\mathfrak{T})$ and if M is a linear subspace of E, then $K \cap M$ is a normal cone in M for the subspace topology; in addition, if E is a vector lattice and M is a lattice ideal in E, then the canonical image of K in the quotient space E/M is a normal cone for the quotient topology. If $\{E_\alpha(\mathfrak{T}_\alpha) : \alpha \in A\}$ is a family of ordered topological vector spaces and if K_α is the positive cone in E_α for each $\alpha \in A$, then the cone $K = \prod_{\alpha \in A} K_\alpha$ (resp. the cone $K = \bigoplus_{\alpha \in A} K_\alpha$) is normal for the product

---

† Recall that a norm $\| \cdot \|_1$ is equivalent to a norm $\| \cdot \|$ on a vector space E if $\| \cdot \|_1$ and $\| \cdot \|$ generate the same topology on E; or equivalently, if there exist positive constants m, M such that $m\|x\| \le \|x\|_1 \le M\|x\|$ for all $x \in E$.

topology on $E = \prod_{\alpha \in A} E_\alpha$ (resp. the topological direct sum topology or the locally convex direct sum topology on $E = \bigoplus_{\alpha \in A} E_\alpha$) if and only if K_α is normal in $E_\alpha(\mathfrak{T}_\alpha)$ for each $\alpha \in A$.

Proof. The statements in the proposition can be verified by a routine check of condition (*b*) in (1.3). (See (4.3) of Chapter 1 in connection with the quotient space assertion.)

1.9 Examples. a. Examples of normal cones in ordered topological vector spaces abound. The cone $K = \{x = (x_k) \in R^n : x_k \geq 0$ for $k = 1, 2, \ldots, n\}$ is normal for the Euclidean topology on R^n since the norm

$$\|x\| = \sup_n \{|x_n|\}$$

generates this topology and it is clear that $\|x\| \leq \|y\|$ whenever $\theta \leq x \leq y$. Therefore, by (1.8), the cones of sequences with non-negative coordinates in ω and φ are normal with respect to the product topology and the locally convex direct sum topology respectively (see (1.6)). It is immediate from (1.7) that the following cones are normal for the topologies indicated:

1. The cone of non-negative functions in the space $C(X)$ of continuous, real-valued functions on a compact Hausdorff space X, or in the space $B(X)$ of bounded real valued functions on the set X, is normal for the topology generated by the norm

$$\|f\| = \sup \{|f(t)| : t \in X\}.$$

2. For an arbitrary measure space (S, Σ, μ), the cone of functions in $L^p(S, \Sigma, \mu)(p \geq 1)$ that are non-negative on S μ-almost everywhere is normal for the topology determined by the norm

$$\|f\| = \{\int |f(t)|^p \, d\mu(t)\}^{1/p}.$$

Note that the unit ball $U = \{f \in L^p(S, \Sigma, \mu) : \|f\| \leq 1\}$ in $L^p(S, \Sigma, \mu)$ is bounded for the norm topology but not order bounded in general.

b. Suppose that H is a real Hilbert space and that K is the cone of positive, self-adjoint operators in the space $\mathscr{L}(H)$ of continuous linear operators on H (see (1.8) of Chapter 1), then, by (1.5) and (1.7); K is normal for the uniform operator topology on $\mathscr{L}(H)$.

c. Consider the collection $\mathscr{D}$ of functions with compact support in R^p having derivatives of all orders. If C is an arbitrary compact subset of R^p, define $\mathscr{D}_C$ to be the linear subspace of $\mathscr{D}$ consisting of those functions in $\mathscr{D}$ with support in C. Topologize $\mathscr{D}_C$ in the following way: If $s = \{s_1, \ldots, s_p\}$ is an arbitrary set of p non-negative integers, define the differential operator D^s by

$$D^s f = \frac{\partial^{|s|} f}{\partial^{s_1} x_1 \partial^{s_2} x_2 \ldots \partial^{s_p} x_p}$$

where $|s| = s_1 + \cdots + s_p$. The family of seminorms $\{q_c^{(m)} : m = 1, 2, \ldots\}$ defined by

$$q_c^{(m)}(f) = \sup \{|D^s f(x)| : x \in C; \quad 0 \le |s| \le m\}$$

clearly generates a complete metrizable locally convex topology $\mathfrak{T}_C$ on $\mathscr{D}_C$. The so-called **Schwartz topology** $\mathfrak{T}$ on $\mathscr{D}$ is the inductive limit topology on $\mathscr{D}$ with respect to the family $\{\mathscr{D}_{C_n} : n = 1, 2, \ldots\}$ of linear subspaces of $\mathscr{D}$ where

$$C_n = \{x = (x_k) \in R^p : |x_k| \le n; \quad k = 1, 2, \ldots, p\}.$$

We shall now show that the cone K of non-negative functions in $\mathscr{D}$ is not normal for the Schwartz topology on $\mathscr{D}$. For a fixed positive integer n, choose a sequence $\{f_k\}$ in $\mathscr{D}_{C_n} \cap K$ such that the sequence of non-negative real numbers $\{\lambda_k\}$ where $\lambda_k = \sup \{f_k(x) : x \in C_n\}$ converges to 0 but $\{f_k\}$ does not converge to θ for $\mathfrak{T}_{C_n}$. Define the sequence g_k on R^p as follows:

$$g_k(x) = \begin{cases} \lambda_k & \text{if} \quad x \in C_{n+1} \\ 0 & \text{if} \quad x \notin C_{n+1} \end{cases}$$

and let h_k be the "regularization" of g_k defined by

$$h_k(x) = \int_{R^p} \theta_\alpha(x - y) g_k(y) \, dy$$

(see Yosida [1], p. 29), then $h_k \in \mathscr{D}_{C_{n+2}}$. Moreover, $0 \le f_k \le h_k$ for all k and $\{h_k\}$ converges to θ for $\mathfrak{T}$; hence, the cone K is not normal for $\mathfrak{T}$ by (1.3).

The cones in R^n, $C(X)$, and $B(X)$ discussed in (1.9)(a) are normal and have nonempty interiors. The following simple result shows that cones of this sort cannot be found in spaces equipped with a topology that cannot be generated by a single norm.

1.10 Proposition. If $E(\mathfrak{T})$ is a Hausdorff topological vector space ordered by a normal cone K with a nonempty interior, then $E(\mathfrak{T})$ is a normable space.

Proof. If x_0 is an interior point of K, the order interval

$$[-x_0, x_0] = (-x_0 + K) \cap (x_0 - K)$$

is a convex neighborhood of θ for $\mathfrak{T}$. Since K is a normal cone, $[-x_0, x_0]$ is $\mathfrak{T}$-bounded by (1.4); hence, $E(\mathfrak{T})$ is normable by Kolmogorov's Theorem (see the Appendix).

We shall now introduce a restriction on the cone of an ordered locally convex space that will turn out to be dual (in a sense that we shall make precise later in this section) to the restriction of normality.

1.11 Definitions. Suppose that $\mathfrak{S}$ is a saturated class of $\mathfrak{T}$-bounded subsets of an ordered locally convex space $E(\mathfrak{T})$ such that $E = \cup \{S : S \in \mathfrak{S}\}$. The cone K in $E(\mathfrak{T})$ is an $\mathfrak{S}$-**cone** (resp. **strict** $\mathfrak{S}$-**cone** if the class

[handwritten: this not a closure Notation]

$$\overline{\mathfrak{S}}_K = \{\overline{(S \cap K) - (S \cap K)} : S \in \mathfrak{S}\}$$
$$(\text{resp. } \mathfrak{S}_K = \{(S \cap K) - (S \cap K) : S \in \mathfrak{S}\})$$

is a fundamental system for $\mathfrak{S}$. An $\mathfrak{S}$-cone (resp. strict $\mathfrak{S}$-cone) for the class $\mathfrak{S}$ of all $\mathfrak{T}$-bounded sets in $E(\mathfrak{T})$ is called a **b-cone** (resp. **strict b-cone**).

Observe that a strict $\mathfrak{S}$-cone is necessarily generating since $E = \cup \{S : S \in \mathfrak{S}\}$. Though $\mathfrak{S}$-cones need not be generating in general, we shall prove later that a closed b-cone in a Banach space or in the weak dual of a barreled space is necessarily generating.

There is an alternate equivalent way to describe the concepts introduced in (1.11) that will prove to be useful: Given any fundamental system $\mathfrak{S}'$ for a saturated class $\mathfrak{S}$ of bounded sets in $E(\mathfrak{T})$, define $\mathfrak{S}_1$ to be the class of all convex circled hulls of sets of the form $S \cap K$ for $S \in \mathfrak{S}'$. Define $\mathfrak{S}_2$ to be the class of all closures of the sets in $\mathfrak{S}_1$. Then it is a routine matter to verify that the positive cone K in $E(\mathfrak{T})$ is an $\mathfrak{S}$-cone (resp. strict $\mathfrak{S}$-cone) if and only if $\mathfrak{S}_2$ (resp. $\mathfrak{S}_1$) is a fundamental system for $\mathfrak{S}$.

By making use of the following results, it will be a simple matter to identify a number of examples of b-cones and strict b-cones in specific spaces.

1.12 Proposition. If E is a normed space ordered by a cone K, then K is a strict b-cone in E if and only if there is a constant $M > 0$ such that each $x \in E$ has a decomposition $x = x_1 - x_2$ where $x_i \in K$, $\|x_i\| \le M \|x\| (i = 1, 2)$.

Proof. If $B_r = \{x \in E : \|x\| \le r\}$ $(r > 0)$, then the condition stated in the proposition is equivalent to the relation

$$B_r \subset (B_{Mr} \cap K) - (B_{Mr} \cap K);$$

therefore, this condition is equivalent to the statement that K is a strict b-cone.

1.13 Proposition. If E is a Banach space ordered by a cone K, the following assertions are equivalent:

a. K is a b-cone.
b. For any $x \in E$, there exist bounded sequences $\{y_n\}$, $\{z_n\}$ in K such that the sequence $\{y_n - z_n\}$ norm converges to x.

Proof. If K is a b-cone and $x \in E$, there is an $r > 0$ such that $x \in \overline{(B_r \cap K) - (B_r \cap K)}$ where $B_r = \{y \in E : \|y\| \le r\}$. But then there exist sequences $\{y_n\}$ and $\{z_n\}$ in $B_r \cap K$ such that $\{y_n - z_n\}$ norm converges to x; hence, (a) implies (b).

On the other hand, if (b) is satisfied, define E_n for each positive integer n as follows:

$$E_n = \{x \in E : x = y - z; y \in K, z \in K, \|y\| \le n, \|z\| \le n\}.$$

Then $E = \bigcup_{n=1}^{\infty} \bar{E}_n$; hence, some $\bar{E}_{n_0}$ must have a nonempty interior by the Baire Category Theorem. Since $\bar{E}_{n_0}$ is convex and circled, the zero element θ must be an interior point of $\bar{E}_{n_0}$. Therefore, if $r > 0$, there is a positive number λ_r such that $B_r \subset \lambda_r \bar{E}_{n_0}$ (where B_r is defined as in the first step of the proof). It follows that B_r is contained in $\overline{(B_{\lambda_r n_0} \cap K) - (B_{\lambda_r n_0} \cap K)}$; hence, K is a b-cone in E.

1.14 Corollary. If E is a Banach space ordered by a generating cone K, then K is a b-cone.

1.15 Proposition. Suppose that $E(\mathfrak{T})$ is a barreled space and that H is a cone in the dual space E' of E. If H is closed for the weak topology $\sigma(E', E)$ and if H is a b-cone in $E'(\sigma(E', E))$, then H is a strict b-cone.

Proof. Suppose that $\mathfrak{S} = \{B_\alpha : \alpha \in A\}$ is the class of all $\sigma(E', E)$-bounded subsets of E' and define C_α to be the $\sigma(E', E)$-closure of $(B_\alpha \cap H) - (B_\alpha \cap H)$ for each $\alpha \in A$. Then $\{C_\alpha : \alpha \in A\}$ is a fundamental system for $\mathfrak{S}$ since H is a b-cone. If B_{α_0} is $\sigma(E', E)$-closed and $z_0 \in C_{\alpha_0}$, choose nets $\{x_\beta\}$, $\{y_\beta\}$ in $(B_{\alpha_0} \cap H)$ such that $\{x_\beta - y_\beta\}$ converges to z_0 for $\sigma(E', E)$. Since $E(\mathfrak{T})$ is a barreled space and H is $\sigma(E',E)$-closed, $B_{\alpha_0} \cap H$ is $\sigma(E',E)$-compact (see, for example, Chap. IV, §2, Theorem 1 in Bourbaki [1]). Hence, the net $\{x_\beta\}$ has a subnet $\{x_{\beta'}\}$ which converges to some $x_0 \in B_{\alpha_0} \cap H$ for $\sigma(E', E)$. But then the corresponding subnet $\{y_{\beta'}\}$ converges to $y_0 = x_0 - z_0$ for $\sigma(E', E)$; hence, $C_{\alpha_0} = (B_{\alpha_0} \cap H) - (B_{\alpha_0} \cap H)$. Therefore, the class $\{(B_\alpha \cap H) - (B_\alpha \cap H) : \alpha \in A\}$ is a fundamental system for $\mathfrak{S}$; that is, H is a strict b-cone.

1.16 Corollary. If $E(\mathfrak{T})$ is a semireflexive locally convex space ordered by a closed b-cone K, then K is a strict b-cone.

Before proceeding to a description of the important duality relations between normal cones and $\mathfrak{S}$-cones, we shall consider a number of examples.

1.17 Examples. a. By making use of (1.12), (1.13), and (1.16), it is an easy matter to verify that the cones discussed in (1.9)(a) are all strict b-cones in the corresponding locally convex spaces.

b. In the space $\mathscr{L}(H)$ of continuous linear operators on a real Hilbert space H equipped with the uniform or strong operator topologies (see (1.8) of Chapter 1 and (1.9)(b)), the cone K of positive, self-adjoint operators in $\mathscr{L}(H)$ is not a strict $\mathfrak{S}$-cone for any class of bounded subsets of $\mathscr{L}(H)$ since K is not a generating cone. In fact, $K - K$ coincides with the closed linear subspace $\mathscr{S}$ of $\mathscr{L}(H)$ consisting of all self-adjoint operators on H. Hence, K is not an $\mathfrak{S}$-cone in $\mathscr{L}(H)$.

c. The cone K of non-negative functions in the space $\mathscr{D}$ of functions with compact support in R^p having derivatives of all orders, equipped with the Schwartz topology (see (1.9)(c)), is a strict b-cone. For if B is a bounded, circled, subset of $\mathscr{D}$ for the Schwartz topology, then all of the functions in B have their support in a common compact set C_{n_0} (where $C_n = \{x = (x_k) \in R^p : |x_k| \leq n\}$ for each positive integer n) and there is a constant $M > 0$ such that $|f(t)| \leq M$ for all $f \in B$, $t \in C_{n_0}$. If we define the function g on R^p as follows:

$$g(t) = \begin{cases} M & \text{if } t \in C_{n_0+1} \\ 0 & \text{if } t \notin C_{n_0+1} \end{cases}$$

then the regularization h of g (cf. Yosida [1], p. 29) has its support in C_{n_0+2} and

$$B \subset (B + h) - \{h\} \subset (B + h) \cap K - (B + h) \cap K$$

Since $(B + h)$ is obviously a bounded set, we conclude that K is a strict b-cone.

d. Consider the vector space $C_0[0, 1]$ of continuous, real valued functions on the unit interval that vanish at 0. If $C_0[0, 1]$ is equipped with the topology generated by the norm

$$\|f\| = \sup \{|f(t)| : 0 \leq t \leq 1\}$$

and the order generated by the cone K of non-negative, convex functions in $C_0[0, 1]$, then K is not a b-cone in $C_0[0, 1]$. In fact, if f is the element of $C_0[0, 1]$ defined by

$$f(t) = \sqrt{t} \qquad 0 \leq t \leq 1$$

and if ε is chosen so that $0 < \varepsilon < \frac{1}{2}$, the relation $\|f - (g - h)\| < \varepsilon$ for g, h in K implies $g(t) > f(t) - \varepsilon$ for all $t \in [0, 1]$. In particular, $g(4\varepsilon^2) > \varepsilon$; hence, since g is convex and $g(0) = 0$, it follows that

$$g(1) = \frac{g(1) - g(0)}{1 - 0} \geq \frac{g(4\varepsilon^2) - g(0)}{4\varepsilon^2 - 0} > \frac{1}{4\varepsilon}.$$

Therefore, $\|g\| \geq \frac{1}{4\varepsilon}$; hence, K is not a b-cone in $C_0[0, 1]$.

We shall now proceed to the development of the duality theory for normal and $\mathfrak{S}$-cones.

1.18 Definitions. Suppose that $\langle E, F \rangle$ is a dual system consisting of a pair of real vector spaces E, F and a real valued bilinear functional $(x, u) \to \langle x, u \rangle$ defined on $E \times F$. If K is a wedge in E, the wedge K' in F defined by

$$K' = \{u \in F : \langle x, u \rangle \geq 0 \quad \text{for all } x \in K\}$$

is the **dual wedge** for K in F. If K' is a cone in F, then K' is called the **dual cone** for K in F.

It is an easy matter to verify that K' is a cone in F if and only if $K - K$ is dense in E for the weak topology $\sigma(E, F)$. Also, since K contains all positive multiples of its elements, it is true that $K' = -K^\circ$ (where K° denotes the polar set of K with respect to the dual system $\langle E, F \rangle$); in particular, the dual wedge K' for K is always a $\sigma(F, E)$-closed subset of F. Moreover, the Bipolar Theorem (see the Appendix) implies that the dual wedge $K'' = (K')'$ for K' coincides with the $\sigma(E, F)$-closure of the given wedge K in E. By making use of these facts, the following result is easily established.

1.19 Proposition. Suppose that $\langle E, F \rangle$ is a dual system, that K is a wedge in E, and that K' is the dual wedge for K in F, then:

a. K is closed for a topology $\mathfrak{T}$ consistent with the dual system $\langle E, F \rangle$ if and only if $x \in K$ precisely when $\langle x, u \rangle \geq 0$ for all $u \in K'$.

b. If $x_0 \in E$, there is a $u \in K'$ such that $\langle x_0, u \rangle < 0$ if and only if x_0 is not in the $\sigma(E, F)$-closure of K.

c. If K is a cone in E, then the closure $\overline{K}$ of K for a topology $\mathfrak{T}$ consistent with the dual system $\langle E, F \rangle$ is a cone in E if and only if $K' - K'$ is dense in F for $\sigma(F, E)$.

1.20 Examples. a. If E is an ordered vector space with a positive cone K and if E^* is the algebraic dual of E (that is, E^* is the vector space of all linear functionals on E), then $\langle E, E^* \rangle$ is a dual system with respect to the bilinear functional that is defined to have the value $f(x)$ at $(x, f) \in E \times E^*$. The dual wedge for K coincides with the collection K^* of all positive linear functionals on E. If E is equipped with a Hausdorff locally convex topology $\mathfrak{T}$ and if E' is the collection of all $\mathfrak{T}$-continuous linear functionals, then $\langle E, E' \rangle$ is a dual system with respect to the restriction of the bilinear functional defined above, and the dual wedge for K is precisely the set of all positive linear functionals on E that are continuous for $\mathfrak{T}$.

b. If E is a Köthe function space ordered by the cone K of functions in E that are non-negative almost everywhere, and if F is the Köthe dual of E (see (1.6) of Chapter 1) then $\langle E, F \rangle$ is a dual system with respect to the bilinear form

$$\langle f, g \rangle = \int fg \, d\mu \qquad (f \in E, g \in F)$$

and the dual cone K' for K coincides with the set of functions in F that are non-negative almost-everywhere.

The following proposition embodies one of the most important consequences of the normality restriction for ordered locally convex spaces.

1.21 Proposition. If $E(\mathfrak{T})$ is a locally convex space ordered by a normal positive cone K, then every continuous linear functional on E is the difference of two positive continuous linear functionals on E.

Proof. If E' denotes the collection of all continuous linear functionals on $E(\mathfrak{T})$ and K' is the dual wedge for K corresponding to the dual system $\langle E, E' \rangle$, then we must show that $E' = K' - K'$. Given $f \in E'$, choose a $\mathfrak{T}$-closed, convex, circled, full neighborhood V of θ such that $|f(x)| \leq 1$ for all $x \in V$. If p and q are the Minkowski functionals of $(V - K)$ and V respectively, then $q(y) = \max \{p(y), p(-y)\}$ for each $y \in E$ since V is full. Define the sets H_p and H_q as follows:

$$H_p = \{g \in E' : g(y) \leq p(y) \quad \text{for all } y \in E\},$$

$$H_q = \{g \in E' : g(y) \leq q(y) \quad \text{for all } y \in E\},$$

then $H_p \subset K'$ since $g(-x) \leq p(-x) = 0$ for all $x \in K$, $g \in H_p$. A simple application of the Hahn-Banach Theorem shows that

$$q(y) = \sup \{g(y) : g \in H_q\} = \sup \{g(y) : g \in H_p \cup (-H_p)\}$$

for each $y \in E$; that is, the elements of E considered as $\sigma(E', E)$-continuous linear functionals on E' have the same suprema on $H_p \cup (-H_p)$ as on H_q. Therefore, by a separation argument,

H_q is the $\sigma(E', E)$-closed convex hull of $H_p \cup (-H_p)$. Moreover, since H_p is $\sigma(E', E)$-compact and convex, it follows that H_q is actually the convex hull of $H_p \cup (-H_p)$. Consequently, there exist λ such that $0 \le \lambda \le 1$ and f_1, f_2 in $H_p \subset K'$ such that $f = \lambda f_1 - (1 - \lambda)f_2$; hence, $E' = K' - K'$ which completes the proof.

We are now in a position to establish the fundamental duality relation between normal cones and $\mathfrak{S}$-cones.

1.22 Proposition (Schaefer). Suppose that $\langle E, F \rangle$ is a dual system consisting of a vector space E ordered by a cone K, and a vector space F equipped with the dual wedge K' for K. If K' is an $\mathfrak{S}$-cone in F for a saturated class $\mathfrak{S}$ of $\sigma(F, E)$-bounded subsets of F, then K is normal for the corresponding $\mathfrak{S}$-topology on E. If K is normal for an $\mathfrak{S}$-topology on E that is consistent with the dual system $\langle E, F \rangle$, then K' is a strict $\mathfrak{S}$-cone in F.

Proof. Suppose K' is an $\mathfrak{S}$-cone in F, then the family $\{p_S : S \in \mathfrak{S}\}$ of seminorms defined by

$$p_S(x) = \sup \{|\langle x, y \rangle| : y \in S \cap K'\}$$

generates the $\mathfrak{S}$-topology on E. Since these seminorms clearly satisfy (b) of (1.5), K is normal for the $\mathfrak{S}$-topology on E.

Now suppose that K is normal for an $\mathfrak{S}$-topology $\mathfrak{T}$ consistent with dual system $\langle E, F \rangle$. If $\mathscr{W}$ is a neighborhood basis of θ for $\mathfrak{T}$ consisting of convex, circled, full sets, then $\mathfrak{S}' = \{V^\circ : V \in \mathscr{W}\}$ is a fundamental system for $\mathfrak{S}$. For a given $V \in \mathscr{W}$, define $E_V = E/p_V^{-1}(0)$ where p_V is the Minkowski functional of V. The seminorm p_V is constant on each equivalence class in the quotient space E_V; hence, if $\dot{x}$ is the equivalence class in E_V containing the element x, then

$$\|\dot{x}\|_V = p_V(x)$$

defines a norm on E_V. Moreover, the image K_V of the cone K under the canonical quotient map $\varphi_V : E \to E_V$ is a normal cone for the corresponding norm topology on E_V. (For if $\dot{x} \in K_V \cap (-K_V)$, then $0 = \|\dot{x} + (-\dot{x})\|_V \ge \|\dot{x}\|_V$; hence, K_V is a cone; the fact that K_V is normal follows immediately from the fact that V is full). Therefore, by (1.21), every norm continuous linear functional on E_V is the difference of two positive norm continuous linear functionals on E_V; that is,

$$E'_V = K'_V - K'_V.$$

There is a natural isomorphism between the space E'_V of norm continuous linear functionals on E_V and the linear subspace of F consisting of those linear functionals that are bounded on V. For if $f \in F$ is bounded on V, then f vanishes on $p_V^{-1}(0)$; hence, the mapping $\dot{f}$ on E_V defined at $\dot{x} \in E_V$ by

$$\dot{f}(\dot{x}) = f(x) \quad \text{for some } x \in \dot{x}$$

is a norm continuous linear functional. On the other hand, if g is a norm continuous linear functional on E_V, the mapping $\bar{g}$ on E defined at each $x \in E$ by $\bar{g}(x) = g(\dot{x})$ is a continuous linear functional on E that is bounded on V; moreover, $\dot{\bar{g}} = g$.

Suppose that E'_V is equipped with the standard dual norm $\|\dot{g}\| = \sup\{|\dot{g}(\dot{x})| : \|\dot{x}\| \le 1\}$. Define a subset M of E'_V as follows:

$$M = \{\dot{f} \in E'_V : \dot{f} = \dot{f_1} - \dot{f_2} ; \dot{f_i} \in K'_V, \|\dot{f_i}\| \le 1 \quad (i = 1, 2)\},$$

then M is a norm closed subset of E'_V. For if $\{\dot{f_m}\}$ is a sequence in M that norm converges to $\dot{f} \in E'_V$, then $\dot{f_m} = \dot{g_m} - h_m$ where $\dot{g_m}$, h_m are elements of K'_V with norms not exceeding 1 for each m. Therefore, by the Alaoglu Theorem, $\{\dot{g_m}\}$ has a $\sigma(E'_V, E_V)$-cluster point $\dot{g}$. Hence, a subsequence of $\{h_m\}$ converges to $h = \dot{g} - \dot{f}$. It is clear that $\|\dot{g}\| \le 1$, $\|h\| \le 1$ and that $\dot{f} = \dot{g} - h$; hence, M is norm closed.

Since $E'_V = \bigcup_{n=1}^{\infty} nM$ by (1.21), the Baire Category Theorem implies that M has a nonempty interior. But M is convex and circled; hence, M is a neighborhood of θ in E'_V. Therefore, there is an integer n_0 such that $n_0 M$ contains the unit ball in E'_V. This means that

$$V^\circ \subset (n_0 V^\circ) \cap K' - (n_0 V^\circ) \cap K';$$

that is, K' is a strict $\mathfrak{S}$-cone in F.

1.23 Corollary. Suppose that $\langle E, F \rangle$ is a dual system consisting of a vector space E ordered by a cone K and a vector space F equipped with dual wedge K' for K, then K is a normal cone for the weak topology $\sigma(E, F)$ if and only if K' generates F. If K is an $\mathfrak{S}$-cone in E and the corresponding $\mathfrak{S}$-topology on F is consistent with $\langle E, F \rangle$, then the closure $\overline{K}$ of K for $\sigma(E, F)$ is a strict $\mathfrak{S}$-cone.

Proof. The first assertion is an immediate consequence of (1.22). If K is an $\mathfrak{S}$-cone in E, then, as in the proof of (1.22), it can be seen that K' is normal for the $\mathfrak{S}$-topology on F. It follows from (1.22) that $K'' = \overline{K}$ is a strict $\mathfrak{S}$-cone.

1.24 Corollary. If $E(\mathfrak{T})$ is a locally convex space ordered by a normal cone K, then K is normal for the weak topology $\sigma(E, E')$.

Proof. This result follows immediately from (1.21) and the first assertion in (1.23).

1.25 Corollary. Suppose that $E(\mathfrak{T})$ is a barreled space ordered by a cone K such that $K - K$ is dense in $E(\mathfrak{T})$, and suppose that K' is the dual cone for K in E', then the following assertions are equivalent:

a. K is a normal cone in $E(\mathfrak{T})$.
b. K' is a b-cone in $E'\big(\sigma(E', E)\big)$.
c. K' is a strict b-cone in $E'\big(\sigma(E', E)\big)$.

Proof. Since $K - K$ is dense in $E(\mathfrak{T})$, the dual wedge K' for K is a cone. Also, the fact that $E(\mathfrak{T})$ is a barreled space implies that $\mathfrak{T}$ is the (consistent) $\mathfrak{S}$-topology determined by the class of all $\sigma(E', E)$-bounded sets in E'. Consequently, the equivalence of the assertions in the proposition follows immediately from (1.22).

1.26 Corollary. Suppose that $E(\mathfrak{T})$ is a reflexive locally convex space ordered by a closed cone K such that $K - K$ is dense in $E(\mathfrak{T})$ then K is a normal cone (resp. a b-cone) in $E(\mathfrak{T})$ if and only if the dual cone K' for K is a b-cone (resp. a normal cone) in $E'\big(\beta(E', E)\big)$.

Proof. This result is an immediate consequence of (1.22) and (1.25) since a subset of E' is $\beta(E', E)$-bounded if and only if it is $\sigma(E', E)$-bounded.

The following result shows that the complete duality between normal cones and b-cones (or strict b-cones by (1.25)) obtained for reflexive spaces in (1.26) persists in Banach spaces, reflexive or not.

1.27 Proposition. Suppose that $E(\mathfrak{T})$ is a Banach space ordered by a closed cone K such that $K - K$ is dense in $E(\mathfrak{T})$, then K is a normal cone (resp. a strict b-cone) in $E(\mathfrak{T})$ if and only if the dual cone K' for K is a strict b-cone (resp. a normal cone) in $E'(\beta(E', E))$.

Proof. We have already observed that if K is a b-cone, then K' is normal in $E'(\beta(E', E))$. Therefore, in view of the equivalence of (a) and (c) in (1.25), it is only necessary to show that if K' is normal in $E'(\beta(E', E))$, then K is a strict b-cone. If U is the unit ball in E, the bipolar of $U \cap K$ with respect to the dual system $\langle E', E'' \rangle$ is the intersection of the unit ball $U^{\circ\circ}$ in E'' and the cone K'' in E''. Hence, since K'' is a strict b-cone in E'' by (1.22), we note that $U \cap K - U \cap K$ is a dense subset of a θ-neighborhood in $E(\mathfrak{T})$. Define E_K to be the linear hull of K, that is, $E_K = K - K$ and equip E_K with the topology $\mathfrak{T}_K$ (see the Appendix). The Banach Homorphism Theorem can now be applied to the embedding map of $E_K(\mathfrak{T}_K)$ into $E(\mathfrak{T})$ to conclude that this mapping is a topological isomorphism; hence, K is a strict b-cone in $E(\mathfrak{T})$.

1.28 Corollary. If E is a Banach space ordered by a closed cone K, the following assertions are equivalent:

a. K generates E.
b. K is a b-cone in E.
c. K is a strict b-cone in E.

Proof. (a) implies (b) by (1.14). If (b) is satisfied, then K' is normal for $\beta(E', E)$; hence, K is a strict b-cone in E by (1.27). Since (c) obviously implies (a), the proof is complete.

As we shall see by example in the next section, the order dual E^+ of an ordered vector space E may not contain sufficiently many linear functionals to separate points of E; in fact, E^+ may reduce to the set consisting of the zero functional only. Since it is important for many considerations to know that E^+ separates points of E, it would be useful to have an "intrinsic" characterization of this property. Such a characterization can be obtained by making use of the preceding results.

1.29 Proposition. Suppose that E is a vector space ordered by a cone K, then the following assertions are equivalent:

a. E^+ separates points of E.
b. The closure of K for the finest locally convex topology on E is a cone in E.
c. There is a Hausdorff locally convex topology $\mathfrak{T}$ on E such that the $\mathfrak{T}$-closure of K is a cone in E.
d. There is a Hausdorff locally convex topology $\mathfrak{T}$ on E for which K is a normal cone.

Proof. If E^+ separates points of E, then E^+ is dense in the algebraic dual E^* of E for $\sigma(E^*, E)$. Therefore, (a) implies (b) by virtue of $(1.19)(c)$. It is obvious that (b) implies (c). If (c) is satisfied and E' is the dual of E for $\mathfrak{T}$, then $K' - K'$ is $\sigma(E', E)$-dense in E' by $(1.19)(c)$. Therefore, $\langle E, K' - K' \rangle$ is a dual system, and K is normal for $\sigma(E, K' - K')$ by (1.23), Finally, if (d) is satisfied, then $E(\mathfrak{T})'$ separates points of E and $E(\mathfrak{T})' = K' - K' \subset K^* - K^* = E^+$ by (1.21); hence, E^+ also separates points of E.

1.30 Definition. An ordered vector space E is **regularly ordered** if E^+ separates points of E.

It is clear from the equivalences established in (1.29) that the regularity requirement is a very mild restriction on the linear and order structures of an ordered vector space. The following result lists a number of pleasant elementary properties of regularly ordered vector spaces.

1.31 Proposition. Each regularly ordered vector space is almost Archimedean. If E is a regularly ordered vector space and M is a linear subspace of E, then M is a regularly ordered vector space. The product and direct sum of any family of regularly ordered vector spaces is regularly ordered.

Proof. If E is regularly ordered, then the closure $\bar{K}$ of K for the finest locally convex topology on E is a cone in E. Hence, if $-\lambda y \leq x \leq \lambda y$ for all $\lambda > 0$ and some $y \in K$, then

$$x \leq \lim_{\substack{\lambda \to 0 \\ \lambda > 0}} \lambda y = \theta, \qquad -x \leq \lim_{\substack{\lambda \to 0 \\ \lambda > 0}} \lambda y = \theta$$

for the ordered structure determined by $\overline{K}$. It follows that $x = \theta$, consequently E is almost Archimedean. The remaining assertions follow from (1.29)(d) and (1.8).

1.32 Notes. The notion of a normal cone was first studied systematically by Krein [see [1]) who considered the concept in normed spaces only. The normality restriction in general ordered topological vector spaces was investigated independently by Bonsall [3], Kist [1], Namioka [1], and Schaefer [2]. Bonsall [4] introduced b-cones in normed spaces, but Schaefer [2] developed the duality theory for normal cones and $\mathfrak{S}$-cones.

Proposition (1.21) was first established for normed spaces by Krein and Grosberg [1]. A number of different proofs of (1.21) in the context of locally convex spaces were provided by Bonsall [3], Kist [1] (see Prop. 4.1), Namioka [1] (see Theorem 6.2), Schaefer [2] (see (1.3)) and Weston [4]; our proof is due to Kist. Ando [1] proved that the cone in an ordered Banach space is necessarily a strict b-cone if the dual cone is normal, thus completing the duality between normal and strict b-cones expressed in (1.27).

§2. THE CONTINUITY OF POSITIVE LINEAR MAPPINGS; EXTENSION THEOREMS

In view of the fact that there is often an intimate relation between the order and topological structures of the ordered vector spaces that occur in analysis, it is not surprising that this relationship is often reflected in the nature of linear mappings on these spaces. For example, one would expect positive linear mappings to be continuous for a fairly wide class of spaces, and extension theorems of the Hahn-Banach type should also be available. This section is devoted to an exposition of some results in this direction.

We begin with the formulation of a rather obvious generalization of the classical Hahn-Banach Theorem.

2.1 Proposition. Suppose that p is a mapping from a real vector space E into an order complete vector lattice F such that

$$p(x + y) \leq p(x) + p(y); \quad p(\lambda x) = \lambda p(x)$$

for all x, y in E and all non-negative real numbers λ. If T is a linear mapping defined on a linear subspace M of E with range in F such that $Tx \leq p(x)$ for all $x \in M$, then T can be extended to a linear mapping T_1 of E into F such that $T_1 x \leq p(x)$ for all $x \in E$.

Since the usual proof of the Hahn-Banach Theorem (see, for example, II.3.10 in Dunford-Schwartz [1]) uses only the fact that the real number system is an order complete vector lattice, the above generalization follows by the same argument.

For the sake of convenience, we shall refer to mappings satisfying (∗) in (2.1) as **sublinear** mappings. The following result is fundamental in our treatment of the extension of positive linear mappings.

2.2 Proposition (Mazur-Orlicz). If p is a sublinear mapping of a real vector space E into an order complete vector lattice F and if $\{x_\alpha : \alpha \in A\}$ and $\{y_\alpha : \alpha \in A\}$ are subsets of E and F respectively, then there is a linear mapping T of E into F such that

a. $y_\alpha \leq Tx_\alpha \qquad$ for all $\alpha \in A$,
b. $Tx \leq p(x) \qquad$ for all $x \in E$,

if and only if

c. for any finite subset $\{\alpha_1, \ldots, \alpha_n\}$ of A and any finite set $\{\lambda_1, \ldots, \lambda_n\}$ of non-negative real numbers, it is true that

$$\sum_{k=1}^{n} \lambda_k y_{\alpha_k} \leq p\left(\sum_{k=1}^{n} \lambda_k x_{\alpha_k}\right) . \qquad (*)$$

Proof. The necessity of (c) is clear since T is a linear mapping. On the other hand, suppose that (c) is satisfied. For a given $x \in E$, and any finite sets $\{\alpha_1, \ldots, \alpha_n\}$, $\{\lambda_1, \ldots, \lambda_n\}$ of the sort described in (c), it is true that

$$\sum_{k=1}^{n} \lambda_k y_{\alpha_k} \leq p\left(x + \sum_{k=1}^{n} \lambda_k x_{\alpha_k}\right) + p(-x);$$

hence,

$$-p(-x) \leq p\left(x + \sum_{k=1}^{n} \lambda_k x_{\alpha_k}\right) - \sum_{k=1}^{n} \lambda_k y_{\alpha_k} .$$

Therefore, since F is an order complete vector lattice, we can define a mapping q from E into F by

$$q(x) = \inf \left\{ p\left(x + \sum_{k=1}^{n} \lambda_k x_{\alpha_k} \right) - \sum_{k=1}^{n} \lambda_k y_{\alpha_k} : \alpha_k \in A,\ \lambda_k \geq 0\ k = 1, 2, \ldots \right\}.$$

It is obvious that $q(\alpha x) = \alpha q(x)$ for all $x \in E$ and all $\alpha \geq 0$. Moreover, if $\alpha_i \in A,\ \lambda_i \geq 0\ (i = 1, \ldots, n)$, if $\alpha'_j \in A,\ \lambda'_j \geq 0\ (j = 1, \ldots, m)$, and if x, x' are elements of E, then

$$p\left(x + \sum_{i=1}^{n} \lambda_i x_{\alpha_i} \right) - \sum_{i=1}^{n} \lambda_i y_{\alpha_i} + p\left(x' + \sum_{j=1}^{m} \lambda'_j x_{\alpha'_j} \right)$$

$$- \sum_{j=1}^{m} \lambda'_j y_{\alpha'_j} \geq p\left(x + x' + \sum_{i=1}^{n} \lambda_i x_{\alpha_i} + \sum_{j=1}^{m} \lambda'_j x_{\alpha'_j} \right)$$

$$- \sum_{i=1}^{n} \lambda_i y_{\alpha_i} - \sum_{j=1}^{m} \lambda'_j y_{\alpha'_j} \geq q(x + x').$$

Consequently, $q(x + x') \leq q(x) + q(x')$ for all x, x' in E. Applying (2.1), we conclude that there exists a linear mapping T of E into F such that $Tx \leq q(x)$ for all $x \in E$. Since it is clear that $q(x) \leq p(x)$ for all $x \in E$, it follows that (b) holds. Moreover, for each $\alpha \in A$

$$q(-x_\alpha) \leq p(-x_\alpha + x_\alpha) - y_\alpha = -y_\alpha;$$

hence, $-T(x_\alpha) \leq q(-x_\alpha) \leq -y_\alpha$, that is, (a) is also satisfied.

2.3 Proposition. Suppose that $E(\mathfrak{T})$ is a locally convex space and that $F(\mathfrak{O})$ is an order complete vector lattice ordered by a normal cone K. If $\{x_\alpha : \alpha \in A\}$ and $\{y_\alpha : \alpha \in A\}$ are subsets of E and F, respectively, then a sufficient (and, if K has a nonempty interior†, necessary) condition for the existence of a continuous linear mapping T of E into F such that $Tx_\alpha \geq y_\alpha$ for all $\alpha \in A$ is that there exists a neighborhood U of θ in $E(\mathfrak{T})$ such that the set

$$\left\{ \sum_{i=1}^{n} \lambda_i y_{\alpha_i} : \lambda_i \geq 0;\ \alpha_i \in A;\ \sum_{i=1}^{n} \lambda_i x_{\alpha_i} \in U \right\} \tag{$*$}$$

is bounded above in F.

† In view of (1.10) the topology $\mathfrak{O}$ on F is then necessarily normable; in fact, as we shall see in Section 4 of this chapter, $F(\mathfrak{O})$ is norm and order isomorphic to the space of all real valued, continuous functions on some extremally disconnected compact Hausdorff space since F is also order complete.

Proof. Suppose that there is a neighborhood U of the sort described in the proposition, and let b be an upper bound for the set (∗). Without loss in generality, we can assume that U is convex and circled. If $\lambda_i \geq 0$, $\alpha_i \in A(i = 1, 2, \ldots, n)$, there is a $\lambda > 0$ such that $\sum_{i=1}^{n} \lambda_i x_{\alpha_i} \in \lambda U$. Hence, $\sum_{i=1}^{n} \frac{\lambda_i}{\lambda} x_{\alpha_i} \in U$ so that $\sum_{i=1}^{n} \lambda_i y_{\alpha_i} \leq \lambda b$. Therefore, if q is the Minkowski functional of U, we obtain $\sum_{i=1}^{n} \lambda_i y_{\alpha_i} \leq q(x) b$ where $x = \sum_{i=1}^{n} \lambda_i x_{\alpha_i}$. Define $p(x) = q(x)b$ for each $x \in E$; then (2.2) implies that there is a linear mapping T of E into F such that $Tx_\alpha \geq y_\alpha$ for all $\alpha \in A$ and $Tx \leq p(x)$ for all $x \in E$. If W is a given full, circled neighborhood of θ in F, choose $\mu > 0$ so that $\mu b \in W$. Then $T(\mu U) \subset [-\mu b, \mu b] \subset W$; hence, T is continuous.

If K has a nonempty interior, if T is a continuous linear mapping of E into F such that $Tx_\alpha \geq y_\alpha$ for all $\alpha \in A$, and if u is an interior point of K, define

$$U = \{x \in E : Tx \leq u\} = T^{-1}(u - K).$$

If $\alpha_i \in A$, $\lambda_i \geq 0(i = 1, 2, \ldots, n)$ and if $\sum_{i=1}^{n} \lambda_i x_{\alpha_i} \in U$, then

$$u \geq T\left(\sum_{i=1}^{n} \lambda_i x_{\alpha_i}\right) = \sum_{i=1}^{n} \lambda_i T x_{\alpha_i} \geq \sum_{i=1}^{n} \lambda_i y_{\alpha_i}.$$

Hence, the set described by (∗) is bounded above in F.

2.4 Proposition. Suppose that $E_1(\mathfrak{T}_1)$ is a locally convex space ordered by a cone K_1, that $E_2(\mathfrak{T}_2)$ is an order complete vector lattice ordered by a normal cone K_2, and that T and i are linear mappings of a vector space H into E_2 and E_1, respectively. Consider the following assertions:

a. There is a positive continuous linear mapping $\bar{T}$ of E_1 into E_2 such that $\bar{T} \circ i = T$.
b. There is a neighborhood U of θ in $E_1(\mathfrak{T}_1)$ such that the set $B = \{Tx : i(x) \leq y \text{ for some } y \in U\}$ is bounded above in E_2.

Statement (*b*) implies statement (*a*) and, if K_2 has a nonempty interior, (*a*) and (*b*) are equivalent.

Proof. By (2.3), there is a continuous linear mapping $\overline{T}$ of E_1 into E_2 such that $\overline{T}z \geq \theta$ for all $z \in K_1$ and $Tx \leq \overline{T}(i(x))$ for all $x \in H$ if there exist a neighborhood U of θ in $E_1(\mathfrak{T}_1)$ and an element b in E_2 such that $Tx \leq b$ whenever $z + i(x) \in U$ for some $z \in K_1$, $x \in H$. If such a mapping $\overline{T}$ exists, then, in particular, $T(-x) \leq \overline{T}(i(-x))$; hence, (*b*) implies (*a*). Moreover, if K_2 has a nonempty interior, then (2.3) implies the equivalence of (*a*) and (*b*).

2.5 Corollary. Suppose T is a linear mapping defined on a linear subspace M of an ordered locally convex space $E_1(\mathfrak{T}_1)$ such that the range of T is contained in an order complete vector lattice $E_2(\mathfrak{T}_2)$ ordered by a normal cone. Then T can be extended to a positive continuous linear mapping $\overline{T}$ of $E_1(\mathfrak{T}_1)$ into $E_2(\mathfrak{T}_2)$ if there is a neighborhood U of θ such that $\{Tx : x \in M; x \leq u \in U\}$ is bounded above in E_2.

Proof. Apply (2.4) to the natural embedding mapping i of M into E_1.

2.6 Corollary. A linear functional f defined on a linear subspace M of an ordered locally convex space $E(\mathfrak{T})$ can be extended to a positive, continuous linear functional on $E(\mathfrak{T})$ if and only if there is a convex neighborhood U of θ such that $\{f(x) : x \in M, x \leq u$ for some $u \in U\}$ is bounded above.

Proof. In (2.4), take E_2 to be the real field in its usual order and topology and let i be the natural embedding mapping of M into E_1.

2.7 Corollary. A linear functional f defined on a linear subspace M of an ordered vector space E can be extended to a positive linear functional on E if and only if there is a convex radial set U such that $\{f(x) : x \in M; x \leq u$ for some $u \in U\}$ is bounded above.

Proof. Equip E with the finest locally convex topology and apply (2.6).

2.8 Corollary. If M is a linear subspace of a vector space E ordered by a cone K and if, for each $x \in K$, there is a $y \in M$ such that $x \leq y$ (in particular, if M contains a point of the positive cone at which the cone is radial), then every positive linear functional on M can be extended to a positive linear functional on E.

Proof. It suffices to show that each positive linear functional on M can be extended to a positive linear functional on the linear subspace $F = K - K$ of E. Since the set $U = \{x \in F : x \leq y$ for some $y \in M$ such that $f(y) \leq 1\}$ is a convex, radial subset of F, the assertion follows from (2.7).

We shall now establish a number of further results that are somewhat less direct consequences of (2.1) and (2.5).

2.9 Proposition. Suppose that E is a vector space ordered by a cone K and suppose that M is a linear subspace of E such that, for each $x \in E$, $(x + M) \cap K \neq \phi$ if and only if $(-x + M) \cap K \neq \phi$.† Then every positive linear mapping T of M into an order complete vector lattice F can be extended to a positive linear mapping of E into F.

Proof. Let N be the linear hull of $K \cup M$ and define a sublinear mapping p on N by

$$p(x) = \inf \{Ty : y \in M, y \geq x\}.$$

(Any $x \in N$ is comparable to some $y \in M$; hence, in view of the main hypothesis, the infimum defining $p(x)$ exists.) Since $Tx \leq p(x)$ for all $x \in M$, (2.1) implies that T can be extended to a linear mapping $\overline{T}$ of N into F such that $\overline{T}x \leq p(x)$ for all $x \in N$. If $x \leq \theta$, then $\overline{T}x \leq p(x) \leq T\theta = \theta$; hence, $\overline{T}$ is a positive linear mapping on N. Since $K \subset N$, any linear extension of $\overline{T}$ to all of E will provide an extension of T of the required sort.

2.10 Corollary. If f is a positive linear functional defined on a linear subspace M of a vector space E ordered by a cone K and if, for each $x \in E$, $(x + M) \cap K \neq \phi$ if and only if $(-x + M) \cap K \neq \phi$, then f can be extended to a positive linear functional on E.

2.11 Proposition. Suppose that E_1 is an ordered locally convex space and that E_2 is a locally convex space ordered by a normal cone K_2. There is a nonzero positive, continuous linear mapping of E_1 into E_2 if and only if the cone K_1 in E_1 is not dense in E_1.

---

† This condition is equivalent to the following requirement: For each $x \in E$, either x is not comparable to any element of M, or x is contained in an order interval with endpoints in M.

Proof. If K_1 is dense in E_1 and T is a positive, continuous linear mapping of E_1 into E_2, then

$$T(E_1) \subset T(\overline{K}_1) \subset \overline{K}_2, \quad T(E_1) \subset T(-\overline{K}_1) \subset -\overline{K}_2 \ ;$$

hence, $T = 0$ since $\overline{K}_2$ is a cone by (1.6). On the other hand, if K_1 is not dense in E_1, choose an element x that is not in the closure of $-K_1$ and choose a circled neighborhood V of θ in E_1 such that $(x + V) \cap (-K_1) = \phi$. If y is a fixed element of K_2, define a linear mapping T on the linear subspace M spanned by x as follows; For each real number α, set $T(\alpha x) = \alpha y$. If $z = \alpha x \in M$, $\alpha > 0$, and $z \leq v \in V$, then $\alpha \leq 1$ since $(x + V) \cap (-K_1) = \phi$. Hence, $\{Tz : z \in M, z \leq v \in V\}$ is bounded above by y; therefore, T can be extended to a nonzero positive, continuous, linear mapping of E_1 into E_2 by (2.5).

2.12 Corollary. If $E(\mathfrak{T})$ is a locally convex space ordered by a cone K, there is a nonzero, positive, continuous linear functional on $E(\mathfrak{T})$ if and only if K is not dense in $E(\mathfrak{T})$.

2.13 Proposition. Suppose that $E(\mathfrak{T})$ is a locally convex space ordered by a cone K with a compact base B and suppose that M is a closed linear subspace of E such that $M \cap B = \phi$. Then every continuous linear mapping T from M into an order complete vector lattice F ordered by a normal cone with a nonempty interior can be extended to a continuous, positive linear mapping on E.

Proof. Choose a neighborhood V_1 of θ in $E(\mathfrak{T})$ such that $B \cap (M + V_1) = \phi$. If u_0 is an interior point of the cone in F, choose a neighborhood V_2 of θ for which $T(V_2 \cap M) \subset [-u_0, u_0]$. If V is a closed, convex, circled neighborhood of θ such that $V \subset V_1 \cap V_2$ and if p is the Minkowski functional of V, then $T(x) \in [-p(x)u_0, p(x)u_0]$ for all $x \in M$. If $x \in M$ and $x \leq v \in V$, then there exist a unique $\lambda \geq 0$ and a $b_0 \in B$ such that $\lambda b_0 = v - x$. Since $B \cap (M + V) = \phi$, it is true that $\lambda < 1$; hence,

$$Tx \leq p(x)u_0 \leq (p(v) + \lambda p(b_0))u_0 \leq (1 + \sup \{p(b) : b \in B\})u_0 \ .$$

We conclude that $\{Tx : x \in M, x \leq v \in V\}$ is bounded above by $(1 + \alpha_0)u_0$ where $\alpha_0 = \sup \{p(b) : b \in B\}$; hence, the result follows from (2.5).

2.14 Corollary. If f is a linear functional defined on a closed linear subspace M of a locally convex space $E(\mathfrak{T})$ ordered by a cone K with a compact base B such that $M \cap B = \phi$, then f can be extended to a continuous, positive linear functional defined on E.

We shall now discuss a number of examples related to the preceding results.

2.15 Examples.

a. In three-dimensional Euclidean space R^3, consider the cone K spanned by the set B defined by

$$B = \{(1, y, z) \in R^3 : z \geq -y^3 \text{ if } y < 0; \quad z \geq 0 \text{ if } y \geq 0\} ;$$

that is, $K = \{\lambda p : p \in B, \lambda \geq 0\}$. If $M = \{(x, y, z) \in R^3 : z = 0\}$ and f is the linear functional defined on the linear subspace M by $f(x, y, 0) = y$, then f is a positive linear functional on M for the order determined by K. However, if f could be extended to a positive linear functional $\bar{f}$ on R^3, then the plane

$$H = \{(x, y, z) \in R^3 : \bar{f}(x, y, z) = 0\}$$

would support K, pass through the origin, and contain the line

$$L = \{(x, y, z) \in R^3 : y = z = 0\}.$$

But then

$$H = \{(x, y, z) \in R^3 : z = 0\},$$

which is impossible; hence, f cannot be extended to a positive linear functional on R^3.

b. If the sequence space φ (see (1.6) of Chapter 1) is ordered by the cone K of all sequences $x = (x_n) \in \varphi$ such that the last nonzero component of x is positive and if φ is equipped with the topology generated by the ℓ^1-norm: $\|x\| = \sum_{n=1}^{\infty} |x_n|$, then the cone K is dense in φ. (In fact, if $x \in \varphi$ and $\varepsilon > 0$ are given, and if x_{n_0} is the last nonzero component of x, define

$$u_n^\varepsilon = \begin{cases} x_n & \text{if } n \neq n_0 + 1 \\ \varepsilon & \text{if } n = n_0 + 1 \end{cases}$$

then $\|x - u^\varepsilon\| = \varepsilon$.) It follows from (2.12) that there do not exist nonzero, positive, continuous linear functionals on φ.

c. If $0 < p < 1$ and $[a, b]$ is a closed interval on the real line equipped with Lebesgue measure, the vector space $L^p[a, b]$ (see (1.6) of Chapter 1) ordered by the cone K of functions in $L^p[a, b]$ that are non-negative almost everywhere on $[a, b]$, and equipped with the complete, metrizable topology determined by the θ-neighborhood basis:

$$V_n = \left\{ f \in L^p[a, b] : \left(\int_a^b |f(t)|^p \, d\mu(t) \right)^{1/p} < \frac{1}{n} \right\}; \; n = 1, 2, \ldots$$

is known to have no nonzero, continuous linear functionals. (This result is due to Day [1]; however, a shorter proof due to Robertson can be found on p. 161 of Köthe [1].) Later in this section, we shall prove a theorem (see (2.16)) that can be applied to $L^p[a, b]$ to conclude that every positive linear functional on this space is continuous. Hence, there do not exist nonzero, positive linear functionals on $L^p[a, b]$.

We shall now turn our attention to the continuity properties of positive linear mappings.

2.16 Proposition (*Nachbin-Namioka-Schaefer*). If $E_1(\mathfrak{T}_1)$ and $E_2(\mathfrak{T}_2)$ are ordered topological vector spaces and if the cone in $E_2(\mathfrak{T}_2)$ is normal, then each of the following conditions implies that every positive linear mapping T of $E_1(\mathfrak{T}_1)$ into $E_2(\mathfrak{T}_2)$ is continuous:

a. The cone K_1 in $E_1(\mathfrak{T}_1)$ has a nonempty interior.

b. $E_1(\mathfrak{T}_1)$ is a bornological space ordered by a sequentially complete strict b-cone and $E_2(T_2)$ is a locally convex space.

c. $E_1(\mathfrak{T}_1)$ is a metrizable topological vector space of second category ordered by a complete generating cone K_1 and $E_2(T_2)$ is a locally convex space.

Proof.   (1) If V is a given full, circled neighborhood of θ in $E_2(\mathfrak{T}_2)$ and if x_0 is an interior point of K_1, choose a $\lambda_0 > 0$ such that $\lambda_0 T x_0 \in V$. Then $W = [-\lambda_0 x_0, \lambda_0 x_0]$ is a neighborhood of θ in $E_1(\mathfrak{T}_1)$ and $T(W) \subset V$ since V is circled and full; hence, T is a continuous linear mapping.

(2) Suppose that T is not continuous, then there is a bounded set B in $E_1(\mathfrak{T}_1)$ such that $T(B)$ is not bounded in $E_2(\mathfrak{T}_2)$ since $E_1(\mathfrak{T}_1)$ is

a bornological space. This in turn implies that there is a sequence $\{x_n\} \subset B$ such that $\{Tx_n\}$ is not bounded in $E_2(\mathfrak{T}_2)$. Since the cone K_2 in $E_2(\mathfrak{T}_2)$ is normal, (1.21) implies that $E_2' = K_2' - K_2'$; hence, the family $\{p_{y'} : y' \in K_2'\}$ of seminorms defined by

$$p_{y'}(y) = |\langle y, y' \rangle| \qquad (y \in E_2)$$

generates the weak topology $\sigma(E_2, E_2')$ on E_2. Therefore, the set $\{\langle Tx_n, y' \rangle : n = 1, 2, \ldots\}$ is not bounded for some choice of y' in K_2'; in fact, we can assume that there is a $y_0' \in K_2'$ such that

$$\langle Tx_n, y_0' \rangle \geq n, \qquad n = 1, 2, \ldots$$

without loss in generality. The sequence $\{z_n\}$ defined by

$$z_n = \sum_{k=1}^{n} \frac{1}{k^2} x_k$$

is a monotone increasing Cauchy sequence in K_1; hence, $\{z_n\}$ converges to some z in K_1 since K_1 is sequentially complete. But then

$$\sum_{k=1}^{n} \frac{1}{k} \leq \langle Tz_n, y_0' \rangle \leq \langle Tz, y_0' \rangle < +\infty$$

for each positive integer n since T is positive and $\{z_n\}$ is monotone increasing. Thus, we have arrived at a contradiction; consequently, T is a continuous linear mapping.

(3) We shall begin by showing that each convex, circled subset V of E_1 that absorbs each order bounded set is a neighborhood of θ for $\mathfrak{T}_1$. Let $\mathscr{W} = \{W_n : n = 1, 2, \ldots\}$ be a countable neighborhood basis of θ for $\mathfrak{T}_1$ consisting of circled sets W_n such that $W_{n+1} + W_{n+1} \subset W_n$ for each positive integer n, and suppose that V is not a neighborhood of θ for $\mathfrak{T}_1$. Now $\mathfrak{T}_1$ coincides with the topology $\mathfrak{T}_{K_1}$ (see the Appendix); hence, corresponding to each $W_n \in \mathscr{W}$ there is an x_n in $W_n \cap K_1$ such that $x_n \notin nV$. (For if $W_{n_0} \cap K_1 \subset n_0 V$, then $V_{n_0} = W_{n_0} \cap K_1 - W_{n_0} \cap K_1 \subset 2n_0 V$ contrary to the supposition that V is not a neighborhood of θ for $\mathfrak{T}_{K_1} = \mathfrak{T}_1$.) The sequence $\{z_n\}$ defined by

$$z_n = \sum_{k=1}^{n} x_k \qquad n = 1, 2, \ldots$$

is a Cauchy sequence in $E_1(\mathfrak{T}_1)$; hence, $\{z_n\}$ converges to $z \in K_1$. It is clear that $\theta \le z_n \le z$ for each positive integer n; hence, since V absorbs $[\theta, z]$, it follows that $x_{n_0} \in n_0 V$ for some positive integer n_0. This contradicts the definition of x_{n_0}; hence, V must be a neighborhood of θ for $\mathfrak{T}_1$. Now, if W is a given convex, circled neighborhood of θ in $E_2(\mathfrak{T}_2)$, then W absorbs each order bounded set in $E_2(\mathfrak{T}_2)$ by (1.4). It follows that $V = T^{-1}(W)$ is a convex circled subset of $E_1(\mathfrak{T}_1)$ that absorbs each order bounded set. Therefore, V is a neighborhood of θ for $\mathfrak{T}_1$; hence, T is continuous.

2.17 Corollary. If $E(\mathfrak{T})$ is a topological vector space ordered by a cone K, each of the following hypotheses on $E(\mathfrak{T})$ implies that every positive linear functional on $E(\mathfrak{T})$ is continuous:

a. K has a nonempty interior.

b. $E(\mathfrak{T})$ is a bornological space and K is a sequentially complete strict b-cone.

c. $E(\mathfrak{T})$ is a metrizable topological vector space of second category ordered by a complete generating cone.

2.18 Proposition. Every positive linear mapping T of a regularly ordered vector space E_1 into a regularly ordered vector space E_2 is continuous for the weak topologies $\sigma(E_1, E_1^+)$ and $\sigma(E_2, E_2^+)$ determined by the order duals of E_1 and E_2, respectively.

Proof. If T^* is the algebraic adjoint of T, then

$$T^*y'(x) = y'(Tx) \ge 0$$

for all $x \ge \theta$ in E_1 and all $y' \ge \theta$ in E_2^+. Hence, T^* maps E_2^+ into E_1^+ which implies that T is continuous for $\sigma(E_1, E_1^+)$ and $\sigma(E_2, E_2^+)$.

2.19 Corollary. If every positive linear functional on a regularly ordered vector space $E_1(\mathfrak{T}_1)$ is continuous and if every continuous linear functional on a regularly ordered vector space $E_2(\mathfrak{T}_2)$ is the difference of two positive linear functionals on E_2, then every positive linear mapping T of E_1 into E_2 is continuous for $\sigma(E_1, E_1')$ and $\sigma(E_2, E_2')$.

Proof. Our assumptions imply that $\sigma(E_1, E_1')$ is finer than $\sigma(E_1, E_1^+)$ and that $\sigma(E_2, E_2')$ is coarser than $\sigma(E_2, E_2^+)$; hence, the conclusion follows immediately from (2.18).

2.20 *Examples.* a. All of the ordered locally convex spaces mentioned in (1.9)(a) satisfy (b) in (2.16) and (b) in (2.17). This implies that the order dual for each of these spaces is contained in the topological dual. On the other hand, the cones in these spaces are normal; hence, in view of (1.21), the order dual coincides with the topological dual for each of these spaces.

b. Suppose that X is a locally compact Hausdorff space and that $\mathscr{K}(X)$ is the vector space of all real-valued, continuous functions with compact support in X, ordered by the cone of non-negative functions in $\mathscr{K}(X)$. If C is a fixed compact subset of X and if $\mathscr{K}(X, C)$ is the lattice ideal in $\mathscr{K}(X)$ consisting of all functions in $\mathscr{K}(X)$ with support in C, equip $\mathscr{K}(X, C)$ with the topology generated by the norm

$$\|f\|_C = \sup \{|f(t)| : t \in C\}.$$

If the space $\mathscr{K}(X)$ is equipped with the inductive limit topology corresponding to the family $\{\mathscr{K}(X, C) : C \text{ compact in } X\}$ of linear subspaces of $\mathscr{K}(X)$, then the continuous linear functionals on $\mathscr{K}(X)$ are the **Radon measures** on X (see Chap. 3 in Bourbaki [2]). It is an easy matter to verify that each $\mathscr{K}(X, C)$ satisfies (b) or (c) in (2.16) and (b) or (c) in (2.17); hence, every positive linear functional on $\mathscr{K}(X)$ is a Radon measure.

c. Since the Schwartz topology $\mathfrak{X}$ on $\mathscr{D}$ is the inductive limit topology for the family $\{\mathscr{D}_{C_n}(\mathfrak{X}_{C_n}) : n = 1, 2, \ldots\}$, a linear functional on $\mathscr{D}$ is continuous for $\mathfrak{X}$ if and only if its restriction to each $\mathscr{D}_{C_n}(\mathfrak{X}_{C_n})$ is continuous. But $\mathscr{D}_{C_n}(\mathfrak{X}_{C_n})$ satisfies (c) of (2.16) and (c) of (2.17); hence, every positive linear functional on $\mathscr{D}$ is continuous for $\mathfrak{X}$. Therefore, the space of distributions on R^p, that is, the topological dual $\mathscr{D}'$ of $\mathscr{D}$, contains the order dual $\mathscr{D}^+$ of $\mathscr{D}$. Moreover, every positive linear functional φ on $\mathscr{D}$ is a Radon measure. (For (2.8) implies that φ can be extended to a positive linear functional $\bar{\varphi}$ on the space $\mathscr{K}(R^p)$(see (b)); hence, $\bar{\varphi}$ is a positive Radon measure on R^p; moreover, $\bar{\varphi}$ is unique since $\mathscr{D}$ is dense in $\mathscr{K}(R^p)$). Hence, it follows that $\mathscr{D}^+$ coincides with the space $\mathscr{M}(R^p)$ of all Radon measures on R^p which is a proper subset of the space $\mathscr{D}'$ of distributions on R^p.

2.21   Notes. (2.2) was established for linear functionals by Mazur-Orlicz [1], and Riedl [1] observed that such results could be obtained for more general linear mappings by making use of (2.1) in place of the classical Hahn-Banach Theorem. The simple proof of (2.2) that we have presented is due to Ptak [1]. (2.3) was established for linear functionals by Hustad [1]. (2.6) and (2.7) are due to Namioka [1], though (2.6) is essentially the same as a theorem proved independently by Bauer [1] (2.8) was proved under the stronger parenthetical hypothesis by Krein-Rutman [1]. (2.14) is due to Bauer [1]. Parts (1) and (2) of our main result (2.16) concerning the continuity of positive linear mappings were proved by Schaefer [3] while part (3) is due to Namioka [1] and Nachbin [1]. Generalizations to linear mappings of the standard separation theorems for convex sets can be obtained by making use of (2.11). (See 10.3 and 10.4 in Riedl [1].) Additional information concerning linear inequalities can be found in Fan [1], while Bauer [3], Hustad [1], [2], [3], Nef [1], [2], [3], Riedl [1] contain further results dealing with the extension of positive linear functionals and mappings. Applications related to the extension theorems established in this section are included in Silverman [1], [2] and Nef [1].

§3. CONVERGENCE THEOREMS

In this section, we shall establish a number of results concerning the topological convergence of monotone or directed families in an ordered topological vector space. For the sake of convenience, we shall employ the term "directed set" to refer to sets that may be either directed ($\leq$) or directed ($\geq$). Also, whenever a result is stated or proved for directed ($\leq$) sets, we shall omit the obvious modifications that are necessary to obtain the corresponding result for directed ($\geq$) sets.

3.1   Proposition. If D is a directed ($\leq$) subset of topological vector space $E(\mathfrak{T})$ ordered by a closed cone K and if x_0 is a cluster point of the filter $\mathfrak{F}(D)$ of sections of D, then $x_0 = \sup(D)$.

Proof. If $x \in D$ and $S_x' = x + K$, then S_x' is a closed set containing the section $S_x = \{z \in D : z \geq x\}$ of D; hence, $x_0 \in \bar{S}_x \subset S_x'$. It follows that $x_0 \geq x$; hence, x_0 is an upper bound for D. On the other hand, if $z \geq x$ for all $x \in D$, then $D \subset z - K$. But $z - K$ is closed; hence, $x_0 \in \bar{D} \subset z - K$, that is, $x_0 \leq z$. It follows that $x_0 = \sup(D)$.

3.2 Corollary. If $\{x_\alpha : \alpha \in A\}$ is a monotone increasing (resp. decreasing) net in a topological vector space ordered by a closed cone K and if $\{x_\alpha : \alpha \in A\}$ converges to x_0 for $\mathfrak{T}$, then $x_0 = \sup \{x_\alpha : \alpha \in A\}$ (resp. $x_0 = \inf \{x_\alpha : \alpha \in A\}$).

3.3 Example. In connection with the preceding results, it is of interest to note that the supremum of a monotone increasing sequence need not be "topologically close" to the elements of the sequence. For example, the sequence $\{x^{(n)}\}$ in ℓ^∞ defined by

$$x_k^{(n)} = \begin{cases} 1 & \text{if } k \leq n \\ 0 & \text{if } k > n \end{cases}$$

has the supremum e in ℓ^∞ defined by $e_n = 1$ for all n. However, if ℓ^∞ is equipped with the norm $\|z\| = \sup_n \{|z_n|\}$, then $\|x^{(n)} - e\| = 1$ for all n.

3.4 Proposition. If D is a directed subset of a locally convex space $E(\mathfrak{T})$ ordered by a normal cone K and if the filter $\mathfrak{F}(D)$ of sections of D converges for the weak topology $\sigma(E, E')$, then $\mathfrak{F}(D)$ converges to the same limit for $\mathfrak{T}$.

Proof. Without loss in generality, we can assume that D is directed $(\geq)$, that $\mathfrak{F}(D)$ converges to θ for $\sigma(E, E')$, and that K is closed since the closure $\bar{K}$ of a normal cone K is normal (see (1.6)) and since D is also directed $(\geq)$ for the order generated by $\bar{K}$. In this case, $\theta = \inf(D)$ by (3.1). Let $\mathcal{W}$ be a neighborhood basis of θ for $\mathfrak{T}$ consisting of convex, open, full sets, and suppose that $\mathfrak{F}(D)$ does not converge to θ for $\mathfrak{T}$. Then there is a $W \in \mathcal{W}$ such that W is disjoint from each section of D since W is full and D is directed $(\geq)$. Then $D \cap W = \phi$; consequently, $(D + K) \cap W = \phi$ since W is full. Moreover, $D + K = \bigcup_{x \in D} (x + K)$ is convex since D is directed $(\geq)$. Therefore, since the convex set $D + K$ is disjoint from the open convex set W, there is a closed hyperplane H separating $D + K$ and W.

The closed semispace containing W determined by H is a $\sigma(E, E')$-neighborhood of θ that is disjoint from D. This contradicts the fact that $\mathfrak{F}(D)$ converges to θ for $\sigma(E, E')$. Consequently, $\mathfrak{F}(D)$ must converge to θ for $\mathfrak{T}$.

3.5 Corollary. If $E(\mathfrak{T})$ is a weakly sequentially complete locally convex space ordered by a normal closed cone K and if $\{x_n\}$ is a monotone increasing sequence in E such that $\sup \{f(x_n)\} < +\infty$ for each continuous positive linear functional f on E, then the supremum x_0 of $\{x_n\}$ exists in E, and $\{x_n\}$ converges to x_0 for $\mathfrak{T}$.

Proof. By (1.21), every continuous linear functional on E is the difference of two positive continuous linear functionals on E since K is a normal cone. Hence, the condition that $\sup \{f(x_n)\} < +\infty$ for each $f \in K'$ implies that $\{x_n\}$ is a Cauchy sequence for the weak topology $\sigma(E, E')$. Since K is closed and normal, it follows from (3.4) and (3.1) that $\{x_n\}$ converges to $x_0 = \sup \{x_n\}$ for $\mathfrak{T}$.

3.6 Examples. a. Suppose that X is a locally compact Hausdorff space and that $C(X)$ is the vector space of all real-valued, continuous functions on X, ordered by the cone K of non-negative functions in $C(X)$, and equipped with the topology of uniform convergence on the compact subsets of X. It is an easy matter to verify that K is a closed, normal cone in $C(X)$. The topological dual of $C(X)$ can be identified with the space $\mathcal{M}_c(X)$ of all Radon measures on X with compact support; in fact, the bilinear functional placing $C(X)$ and $\mathcal{M}_c(X)$ in duality is given by

$$\langle f, \mu \rangle = \int_X f(t) \, d\mu(t).$$

A sequence $\{f_n\}$ of functions in $C(X)$ converges to $f_0 \in C(X)$ for the weak topology $\sigma(C(X), \mathcal{M}_c(X))$ if and only if the sequence $\{f_n\}$ is uniformly bounded on each compact subset of X and $\{f_n\}$ converges to f_0 at each point of X. (See, for example, 4.10.2 in Edwards [1].)

By making use of (3.4) it is possible to establish the following classical theorem due to Dini:

Proposition. If $\{f_n\}$ is a monotone sequence of real-valued, continuous functions on a locally compact Hausdorff space X and if there is a continuous, real-valued function f_0 on X such that $\{f_n(x)\}$

converges to $f_0(x)$ for each $x \in X$, then f_n converges uniformly to f_0 on each compact subset of X.

Proof. The hypotheses imply that $\{f_n\}$ converges to f_0 for $\sigma(C(X),$ $\mathcal{M}_c(X))$; hence, $\{f_n\}$ converges to f_0 for the topology of compact convergence by (3.4) since $\{f_n\}$ is a monotone sequence and K is closed and normal.

b. Suppose that X is a locally compact Hausdorff space, that $\mathcal{K}(X)$ is the space of real-valued, continuous, functions with compact support in, X, and that $\mathcal{M}^1(X)$ is the vector space of all bounded Radon measures on X (see Chap. III, §2, in Bourbaki [2]), equipped with the topology generated by the norm

$$\|\mu\| = \sup \left\{ \left| \int_X f \, d\mu \right| : f \in \mathcal{K}(X), |f(t)| \leq 1 \text{ for all } t \in X \right\}$$

and ordered by the cone K of positive Radon measures on X. It is clear that K is a normal, closed cone in the Banach space $\mathcal{M}^1(X)$. Moreover, $\mathcal{M}^1(X)$ is known to be weakly sequentially complete. Therefore, the following measure theoretic result can be derived from (3.5):

Proposition. If $\{\mu_n\}$ is a sequence of bounded, regular, Borel measures on a locally compact Hausdorff space X, if $\mu_n(A) \leq \mu_{n+1}(A)$ for each positive integer n and each Borel set A, and if $\sup \{\mu_n(A)\} < +\infty$ for each Borel set A, then $\{\mu_n\}$ converges to a bounded regular Borel measure μ_0 uniformly on the class of Borel sets in X.

Observe that the classical Monotone Convergence Theorem is a special case of the preceding proposition.

3.7 Proposition. Suppose that $E(\mathfrak{T})$ is a semireflexive locally convex space ordered by a normal cone K. If D is a directed ($\leq$) subset of E that satisfies one of the following conditions:

a. D is majorized in E.
b. Some section of D is $\mathfrak{T}$-bounded in $E(\mathfrak{T})$.
Then the filter $\mathfrak{F}(D)$ of sections of D converges for $\mathfrak{T}$.

Proof. If D is majorized by some element x_0 in E and if $y_0 \in D$, then the section $S_{y_0} = \{z \in D : z \geq y_0\}$ is contained in the order interval $[y_0, x_0]$. Since K is normal for $\mathfrak{T}$, this order interval is $\mathfrak{T}$-bounded by (1.4). Therefore, it suffices to establish the conclusion under condition (b).

If S_{z_0} is a $\mathfrak{T}$-bounded section of D, then the $\sigma(E, E')$-closure B of S_{z_0} is $\sigma(E, E')$-compact since E is semireflexive. Therefore, the trace $\mathfrak{F}$ on B of $\mathfrak{F}(D)$ has a $\sigma(E, E')$-cluster point $x_1 \in B$. As in (3.1), we see that $x_1 = \sup(S_{z_0})$ for the order structure generated by the closure $\bar{K}$ of K; hence, x_1 is the only cluster point of $\mathfrak{F}$ in B for $\sigma(E, E')$. Since B is compact, it follows that $\mathfrak{F}$ converges to x_1 for $\sigma(E, E')$. But $B \in \mathfrak{F}(D)$; hence, $\mathfrak{F}(D)$ converges to x_1 for $\sigma(E, E')$. The fact that $\mathfrak{F}(D)$ converges to x_1 for $\mathfrak{T}$ now follows from (3.4).

3.8 Example. The space $\mathscr{D}'$ of distributions (see (2.20)(c)) equipped with the strong topology $\beta(\mathscr{D}', \mathscr{D})$ and ordered by the dual cone K' of the cone K on non-negative functions in $\mathscr{D}$ is a reflexive space ordered by a closed normal cone. The normality of K' for $\beta(\mathscr{D}', \mathscr{D})$ follows from (1.26) and the fact that K is a strict b-cone (see (1.17)(c)). Consequently, the following result is an immediate consequence of (3.7).

Proposition. If D is a directed $(\leq)$ set of distributions that is either majorized in $\mathscr{D}'$ or contains a $\beta(\mathscr{D}', \mathscr{D})$-bounded section, then the supremum of D exists in $\mathscr{D}'$ and the filter $\mathfrak{F}(D)$ of sections of D converges to $\sup(D)$ for $\beta(\mathscr{D}', \mathscr{D})$.

Considerations similar to those employed in (3.7) can be used to obtain results concerning the existence of the supremum and the infimum of each relatively compact set or each relatively compact, directed set in certain ordered topological vector spaces. Apart from their intrinsic interest, we shall see that such results will be quite useful in our study of the order properties of compact linear mappings (see Section 3 of Chapter 4). Consequently, we shall now digress from our study of convergence theorems to consider this topic briefly.

3.9 Proposition. If $E(\mathfrak{T})$ is a topological vector space ordered by a closed cone K and if C is a relatively compact, directed $(\leq)$ subset of $E(\mathfrak{T})$, then the supremum of C exists.

Proof. Since $\bar{C}$ is compact in $E(\mathfrak{T})$, the trace $\mathfrak{F}$ on $\bar{C}$ of the filter $\mathfrak{F}(C)$ of sections of C has a cluster point $x_0 \in \bar{C}$, and x_0 can be shown to be the supremum of C just as in the proof of (3.1).

If C is an arbitrary subset of a vector lattice E, it is possible to associate a "minimal" directed ($\leq$) set $D(C)$ containing C, namely, the set $D(C)$ of all suprema of finite subsets of C. However, if C is relatively compact, the set $D(C)$ need not be relatively compact in general. (For example, it is clear that the subset C of ℓ^2 consisting of θ and the elements $\dfrac{1}{\sqrt{n}} \, e^{(n)}$ for $n = 1, 2, \ldots$ (where $e_k^{(n)} = \delta_{nk}$ for $n, k = 1, 2, \ldots$) is compact for the topology generated by the norm

$$\|x\| = \left(\sum_{k=1}^{\infty} |x_k|^2 \right)^{1/2}.$$

However, if ℓ^2 is ordered by the cone of sequences with non-negative components, the set $D(C)$ is not even norm bounded in ℓ^2.) On the other hand, we have the following result.

3.10 Proposition. Suppose that E is a Banach space ordered by a normal, closed cone K and that E is a vector lattice with an order unit e, then every relatively compact subset C of E has a supremum in E and the set

$$C' = \{\sup A : A \subset C\}$$

is relatively compact.

Proof. Since $[-e, e]$ is a bounded barrel, we can assume that the norm on E is the Minkowski functional of the order interval $[-e, e]$. Choose a sequence $\{x_k\}$ in C with the following property: For each integer n, there is an integer N_n such that

$$C \subset \bigcup_{k=1}^{N_n} S\left(x_k, \frac{1}{n}\right)$$

(where $S(x, \alpha) = \{z \in E : \|z - x\| < \alpha\}$). For each positive integer n, define y_n as follows:

$$y_n = \sup\{x_1, \ldots, x_n\}$$

Given $\varepsilon > 0$, choose a positive integer n so that $\dfrac{1}{n} \leq \varepsilon$. If

$p \geq N_n$ and $1 \leq q \leq p$, there is an integer j such that $1 \leq j \leq N_n$ and $x_q \in S\left(x_j, \dfrac{1}{n}\right)$. Then

$$x_q \leq x_j + \frac{1}{n} e \leq y_{N_n} + \frac{1}{n} e;$$

hence, $y_{N_n} \leq y_p \leq y_{N_n} + \varepsilon e$ for all $p \geq N_n$. Therefore, $\{y_k\}$ is a Cauchy sequence in E; hence, $\{y_k\}$ converges to $y \in E$. But $\{y_k\}$ is monotone increasing and K is closed; hence, $y = \sup \{y_k\}$ by (3.2). If $x \in C$ and $\varepsilon > 0$, there is a positive integer n_0 such that $\|x - x_{n_0}\| \leq \varepsilon$. But then

$$x \leq x_{n_0} + \varepsilon e \leq y_{n_0} + \varepsilon e \leq y + \varepsilon e.$$

Since ε is an arbitrary positive number, it follows that $x \leq y$ since K is closed. Therefore, y is an upper bound of C. If z is any other upper bound of C, then z is an upper bound of $\{y_k\}$; hence, $z \geq y$. It follows that $y = \sup (C)$.

To prove the second part of the assertion, suppose that $\varepsilon > 0$ is given, that n is a positive integer such that $\dfrac{1}{n} < \varepsilon$, and that $\mathscr{A}$ is the class of all finite subsets of the set $\{1, \ldots, N_n\}$. If $A \subset C$, choose $\{k_1, \ldots, k_r\} \in \mathscr{A}$ so that

a. For each $x \in A$, there is an $x_{k_j} (1 \leq j \leq r)$ such that $x \in S\left(x_{k_j}, \dfrac{1}{n}\right)$.

b. $S\left(x_{k_j}, \dfrac{1}{n}\right) \cap A \neq \phi$ for $j = 1, \ldots, r$.

By (*b*), we conclude that, for each j in the range $\{1, \ldots, r\}$, there is an $x \in A$ such that

$$x_{k_j} \leq x + \frac{1}{n} e.$$

But $\sup (A)$ exists by virtue of the result established in the first part of the proof; hence,

$$x_{k_j} \leq \sup (A) + \frac{1}{n} e \qquad j = 1, \ldots, r.$$

It follows that

$$\sup \{x_{k_j} : j = 1, 2, \ldots, r\} \leq \sup (A) + \frac{1}{n} e. \qquad (*)$$

On the other hand, if $x \in A$, there is an integer j such that $1 \le j \le r$ and

$$x \le x_{k_j} + \frac{1}{n} e$$

by virtue of (a). Therefore,

$$x \le \sup \{x_{k_j} : j = 1, \ldots, r\} + \frac{1}{n} e$$

for all $x \in A$; hence,

$$\sup (A) \le \sup \{x_{k_j} : j = 1, \ldots, r\} + \frac{1}{n} e. \qquad (**)$$

Combining $(*)$ and $(**)$, we conclude that

$$\| \sup (A) - \sup \{x_{k_j} : j = 1, \ldots, r\} \| \le \frac{1}{n} < \varepsilon.$$

It follows that the finite set $\{\sup_{j \in \alpha} (x_j) : \alpha \in \mathscr{A}\}$ is an ε-net covering $\{\sup (A) : A \subset C\}$, which implies the desired result.

Though the class of ordered topological vector spaces with the property that every relatively compact subset has a supremum and and infimum does not seem to be particularly broad, the following example shows that this property is sometimes enjoyed by spaces without order units.

3.11 Example. Suppose that A is a relatively compact subset of the vector space (c_0) of all null sequences of real numbers equipped with the topology generated by the norm

$$\|x\| = \sup \{|x_n| : n = 1, 2, \ldots\}. \qquad (*)$$

Then A is a relatively compact subset of the vector space ℓ^∞ of bounded sequences of real numbers equipped with the norm $(*)$ and ordered by the cone of sequences with non-negative components. Therefore, (3.10) implies that A has a supremum $y^{(0)} \in \ell^\infty$. If $y^{(0)} \notin (c_0)$, there is a positive number ε_0 such that, for each positive integer N, there is a positive integer $n > N$ for which

$$|y_n^{(0)}| > \varepsilon_0 \qquad (**)$$

But, since A is relatively compact in (c_0), there is a positive integer N_0 such that

$$\sup_{x \in A} \{|x_n|\} \leq \frac{\varepsilon_0}{2} \qquad (***)$$

for all $n > N_0$ (see IV.13.9 in Dunford-Schwartz [1]). The relations $(**)$ and $(***)$ are contradictory since $y_n^{(0)} = \sup_{x \in A} \{x_n\}$ for all n; hence, we conclude that $y_0 \in (c_0)$. Thus, every relatively compact subset of (c_0) has a supremum (and an infimum) for the order induced by ℓ^∞, yet (c_0) does not contain an order unit.

We now return to our study of convergence theorems in ordered locally convex spaces.

3.12 Proposition. Suppose that E is a locally convex space ordered by a cone K with a nonempty interior. If $\{y_\alpha : \alpha \in I\}$ is a net in the dual cone K' of K in E' that converges to θ for $\sigma(E', E)$, then $\{y_\alpha : \alpha \in I\}$ converges to θ for $\beta(E', E)$.

Proof. Suppose that V is a $\beta(E', E)$-neighborhood of θ and that x_0 is an interior point of K, then the polar set M of $\{x_0\}$ is a $\sigma(E', E)$-neighborhood of θ and the order interval $[\theta, x_0]$ has a nonempty interior. Since the elements of $M \cap K'$ are uniformly bounded on $[\theta, x_0]$, it follows that $M \cap K'$ is an equicontinuous subset of E'. Therefore, there is a positive number λ_0 such that $(\lambda_0 M) \cap K' = \lambda_0(M \cap K') \subset V$. Since $\{y_\alpha : \alpha \in I\}$ converges to θ for $\sigma(E', E)$, there is an $\alpha_0 \in I$ such that $y_\alpha \in \lambda_0 M$ for all $\alpha \geq \alpha_0$. But then $y_\alpha \in V$ for $\alpha \geq \alpha_0$; hence, $\{y_\alpha : \alpha \in I\}$ converges to θ for $\beta(E', E)$.

The following result draws a conclusion similar to that in (3.12) from quite different hypotheses.

3.13 Proposition. If E is a Banach space ordered by a generating normal cone K and if E' is separable for the strong topology $\beta(E', E)$, then every monotone increasing sequence $\{y_n\}$ in E' that is either majorized or $\sigma(E', E)$-bounded has a supremum $\bar{y}$ and $\{y_n\}$ converges to $\bar{y}$ for $\beta(E', E)$.

Proof. For each $x \in K$, $\{y_n(x)\}$ is a monotone increasing sequence that is bounded above; hence, there is a $\bar{y} \in E'$ such that $\{y_n\}$

converges to $\bar{y}$ for $\sigma(E', E)$ since E' is $\sigma(E', E)$-sequentially complete and K is generating. If we regard K to be a cone in the bidual E'' of E, the $\sigma(E'', E')$-closure of K in E'' coincides with the dual cone $(K')'$ of K' for the dual system $\langle E', E'' \rangle$ by the Bipolar Theorem. Therefore, if $x'' \in (K')'$, there is a sequence $\{x_m\}$ in K such that

$$x''(y) = \lim_m y(x_m)$$

for each $y \in E'$ since E' is separable. If we can justify the interchange of limits in the relation

$$\lim_n x''(y_n) = \lim_n \lim_m y_n(x_m) = \lim_m \lim_n y_n(x_m) = \lim_m \bar{y}(x_m) = x''(\bar{y}), \quad (*)$$

it will follow that $\{y_n\}$ converges to $\bar{y}$ for $\sigma(E', E'')$. But, since K is a generating cone in E, the dual cone K' in E' is normal for $\beta(E', E)$ by (1.14). It would then follow from (3.4) that $\{y_n\}$ converges to $\bar{y}$ for $\beta(E', E)$.

In order to establish the validity of the interchange of limits in $(*)$, define a mapping T on E by

$$Tx = \left(y_n(x) - y_{n-1}(x) : n = 1, 2, \ldots\right)$$

(where y_0 is the zero element of E'). If $x \in K$, then

$$\sum_{n=1}^{\infty} |y_n(x) - y_{n-1}(x)| = \sum_{n=1}^{\infty} \{y_n(x) - y_{n-1}(x)\} = \lim_n y_n(x) < +\infty;$$

hence, since the cone K in E is generating, T maps E into ℓ^1. It is an easy matter to verify that T is closed; hence, T is continuous for the respective norm (and weak) topologies on E and ℓ^1. Since $\{x_m\}$ is a $\sigma(E, E')$-Cauchy sequence, it follows that $\{Tx_m\}$ is a $\sigma(\ell^1, \ell^\infty)$-Cauchy sequence. Therefore, by a well-known property of ℓ^1, $\{Tx_m\}$ is a Cauchy sequence for the norm topology on ℓ^1. Consequently, given $\varepsilon > 0$, there is an integer m such that

$$\sum_{n=1}^{N} |\{y_n(x_{m_1}) - y_{n-1}(x_{m_1})\} - \{y_n(x_{m_2}) - y_{n-1}(x_{m_2})\}| \le \varepsilon$$

for all N and for all $m_1 \geq m$, $m_2 \geq m$. Hence

$$\left| \lim_{m_1 \to \infty} \sum_{n=1}^{\infty} \{y_n(x_{m_1}) - y_{n-1}(x_{m_1})\} - \sum_{n=1}^{\infty} \{x''(y_n) - x''(y_{n-1})\} \right| \leq \varepsilon \qquad (**)$$

for $m_1 \geq m$. Hence, since

$$\lim_m \lim_n y_n(x_m) = \lim_m \sum_{n=1}^{\infty} \{y_n(x_m) - y_{n-1}(x_m)\}$$

and

$$\lim_n \lim_m y_n(x_m) = \lim_n \lim_m \sum_{j=1}^{n} \{y_j(x_m) - y_{j-1}(x_m)\}$$

$$= \lim_n \sum_{j=1}^{n} \{x''(y_j) - x''(y_{j-1})\} = \sum_{n=1}^{\infty} \{x''(y_n) - x''(y_{n-1})\},$$

it follows from $(**)$ that the interchange of limits in $(*)$ is justified.

3.14   Notes. Proposition (3.4) was first established for monotone sequences in certain normed spaces by Krein [1], and was later generalized to monotone sequences in a locally convex space ordered by a normal cone by Bonsall [3], though Bonsall did not identify the concept of normality as such. Weston [1] gave a simpler proof of the Bonsall result. (3.4) was established in its present form by Schaefer [3]. His proof, which is presented in our exposition, not only establishes a more general result than the theorems of Bonsall and Krein, but also seems to be more geometric and intuitive in character. Moreover, by making use of a representation theorem for locally convex spaces ordered by a normal cone (see (5.1) in Schaefer [2]), he established the equivalence of (3.4) with the version of Dini's Theorem valid for directed sets of continuous functions on a locally compact Hausdorff space. (See 7 on p. 141 in Schaefer [4]).

Proposition (3.7) was established for sequences in reflexive Banach spaces by Amemiya [1]; the result in its present form is due to Schaefer [3]. In Section 3 of Chapter 4, we shall apply (3.7) to obtain a convergence theorem for directed families of continuous linear mappings on certain ordered locally convex spaces.

Proposition (3.12) is due to Schaefer [3] and Karlin [1] proved (3.13).

§4. LOCALLY CONVEX LATTICES

In this section, we shall study the special properties of a vector lattice equipped with a topology that is "compatible" with the lattice structure of the space. We shall see, among other things, that the order structure of the duals of such a space is quite rich. Solid subsets of a vector lattice (see (4.1) of Chapter 1) play a fundamental role in these considerations; consequently, we shall devote the initial portion of this section to a discussion of their properties.

4.1 Proposition. If A is a solid subset of a vector lattice E, then A is circled and the convex hull of A is solid.

Proof. It is obvious that A is circled. To prove that the convex hull of A is solid, we shall first establish the following fact: If $x_i \in E$ $(i = 1, 2, \ldots, n)$, $y \in E$, and $|y| \leq |x_1 + \cdots + x_n|$, then there exist $y_i \in E$ $(i = 1, 2, \ldots, n)$ such that $|y_i| \leq |x_i|$ $(i = 1, 2, \ldots, n)$ and $y = y_1 + \cdots + y_n$. It is clear that if we can establish this result for $n = 2$, the general result will follow by induction. Consequently, suppose $|y| \leq |x_1 + x_2|$ and define $y_1 = \{y \cap |x_1|\} \cup \{-|x_1|\}$. Then $y_1 = \{y \cup (-|x_1|)\}$ $|x_1|$ by (1.1) of Chapter 1; in particular, $|y_1| \leq |x_1|$. Now define $y_2 = y - y_1$, then

$$y_2 = y - \{y \cap |x_1|\} \cup (-|x_1|) = \{y - (y \cap |x_1|)\} \cap \{y + |x_1|\}$$

$$= \{\theta \cup (y - |x_1|)\} \cap \{y + |x_1|\} = \{\theta \cap (y + |x_1|)\} \cup \{y - |x_1|\}.$$

Since $-|x_1| - |x_2| \leq y \leq |x_1| + |x_2|$, it follows that $-|x_2| \leq y + |x_1|$ and $y - |x_1| \leq |x_2|$; hence,

$$-|x_2| = (-|x_2|) \cap \theta \leq (y + |x_1|) \cap \theta \leq y_2$$

$$\leq \theta \cup (y - |x_1|) \leq \theta \cup |x_2| = |x_2|.$$

Therefore, $|y_1| \leq |x_1|$, $|y_2| \leq |x_2|$, and $y = y_1 + y_2$.

Now suppose that B is the convex hull of A and that $|y| \leq |x|$ for some $x \in B$. Then

$$x = \sum_{n=1}^{k} \lambda_n x_n; \qquad \sum_{n=1}^{k} \lambda_n = 1; \qquad \lambda_n \geq 0, \qquad x_n \in A \qquad (n = 1, \ldots, k);$$

hence, there exist $y_n \in E$ $(n = 1, \ldots, k)$ such that $y = \sum_{n=1}^{k} y_n$, and $|y_n| \leq \lambda_n |x_n|$ for all n. But then $y = \sum_{n=1}^{k} \lambda_n \left(\dfrac{y_n}{\lambda_n}\right) \in B$; therefore, B is solid.

4.2 Definition. If A is a subset of a vector lattice E, the **solid hull** of A is the set of all $y \in E$ such that $|y| \leq |x|$ for some $x \in A$.

It is clear that the solid hull of a set A in a vector lattice E is the intersection of all solid subsets of E that contain A. Moreover, the operation of forming the solid hull of a set is idempotent on the class of all subsets of E. Observe that the union of solid sets is solid. In particular, solid sets need not be convex.

The following result will be useful in our development of the duality properties of vector lattices.

4.3 Proposition. Suppose that E is a regularly ordered vector lattice and that A is a subset of E (resp. E^+), then the polar of the solid hull B of A with respect to the dual system $\langle E, E^+ \rangle$ is given by

$$B^\circ = \bigcap_{x \in A} \{y \in E^+ : \langle |x|, |y| \rangle \leq 1\},$$

$$\left(\text{resp. } B^\circ = \bigcap_{y \in A} \{x \in E : \langle |x|, |y| \rangle \leq 1\}\right).$$

Proof. Since E^+ is a total set of linear functionals on E, it is sufficient to prove the relation when A is a subset of E (see (4.17)). We have $B^\circ = \{z \in E : |z| \leq |x| \text{ for some } x \in A\}^\circ = \left(\bigcup_{x \in A} \{z \in E : |z| \leq |x|\}\right)^\circ = \bigcap_{x \in A} \{z \in E : |z| \leq |x|\}^\circ = \bigcap_{x \in A} \{y \in E^+ : \sup_{|z| \leq |x|} |\langle z, y \rangle| \leq 1\}$ $= \bigcap_{x \in A} \{y \in E^+ : \langle |x|, |y| \rangle \leq 1\}$ (the last equality follows from Equation (6) in (2.3) of Chapter 1).

4.4 Corollary. If $\langle E, F \rangle$ is a dual system in which E is a regularly ordered vector lattice and F is a sublattice of E^+, then the polar of a solid subset of E is a solid subset of F. If F is a lattice ideal in E^+, then the polar of a solid subset of F is a solid subset of E.

We now turn to some elementary topological considerations.

4.5 Proposition. If $E(\mathfrak{T})$ is an ordered topological vector space which is a vector lattice, then the following assertions are equivalent:

a. $(x, y) \to x \cap y$ is a continuous mapping of $E(\mathfrak{T}) \times E(\mathfrak{T})$ into $E(\mathfrak{T})$.

b. $(x, y) \to x \cup y$ is a continuous mapping of $E(\mathfrak{T}) \times E(\mathfrak{T})$ into $E(\mathfrak{T})$.

c. $x \to x^+$ is a continuous mapping on $E(\mathfrak{T})$.

d. $x \to x^-$ is a continuous mapping on $E(\mathfrak{T})$.

e. $x \to |x|$ is a continuous mapping on $E(\mathfrak{T})$.

If the cone in $E(\mathfrak{T})$ is normal, the continuity of each the mappings in (c), (d), (e) is equivalent to its continuity at the zero element θ.

Proof. (a) implies (b) since $x \cup y = -\{(-x) \cap (-y)\}$. Since $E \times \{\theta\}$ equipped with the topology induced by $E(\mathfrak{T}) \times E(\mathfrak{T})$ is isomorphic with $E(\mathfrak{T})$, it follows that (b) implies (c). (d) follows from (c) by virtue of the relation $x^- = (-x)^+$; (d) implies (e) since $|x| = x + 2x^-$. Finally, (a) is a consequence of (e), since $x \cap y = -\frac{1}{2}\{|x - y| - (x - y)\} + y$.

If the cone in $E(\mathfrak{T})$ is normal, there is a neighborhood basis of θ consisting of full sets. Hence, the inequalities (15) and (17) in (1.2) of Chapter 1 show that continuity at θ implies continuity on $E(\mathfrak{T})$ for each of the mappings in (c), (d), (e).

We shall refer to the mappings defined in (a) through (e) of (4.5) as the **lattice operations**.

4.6 Definitions. An ordered topological vector space $E(\mathfrak{T})$ which is a vector lattice is a **topological vector lattice** if there is a neighborhood basis of θ for $\mathfrak{T}$ consisting of solid sets. In addition, if $E(\mathfrak{T})$ is a locally convex space, then $E(\mathfrak{T})$ is a **locally convex lattice**. A vector lattice E equipped with a norm $\| \cdot \|$ is a **normed vector lattice** if $|x| \leq |y|$ implies $\|x\| \leq \|y\|$; if E is complete for this norm, E is called a **Banach lattice**.

If $E(\mathfrak{T})$ is a locally convex lattice, it follows from (4.1) that there is a neighborhood basis of θ for $\mathfrak{T}$ consisting of convex, circled, solid sets. Also, if E is a normed vector lattice, the unit ball in E is solid; in particular, E is a locally convex lattice for the topology generated by the norm.

Though the formulation of (4.6) is most convenient from the technical point of view, the following result more clearly indicates the real significance of the restriction imposed in the definition of a topological vector lattice.

4.7 Proposition. If $E(\mathfrak{T})$ is a topological vector space which is a vector lattice, then $E(\mathfrak{T})$ is a topological vector lattice if and only if the cone in $E(\mathfrak{T})$ is normal and the lattice operations are continuous.

Proof. Since a solid neighborhood V of θ for $\mathfrak{T}$ has the property that $\theta \le x \le y \in V$ implies $x \in V$, the positive cone in a topological vector lattice $E(\mathfrak{T})$ is normal by $(1.3)(b)$. Moreover, the mapping $x \to |x|$ is obviously continuous at θ in a topological vector lattice $E(\mathfrak{T})$; hence, (4.5) implies that the lattice operations are continuous.

Conversely, suppose that the cone K in $E(\mathfrak{T})$ is normal and that the lattice operations are continuous; then there is a neighborhood basis $\mathscr{W}$ of θ in $E(\mathfrak{T})$ consisting of full, circled sets. If $U \in \mathscr{W}$, choose $W \in \mathscr{W}$ so that $W + W \subset U$, and then choose $V \in \mathscr{W}$ so that $x^+ \in W$ whenever $x \in V$. Now, if $x \in V$, then $-x \in V$; hence, x^+ and $x^- = (-x)^+$ are both in W. It follows that $|x| = x^+ + x^- \in U$ whenever $x \in V$. Thus, $|y| \le |x|$ and $x \in V$, then $y \in [-|x|, |x|] \subset U$; that is, the solid hull of V is contained in U. We conclude that $E(\mathfrak{T})$ is a topological vector lattice.

The following simple facts concerning topological vector lattices will prove to be useful later on.

4.8 Proposition. The closure $\bar{B}$ of a solid set B in a topological vector lattice $E(\mathfrak{T})$ is solid.

Proof. If $x \in \bar{B}$, choose a net $\{x_\alpha : \alpha \in I\}$ in B such that $\{x_\alpha : \alpha \in I\}$ converges to x for $\mathfrak{T}$, then $x = x_\alpha + u_\alpha$ $(\alpha \in I)$ where $\{u_\alpha : \alpha \in I\}$ converges to θ for $\mathfrak{T}$. Now, if $|y| \le |x|$, then, since $|y| \le |x_\alpha + u_\alpha|$ for all $\alpha \in I$, there exist nets $\{y_\alpha : \alpha \in I\}$, $\{v_\alpha : \alpha \in I\}$ such that $y = y_\alpha + v_\alpha$; $|y_\alpha| \le |x_\alpha|$; $|v_\alpha| \le |u_\alpha|$ for each $\alpha \in I$ (see the proof of (4.1)). In view of the continuity of the lattice operations in $E(\mathfrak{T})$, the net $\{|u_\alpha| : \alpha \in I\}$ converges to θ for $\mathfrak{T}$; hence, $\{v_\alpha : \alpha \in I\}$ converges to θ for $\mathfrak{T}$ since the cone in $E(\mathfrak{T})$ is normal. Consequently, $\{y_\alpha : \alpha \in I\}$ converges to y for $\mathfrak{T}$; hence, $y \in \bar{B}$ since $y_\alpha \in B$ for all $\alpha \in I$. Therefore, B is a solid set.

4.9 Proposition. If $E(\mathfrak{T})$ is a topological vector lattice, there is a neighborhood basis of θ consisting of closed, solid sets. If M is a lattice ideal in $E(\mathfrak{T})$, the closure $\overline{M}$ of M is a lattice ideal in $E(\mathfrak{T})$. If $E(\mathfrak{T})$ is an order complete vector lattice and M is a band in $E(\mathfrak{T})$, then the projection P_M of E onto M that vanishes on $M^\perp$ is continuous.

Proof. The first two assertions are immediate from (4.8). Moreover, in view of the relation $|P_M x| = P_M |x| \le |x|$, P_M maps each solid neighborhood of θ into itself.

4.10 Proposition. If $E(\mathfrak{T})$ is a locally convex space that is a vector lattice, then the following assertions are equivalent:

a. $E(\mathfrak{T})$ is a locally convex lattice.
b. For any nets $\{x_\alpha : \alpha \in I\}$, $\{y_\alpha : \alpha \in I\}$ in E, the assumptions that $\{y_\alpha : \alpha \in I\}$ converges to θ for $\mathfrak{T}$ and $|x_\alpha| \le |y_\alpha|$ for all α imply $\{x_\alpha : \alpha \in I\}$ converges to θ for $\mathfrak{T}$.
c. There is a family $\{p_\beta : \beta \in B\}$ of seminorms on E that generates $\mathfrak{T}$ such that $|x| \le |y|$ implies $p_\beta(x) \le p_\beta(y)$ for all $\beta \in B$.

Proof. It is clear that (*a*) implies (*b*). If (*b*) holds and if $\{q_\beta : \beta \in B\}$ is a family of seminorms on E that generates $\mathfrak{T}$, the family $\{p_\beta : \beta \in B\}$ of seminorms on E defined by

$$p_\beta(x) = \sup\{q_\beta(y) : \theta \le y \le |x|\} \qquad (*)$$

will clearly satisfy (*c*) if we can show that this family generates $\mathfrak{T}$. It is immediate from the definition (*) that $2p_\beta(x) \ge q_\beta(x)$ for each $x \in E$ and each $\beta \in B$; hence, the family $\{p_\beta : \beta \in B\}$ certainly generates a topology that is finer than $\mathfrak{T}$. On the other hand, if $\{x_\alpha : \alpha \in I\}$ is a net in $E(\mathfrak{T})$ that converges to θ for $\mathfrak{T}$ and if there exist $\beta \in B$ and $\varepsilon > 0$ such that $p_\beta(x_\alpha) \ge \varepsilon$ for all $\alpha \in I$, choose $y_\alpha \in E$ such that $\theta \le y_\alpha \le |x_\alpha|$ and $q_\beta(y_\alpha) \ge \dfrac{\varepsilon}{2}$ for each $\alpha \in I$. But then $\{y_\alpha\}$ converges to θ while $q_\beta(y_\alpha) \ge \dfrac{\varepsilon}{2}$, which contradicts the continuity of q_β. It follows that p_β is a continuous seminorm on $E(\mathfrak{T})$ for each $\beta \in B$; hence, the family $\{p_\beta : \beta \in B\}$ generates the topology $\mathfrak{T}$.

Finally, if $\{p_\beta : \beta \in B\}$ is a family of seminorms satisfying (*c*) and if, for each $\beta \in B$, the set V_β is defined to be the gauge set of p_β then the class $\mathscr{W}$ of all finite intersections of sets in the class $\left\{\dfrac{1}{n} V_\beta : \beta \in B;\right.$

$n = 1, 2, \ldots \}$ is a neighborhood basis of θ for $\mathfrak{T}$ consisting of convex solid sets. Therefore, $E(\mathfrak{T})$ is a locally convex lattice.

4.11 Corollary. If $E(\mathfrak{T})$ is a bornological space which is a vector lattice, then $E(\mathfrak{T})$ is a locally convex lattice if and only if $\{x_n\}$ converges to θ for $\mathfrak{T}$ whenever $\{x_n\}$ is a sequence in E such that $|x_n| \leq |y_n|$ for some sequence $\{y_n\}$ in E that converges to θ for $\mathfrak{T}$.

Proof. It is only necessary to observe that if p_β is defined by (*) (see the proof of (4.10)), then the sequential condition in this corollary implies that each p_β is continuous since $E(\mathfrak{T})$ is bornological.

4.12 Examples. a. All of the vector lattices mentioned in (1.9)(a) are obviously locally convex lattices for the topologies described there; in fact, all of the normed spaces listed in (1.9)(a) are Banach lattices for the given norm.

b. A simple example of a vector lattice equipped with a norm that is not even a locally convex lattice for the resulting norm topology is provided by the space $BV_0[a, b]$ of all functions of bounded variation on the closed interval $[a, b]$ of the real line that vanish at a, ordered by the cone of functions in $BV_0[a, b]$ that are non-negative throughout $[a, b]$, and normed by the total variation norm. It is easy to see that an order interval $[\theta, g]$ may contain functions of arbitrarily large variation; hence, $(4.10)(b)$ is not satisfied by the total variation norm topology.

c. The cone K of functions in $L^1(S, \Sigma, \mu)$ that are non-negative almost everywhere is normal for the topology generated by the norm

$$\|f\| = \int |f(t)| \, d\mu(t)$$

$\left(\text{see } (1.9)(a)\right)$ and therefore, by (1.24), K is normal for the corresponding weak topology. However, the lattice operations in $L^1(S, \Sigma, \mu)$ need not be weakly continuous, or even weakly sequentially continuous. In fact, if (S, Σ, μ) is taken to be the unit interval $[0, 1]$ equipped with Lebesgue measure, the sequence $\{f_n\}$ in L^1 defined by

$$f_n(t) = \sin nt \qquad (0 \leq t \leq 1)$$

converges to θ for $\sigma(L^1, L^\infty)$, yet $\{|f_n|\}$ does not converge to θ for this topology.

In Section 2 of Chapter 3, we shall prove that the lattice operations in a normed vector lattice are weakly continuous if and only if the vector lattice is finite dimensional.

d. If $0 < p < 1$, the space $L^p[a, b]$ (see (2.15)(c)) is a vector lattice (for the order determined by the cone of functions in $L^p[a, b]$ that are non-negative almost everywhere on $[a, b]$), and a topological vector lattice for the metrizable topology generated by the θ-neighborhood basis:

$$V_n = \left\{ f \in L^p[a, b] : \left(\int_a^b |f(t)|^p \, d\mu(t) \right)^{1/p} < \frac{1}{n} \right\} \qquad n = 1, 2, \ldots$$

since each V_n is obviously solid. It is clear from (2.15)(c) that $L^p[a, b]$ is not a locally convex lattice for this topology. Observe that each V_n is solid but not convex.

4.13 Proposition. If $E(\mathfrak{T})$ is a topological vector space which is a vector lattice and if the lattice operations in $E(\mathfrak{T})$ are continuous, then the cone K in $E(\mathfrak{T})$ is a strict b-cone. In addition, if $\mathfrak{T}$ is a Hausdorff topology, then K is closed.

Proof. To prove the first assertion, it would suffice to show that the mapping $x \to x^+$ transforms bounded sets into bounded sets in $E(\mathfrak{T})$. For, if B is a bounded, circled set in $E(\mathfrak{T})$ and if $B^+ = \{x^+ : x \in B\}$, then $B \subset B^+ - B^+$ and $B^+ \subset K$. Now, if $\{x_n\}$ is a sequence in a bounded set B and if $\{\lambda_n\}$ is a null sequence of positive real numbers, then $\lambda_n x_n^+ = (\lambda_n x_n)^+$; hence, $\{\lambda_n x_n^+\}$ converges to θ for $\mathfrak{T}$ since B is bounded and the mapping $x \to x^+$ is continuous on $E(\mathfrak{T})$. Therefore, B^+ is bounded; hence, K is a strict b-cone. Also $K = \{x \in E : x^- = \theta\}$ is closed if $\mathfrak{T}$ is a Hausdorff topology since $\{\theta\}$ is a closed set in that case.

4.14 Proposition. If $E(\mathfrak{T})$ is a topological vector lattice and if M is a vector sublattice of E, then M is a topological vector lattice for the topology induced by $E(\mathfrak{T})$. If M is a lattice ideal in $E(\mathfrak{T})$, then the quotient space E/M is a topological vector lattice for the quotient topology. An arbitrary product of topological vector lattices is a topological vector lattice.

Proof. The first assertion is obvious. By virtue of (4.3) of Chapter 1, E/M is a vector lattice; moreover, if φ is the canonical mapping of E onto E/M, then φ is positive and $\varphi(|x|) = |\varphi(x)|$ (see the proof of the result just cited). Thus, the cone is normal and the lattice operations are continuous in E/M; i.e., E/M is a topological vector lattice for the quotient topology. The final assertion follows directly from the definitions of order and neighborhoods of θ in product spaces.

4.15 Proposition. If $E(\mathfrak{T})$ is a locally convex lattice ordered by a cone K, then the completion $\tilde{E}(\tilde{\mathfrak{T}})$ of $E(\mathfrak{T})$ is a locally convex lattice for the order structure determined by the closure $\tilde{K}$ of K in $\tilde{E}(\tilde{\mathfrak{T}})$.

Proof. If $\{p_\alpha : \alpha \in A\}$ is a family of seminorms generating $\mathfrak{T}$ and satisfying the restriction in (4.10)(c), then, for each $\alpha \in A$, p_α can be uniquely extended to a continuous seminorm $\tilde{p}_\alpha$ on $\tilde{E}(\tilde{\mathfrak{T}})$. Moerover, the family $\{\tilde{p}_\alpha : \alpha \in A\}$ generates $\tilde{\mathfrak{T}}$ and satisfies (4.10)(c). Hence, $\tilde{E}(\tilde{\mathfrak{T}})$ is a locally convex lattice.

4.16 Proposition. If $\{E_\alpha(\mathfrak{T}_\alpha) : \alpha \in A\}$ is a family of locally convex lattices that are lattice ideals in a vector lattice E and if $E = \bigcup_{\alpha \in A} E_\alpha$, then E is a locally convex lattice for the inductive topology $\mathfrak{T}$ with respect to the family $\{E_\alpha(\mathfrak{T}_\alpha) : \alpha \in A\}$.

Proof. If $\mathscr{W}_\alpha$ is a neighborhood basis of θ in $E_\alpha(\mathfrak{T}_\alpha)$ consisting of convex, solid sets, the typical element of a neighborhood basis of θ for $\mathfrak{T}$ is obtained by forming the convex hull W of $\bigcup_{\alpha \in A} W_\alpha$ where $W_\alpha \in \mathscr{W}_\alpha$. Since $\bigcup_{\alpha \in A} W_\alpha$ is solid, it follows from (4.1) that W is solid; hence, $E(\mathfrak{T})$ is a locally convex lattice.

4.17 Proposition. If $E(\mathfrak{T})$ is a locally convex lattice, then the topological dual E' of E is a lattice ideal in the order dual E^+ of E. E' is a locally convex lattice for the strong topology. $\beta(E', E)$ and the canonical embedding of E into E'' preserves the lattice operations.

Proof. If $f \in E'$, then $f \in E^+$ since the cone K in E normal (see (1.21) and (4.7)). Suppose that $|g| \le |f|$ for $f \in E'$ and $g \in E^+$. If $\{x_\alpha : \alpha \in I\}$ is a net in $E(\mathfrak{T})$ that converges to θ and if $\varepsilon > 0$, choose y_α so that $|y_\alpha| \le |x_\alpha|$ and $|f|(|x_\alpha|) \le f(y_\alpha) + \varepsilon$ for each $\alpha \in I$ (see formula (6) in Section 2 of Chapter 1). Now, $\{y_\alpha : \alpha \in I\}$ converges to θ

for $\mathfrak{T}$ by (4.10); hence, since ε is an artibrary positive number, we conclude that $\{|f|(|x_\alpha|) : \alpha \in I\}$ converges to 0. Consequently, in view of the relation

$$|g(x_\alpha)| \leq |g|(|x_\alpha|) \leq |f|(|x_\alpha|) \qquad (\alpha \in I),$$

it follows that $g \in E'$. Therefore, E' is a lattice ideal in E^+.

Since $E(\mathfrak{T})$ is a locally convex lattice, the class of all solid, bounded subsets of $E(\mathfrak{T})$ is a fundamental system for the class of all bounded subsets of $E(\mathfrak{T})$. Therefore, E' is a locally convex lattice for $\beta(E', E)$ by (4.4).

To show that the canonical embedding $x \to \bar{x}$ of E into E'' preserves the lattice operations, it is sufficient to show that $\bar{x}^+(f) = f(x^+)$ for each element f of the dual cone K' of K in E'. In view of Equation (1) of Section 2 in Chapter 1 and the definition of the canonical embedding $x \to \bar{x}$, $\bar{x}^+$ is given by

$$\bar{x}^+(f) = \sup \{g(x) : \theta \leq g \leq f; g \in K'\}.$$

Define the functional h on the cone K in E by

$$h(u) = \sup \{f(z) : \theta \leq z \leq u; z \leq rx^+ ; r \geq 0\},$$

then h is clearly positively homogeneous on K. By making use of (1.4) of Chapter 1, it is an easy matter to verify that h is additive on K. Hence, h can be extended uniquely to a linear functional h on E which is clearly positive. For each $y \in K$, it is true that $f(y) \geq h(y)$; hence, h is in the class used to define $\bar{x}^+(f)$. Also, $h(x^+) = f(x^+)$ and $h(x^-) = 0$ since x^+ and x^- are disjoint elements of E. Therefore, $f(x^+) = h(x^+) = h(x) \leq \bar{x}^+(f)$; on the other hand, $\bar{x}^+(f) \leq \sup \{g(x^+) : \theta \leq g \leq f\} \leq f(x^+)$ which completes the proof.

4.18 Proposition. If $E(\mathfrak{T})$ is a locally convex lattice which is barreled, the topological dual E' of E is a band in the order dual E^+ of E.

Proof. Since (4.17) asserts that E' is a lattice ideal in the order complete vector lattice E^+, it is only necessary to prove that $\sup (\mathscr{M}) \in E'$ whenever $\mathscr{M}$ is a directed ($\leq$) subset of E' that is majorized in E^+. By Equation (10) of Section 2 in Chapter 1, the supremum of $\mathscr{M}$ is defined by

$$\sup (\mathscr{M})(x) = \sup \{f(x) : f \in \mathscr{M}\} \qquad (*)$$

for each $x \geq \theta$. Since the cone in E is generating, it follows from (∗) that the filter $\mathfrak{F}(\mathscr{M})$ of sections of $\mathscr{M}$ converges to sup $(\mathscr{M})$ for $\sigma(E^+, E)$. Each section of $\mathscr{M}$ is $\sigma(E^+, E)$-bounded since the cone K^* of all positive linear functionals on E is normal for $\sigma(E^+, E)$. Hence, each such section is $\sigma(E', E)$-relatively compact since E is barreled. Therefore, sup $(\mathscr{M}) \in E'$, which completes the proof.

4.19 Proposition. If M is a lattice ideal in a locally convex lattice $E(\mathfrak{T})$, then the polar $M°$ of M for the dual system $\langle E, E' \rangle$ is a band in E'.

Proof. E' is an order complete vector lattice by (4.17), and (4.3) implies that $M°$ is solid and

$$M° = \{f \in E' : |f|(|x|) = 0 \quad \text{for all } x \in M\}. \tag{∗}$$

From the description of $M°$ given in (∗), it is clear that $M°$ is a band in E'.

Our next task will be to relate the continuity of linear mappings with respect to the topology of a locally convex lattice to their order continuity as defined in (5.11) of Chapter 1. We shall begin by considering some examples.

4.20 Examples. a. (Roberts [1]) If C is an arbitrary compact subset of a locally compact Hausdorff space X, and if $\mathscr{K}(X, C)$ is the vector lattice of all continuous, real-valued functions on X with support contained in C equipped with the norm

$$\|f\|_C = \sup \{|f(t)| : t \in C\},$$

then the vector lattice $\mathscr{K}(X)$ of all continuous, real-valued functions with compact support in X is a locally convex lattice for the inductive limit topology with respect to the family $\{\mathscr{K}(X, C) : C$ compact in $X\}$ by (4.16). (See (2.20) (b).) Since the cone of non-negative functions on X is normal for this topology, the dual of $\mathscr{K}(X)$, that is, the space $\mathscr{M}(X)$ of all Radon measures on X, is contained in the order dual $\mathscr{K}(X)^+$. On the other hand, every positive linear functional on $\mathscr{K}(X)$ is continuous $\big($see (2.20)(b)$\big)$; hence, $\mathscr{K}(X)^+ = \mathscr{M}(X)$. Therefore, by (5.15) of Chapter 1, every order continuous linear functional on $\mathscr{K}(X)$ is a Radon measure. However, the converse is not true as the following result shows.

Proposition. If X is a σ-compact, locally compact Hausdorff space, a linear functional on $\mathscr{K}(X)$ is order continuous if and only if it is a Radon measure that vanishes on every set of first category in X.

Proof. Suppose that N is a relatively compact, nowhere dense subset of X, and define D to be the directed ($\geq$) set of all non-negative functions f in $\mathscr{K}(X)$ such that $f(t) \geq 1$ for all $t \in N$. If $t_0 \notin \overline{N}$, there is a continuous, real-valued function f on X with values in the closed interval $[0, 1]$ such that $f(t) = 1$ for all $t \in \overline{N}$ and $f(t) = 0$ for all t in the complement of a compact neighborhood of $\overline{N}$ that does not include t_0. Since such a function is in D, it is clear that any non-negative lower bound for D in $\mathscr{K}(X)$ must vanish on the complement of $\overline{N}$. But the set of points at which such a lower bound takes on positive values is open; hence, inf $(D) = \theta$ since $\overline{N}$ has an empty interior. Therefore, if μ is an order continuous Radon measure on X and if D is regarded as a net $\{f_\alpha\}$ decreasing to θ, it follows that

$$\int f_\alpha \, d|\mu| \to 0$$

since $|\mu|$ is also order continuous (see (5.22) of Chapter 1). Since $f_\alpha(t) \geq 1$ for all $t \in N$ and $f_\alpha \in D$, it is clear that

$$|\mu(N)| \leq \int f_\alpha \, d|\mu|$$

for all α; hence, $\mu(N) = 0$. Consequently, since X is σ-compact, μ vanishes on each set of first category in X.

Now suppose that μ is a positive Radon measure on X such that every set of first category in X has μ-measure zero. If $\{f_\alpha : \alpha \in I\}$ is a net that decreases to θ and if

$$D_n = \left\{ t \in X : f_\alpha(t) \geq \frac{1}{n} \text{ for all } \alpha \in I \right\} \qquad n = 1, 2, \ldots$$

then each D_n is closed. Also, since X is completely regular, each D_n has an empty interior; for otherwise, it would be possible to construct a lower bound f_0 for D such that $f_0 > \theta$. But then the set $\{t \in X : \inf f_\alpha(t) \neq 0\} = \bigcup_{n=1}^{\infty} D_n$ has μ-measure zero, that is, $\{f_\alpha : \alpha \in I\}$ converges to θ μ-almost everywhere. To show that

$$\int f_\alpha \, d\mu \to 0, \qquad (*)$$

it is only necessary to note that, if $\alpha_0 \in I$, the support of each f_α for $\alpha \geq \alpha_0$ is contained in the support f_{α_0}; hence, $\{f_\alpha : \alpha \geq \alpha_0\}$ converges in L_μ^1 (support f_{α_0}). Consequently, (*) holds, that is, μ is order continuous.

If μ is any Radon measure that assigns measure zero to every set of first category in X, we can apply the conclusion of the preceding paragraph to the components of the Jordon decomposition of μ to conclude that μ is order continuous. This completes the proof of the proposition.

b. Consider the sequence space φ of all sequences of real numbers with only a finite number of nonzero components, equipped with the norm

$$\|x\| = \sup_n \{|x_n|\}$$

and ordered by the cone of sequences in φ with non-negative components. φ is obviously a normed vector lattice, and the topological dual of φ can be identified with ℓ^1. However, according to (5.24) of Chapter 1, every sequence $u = (u_n)$ of real numbers determines an order continuous linear functional f_u on φ by means of the equation:

$$f_u(x) = \sum_{n=1}^\infty x_n u_n \qquad x = (x_n) \in \varphi.$$

Consequently, there exist order continuous linear functionals on φ that are not continuous for the norm topology.

4.21 Proposition. Suppose that $E(\mathfrak{T})$ and $F(\mathfrak{S})$ are locally convex spaces that are also vector lattices. If E has the property that every sequence (resp. net) that decreases to θ converges to θ for $\sigma(E, E')$ and if F is an order complete vector lattice ordered by a closed cone, then every positive, weakly continuous linear mapping T of E into F is sequentially order continuous (resp. order continuous).

Proof. Suppose that $\{x_n\}$ is a sequence in E that order converges to θ, then $|x_n| \leq y_n$ for some sequence $\{y_n\}$ that decreases to θ. By hypothesis, $\{y_n\}$ converges to θ for $\sigma(E, E')$; hence, $\{Ty_n\}$ converges to θ for $\sigma(F, F')$. Moreover, $\{Ty_n\}$ is a decreasing sequence since T

is positive; hence, $\{Ty_n\}$ decreases to θ by (3.1). Therefore, the relation

$$|T(x_n)| \leq T|x_n| \leq Ty_n$$

implies that T is order sequentially continuous. An obvious modification of the preceding argument yields the assertion concerning order continuity.

4.22 Corollary. Suppose that E is a locally convex space that is a vector lattice with a weakly normal cone. If every sequence (resp. net) that decreases to θ in E converges to θ for $\sigma(E, E')$, then every continuous linear functional on E is order sequentially continuous (resp. order continuous).

Note that a linear functional on a vector lattice is sequentially order continuous if and only if it is sequentially order *-continuous. Also, for a fairly wide class of vector lattices including the class of σ-order complete vector lattices with the diagonal property (see (5.9) of Chapter 1), relative uniform convergence coincides with order convergence. Since it is possible to identify relative uniform *-convergence with convergence with respect to the given topology in some interesting classes of topological vector lattices (see, for example, (2.4) in Chapter 4), and since such topological vector lattices often have the diagonal property (see (2.6) of Chapter 4), it is often possible to identify the collection of order continuous linear functionals with the dual of a topological vector lattice. We shall elaborate on this point in Section 2 of Chapter 4 after we have developed the necessary preliminary material concerning order topologies in Chapter 3.

4.23 Notes. The early basis of the theory of Banach lattices was developed primarily by Birkhoff [2], Kakutani [1], [2] Kantorovitch [2], Krein [1], and Nakano (see [5] for a collection of early papers) Roberts [2] was the first to investigate the duality theory for locally convex lattices. This theory has undergone very substantial development during recent years through the works of Amemiya-Mori [1], Goffman [2], Gordon [1], [2]; Kawai [1]; Kist [1]; Kuller

[1]; Namioka [1]; Schaefer [2], [3], [4], [5]; Weston [2]; the author [1], [2], and others. Many of the results to be found in these papers are discussed in other sections of this book. The object of this section is to present only the basic structure theory of locally convex lattices and to prepare the way for a detailed account of some special aspects of the theory in Chapters 3 and 4.

We shall not present a detailed account of the fundamental representation theorems due to Kakutani [1], [2] for (M)-spaces and (L)-spaces since excellent accounts (both summary and detailed) of this subject already have appeared in a number of books on functional analysis (see, for example, Birkhoff [2], Day [2], Edwards [1], Kelley-Namioka [1], and Schaefer [1]). Instead, we shall confine ourselves to a presentation of the following brief summary of the basic definitions and results in this theory.

A Banach lattice E is an **M-space** (resp. **L-space**) if the norm on E satisfies the following relation: $\|x \vee y\| = \sup\{\|x\|, \|y\|\}$ for all $x \geq \theta$, $y \geq \theta$ (resp. $\|x + y\| = \|x\| + \|y\|$ for all $x \geq \theta$, $y \geq \theta$). An element u of a Banach lattice E is a **unit element** if $\|u\| = 1$ and $x \leq u$ whenever $x \in E$ and $\|x\| \leq 1$. An element $e \geq \theta$ of a vector lattice E is called a **weak order unit** if $e \cap |x| = \theta$ implies $x = \theta$ for any $x \in E$. Of course, the space $C(X)$ of continuous real-valued functions on a compact Hausdorff space X is an obvious example of an M-space with a unit element, while the Banach lattice $L^1(S, \Sigma, \mu)$ corresponding to a measure space (S, Σ, μ) is clearly an L-space. The point of the Kakutani representation theorems is that any M-space with a unit element can be regarded as $C(X)$ for an appropriate compact Hausdorff space X and that any L-space is essentially the L^1-space corresponding to a suitable measure space (S, Σ, μ). Specifically, the following results can be established:

1. If E is an M-space with a unit element u then there is a compact Hausdorff space X and a norm preserving isomorphism φ of E onto $C(X)$ such that $\varphi(x \vee y) = \varphi(x) \vee \varphi(y)$ and $\varphi(x \cap y) = \varphi(x) \cap \varphi(y)$ for all x, y in E. (In fact, the space X can be identified with the set of extreme points of $\{x' \in E' : x'(u) = 1; x'(x) \geq 0 \text{ for all } x \geq \theta\}$ equipped with the topology induced by $\sigma(E', E)$; the isopmorhism φ can be defined for $x \in E$ by $\varphi(x) = f$ where $f(t) = t(x)$ for all $t \in X$.)

E is order complete if and only if X is extremally disconnected (see (1.7) of Chapter 1). If E is an M-space, but E does not contain a unit element, then E can be identified with a closed vector sublattice of $C(X)$.

2. If E is an abstract L-space, there is a locally compact Hausdorff space S and a positive Radon measure μ defined on S with the following property: There is a norm preserving isomorphism ψ of E onto $L^1(S, \Sigma, \mu)$ such that $\psi(x \cup y) = \psi(x) \cup \psi(y)$ and $\psi(x \cap y) = \psi(x) \cap \psi(y)$ for all x, y in E. If E contains a weak order unit, then S may be chosen to be compact.

3. If E is an M-space (resp. L-space), then the dual E' of E, ordered by the dual cone and equipped with the norm

$$\|x'\| = \sup \{|x'(x)| : \|x\| \leq 1\},$$

is an L-space (resp. M-space). Thus, in view of (4.17), the dual of an L-space can be identified with the order complete Banach lattice $C(X)$ for an appropriate extremally disconnected, compact Hausdorff space X.

Intrinsic topological characterizations of M-spaces and L-spaces have been obtained by Braunschweiger [1], [3], Clarkson [1], Fullerton [2], Weston [2], and the author [2]. For example, in the author's paper [2], it is shown that any complete metrizable locally convex lattice $E(\mathfrak{T})$ is the inductive limit of a family of linear subspaces that are M-spaces; in particular, if E contains an order unit, then $\mathfrak{T}$ can be generated by a norm for which $E(\mathfrak{T})$ is an M-space with unit element. Also, Braunschweiger [1] and Weston [2] show that the topology of a complete Hausdorff topological vector space $E(\mathfrak{T})$ which is a vector lattice can be generated by a norm for which E is an L-space if and only if

a. the lattice operations in E are continuous at θ;
b. there is an $f \in E'$ such that $\{x \in E : x \geq \theta, f(x) = 1\}$ is bounded and nonempty.

Kuller [1] has considered the representation of complete locally convex lattices $E(\mathfrak{T})$ for which there is a generating system $\{p_\alpha : \alpha \in A\}$

of seminorms such that $p_\alpha(x) \le p_\alpha(y)$ for all $\alpha \in A$ whenever $|x| \le |y|$, and either

a. $\quad p_\alpha(x \cup y) = \sup \{p_\alpha(x), p_\alpha(y)\}$ $\quad$ for all $x \ge \theta,\, y \ge \theta,\, \alpha \in A$

or

b. $\quad p_\alpha(x + y) = p_\alpha(x) + p_\alpha(y)$ $\quad$ for all $x \ge \theta,\, y \ge \theta,\, \alpha \in A$.

Other related papers: Bonsall-Reuter [1], Cunningham [1], Geba-Semadeni [1], Gordon [4], Heider [1], [2], Kaplan [1], [2], [3], Mack [1], Rota [1], Tsuji [1].

Chapter Three

Intrinsic Topologies
of Ordered Vector Spaces

Certain topologies on an ordered vector space can be defined in terms of the order structure of the space. This chapter is devoted to a systematic study of the basic properties of two such topologies, the so-called order topology and the $\mathfrak{S}$-topology corresponding to the class $\mathfrak{S}$ of all order bounded subsets of the dual space. As we shall see, these two topologies lie at opposite extremes of the spectrum of topologies compatible with the lattice structure of a vector lattice. We shall show that the order topology agrees with the given topology in any complete, metrizable, locally convex lattice, thereby providing an entirely order theoretic description of the topological structure of this wide and interesting class of spaces. On the other hand, the topology of uniform convergence on order bounded sets will prove to be useful in our study of the relations between order completeness and topological completeness of vector lattices and in our description of the topological properties of bands in order complete vector lattices.

§1. THE ORDER TOPOLOGY

1.1 Definition. If E is an ordered vector space, the **order topology** $\mathfrak{T}_0$ on E is the finest locally convex topology $\mathfrak{T}$ for which every order bounded set is $\mathfrak{T}$-bounded.

The following result is easily verified.

1.2 Proposition. If E is an ordered vector space, a neighborhood basis of θ for the order topology is given by the class of all convex, circled sets that absorb all order bounded sets.

1.3 Corollary. If E is an ordered vector space, the order topology is finer than any locally convex topology on E for which the cone in E is normal. If E is a regularly ordered vector space, then $\mathfrak{T}_0$ is a Hausdorff topology and E is almost Archimedean.

Proof. The assertions follow immediately from (1.4), (1.29), (1.31) of Chapter 2.

The following result gives a particularly simple description of the order topology if the underlying space contains an order unit.

1.4 Proposition. If E is an almost Archimedean ordered vector space containing an order unit e, then the Minkowski functional of the order interval $[-e, e]$ is a norm generating the order topology $\mathfrak{T}_0$ and the cone in E is normal for $\mathfrak{T}_0$.

Proof. The Minkowski functional p_e of $[-e, e]$ is a norm on E since E is almost Archimedean. The topology generated by this norm is certainly finer than $\mathfrak{T}_0$ since the order interval $[-e, e]$ is $\mathfrak{T}_0$-bounded. On the other hand, $[-e, e]$ is a convex, circled set that absorbs each order bounded set since e is an order unit. Hence, $[-e, e]$ is a neighborhood of θ for $\mathfrak{T}_0$. Consequently, the norm p_e generates $\mathfrak{T}_0$. It is obvious that $\theta \leq x \leq y$ implies $p_e(x) \leq p_e(y)$; hence, the cone in E is normal for $\mathfrak{T}_0$ by (1.7) of Chapter 2.

It follows from (1.4) that the norm topology of an M-space with a unit (in particular, the topology of uniform convergence on X in the space $C(X)$ of continuous, real-valued functions on a compact Hausdorff space X) coincides with the order topology. In fact, the following result can be established.

1.5 Proposition. If $E(\mathfrak{T})$ is a Banach space ordered by a closed cone K containing an order unit e, then $\mathfrak{T} = \mathfrak{T}_o$ if and only if K is normal in $E(\mathfrak{T})$.

Proof. The necessity of the condition follows from (1.4) since E is almost Archimedean by (1.29) and (1.31) of Chapter 2. On the other hand, since K is closed, the order interval $[-e, e]$ is a closed, convex, radial, circled subset of E; hence, $[-e, e]$ is a neighborhood of θ for $\mathfrak{T}$ since $E(\mathfrak{T})$ is barreled. Since K is normal, $[-e, e]$ is $\mathfrak{T}$-bounded; hence, $\mathfrak{T}_o = \mathfrak{T}$.

1.6 Proposition. Suppose E is an Archimedean ordered vector space with an order unit e, then the following assertions are equivalent:

a. $E(\mathfrak{T}_o)$ is complete.

b. For each sequence $\{x_n\}$ of elements of E such that $\theta \leq x_n \leq \lambda_n z$ where $\{\lambda_n\} \in \ell^1$ and $z \geq \theta$, it is true that the supremum of the sequence $\left\{ \sum_{k=1}^{n} x_k : n = 1, 2, \ldots \right\}$ exists in E.

Proof. If p_e is the Minkowski functional of the order interval $[-e, e]$, then p_e generates $\mathfrak{T}_o$ by (1.4). If $\{x_n\}$ is a sequence in E such that $\theta \leq x_n \leq \lambda_n z$ where $\{\lambda_n\} \in \ell^1$ and $z \geq \theta$, the sequence $\{y_n\}$ defined by

$$y_n = \sum_{k=1}^{n} x_k \qquad n = 1, 2, \ldots$$

is a Cauchy sequence for the norm p_e. Therefore, if $E(\mathfrak{T}_o)$ is complete, $\{y_n\}$ converges to $y_0 \in E$, and $y_0 = \sup_n \{y_n\}$ by (3.2) of Chapter 2. (K is closed since $x \in \overline{K}$ and $e \in \text{Int}(K)$ imply $x + \dfrac{1}{n} e \in K$ for all n.)

On the other hand, if (2) is satisfied and if $\{x_n\}$ is a Cauchy sequence in $E(\mathfrak{T}_o)$, then, to show that $\{x_n\}$ converges, we can assume that

$$x_{n+1} - x_n \in \left[-\frac{1}{n^2} e, \frac{1}{n^2} e \right] \qquad n = 1, 2, \ldots$$

without loss in generality. But then

$$x_{n+1} - x_n = \frac{1}{n^2} e + (x_{n+1} - x_n) - \frac{1}{n^2} e$$

and

$$\theta \le \frac{1}{n^2} e + (x_{n+1} - x_n) \le \frac{2}{n^2} e;$$

hence,

$$y = \sup \left\{ \sum_{k=1}^{n} \left(\frac{1}{k^2} e + (x_{k+1} - x_k) \right) : n = 1, 2, \ldots \right\}$$

in E. Since

$$\theta \le y - \sum_{k=1}^{n} \left(\frac{1}{k^2} e + (x_{k+1} - x_k) \right)$$

$$\le \sup_{p > n} \sum_{k=n+1}^{p} \left(\frac{1}{k^2} e + (x_{k+1} - x_k) \right) \le 2 \left\{ \sum_{k=n+1}^{\infty} \frac{1}{k^2} \right\} e,$$

it follows that

$$y = \lim_{n} \left\{ \sum_{k=1}^{n} \left(\frac{1}{k^2} e + (x_{k+1} - x_k) \right) \right\}$$

for $\mathfrak{T}_0$. Therefore, $\{x_n\}$ converges for $\mathfrak{T}_0$, that is, $E(\mathfrak{T}_0)$ is complete.

1.7 Proposition. Suppose that there is a fundamental system $\mathfrak{S}'$ for the class of all order bounded sets in a regularly ordered vector space E such that each $B \in \mathfrak{S}'$ is a convex, circled set and the linear hull E_B of B is complete with respect the Minkowski functional p_B of B. Then $E(\mathfrak{T}_0)$ is a barreled space.

Proof. Suppose that A is a closed, convex, circled, radial subset of $E(\mathfrak{T}_0)$ and let B be any member of $\mathfrak{S}'$. Since each neighborhood of θ for $\mathfrak{T}_0$ absorbs B, $\mathfrak{T}_0$ induces a topology on E_B that is coarser than the topology generated by p_B. Therefore, $A \cap E_B$ is a p_B-closed, convex, circled, radial subset of E_B; hence, $A \cap E_B$ absorbs B since

E_B is a barreled space for the topology generated by p_B. But then A absorbs B; consequently, A is a neighborhood of θ for $\mathfrak{T}_0$ since $\mathfrak{S}'$ is a fundamental system for the class of all order bounded subsets of E. It follows that $E(\mathfrak{T}_0)$ is a barreled space since $\mathfrak{T}_0$ is a Hausdorff topology by (1.3).

1.8 Corollary. If $E(\mathfrak{T})$ is a Hausdorff topological vector space that is regularly ordered by a normal, generating cone, and if every order interval in E is sequentially complete, then $E(\mathfrak{T}_0)$ is a barreled space.

Proof. Since the cone in E is generating, every order bounded set in E is contained in an order interval of the form $[-x, x]$ for some $x \geq \theta$. The normality of the cone implies that, for each $x \geq \theta$, the order interval $[-x, x]$ is $\mathfrak{T}$-bounded; hence, the Minkowski functional p_x of $[-x, x]$ generates a topology on $E_x = $ linear hull $\{[-x, x]\}$ that is finer than the topology induced by $E(\mathfrak{T})$.

Suppose that $\{x_n\}$ is a Cauchy sequence in E_x for the norm p_x, then $\{x_n\}$ is a Cauchy sequence for $\mathfrak{T}$. Hence, $\{x_n\}$ converges to $x_0 \in E_x$ for $\mathfrak{T}$. But then, if $\varepsilon > 0$, there is an integer n_ε such that $x_n - x_m \in \varepsilon[-x, x]$ for $n \geq n_\varepsilon$, $m \geq n_\varepsilon$. Hence, $x_n - x_0 \in \varepsilon[-x, x]$ for $n \geq n_\varepsilon$, that is, $\{x_n\}$ converges to x_0 for p_B. It follows that E_x is complete for p_B; hence, the result follows from (1.7).

1.9 Corollary. If $E(\mathfrak{T})$ is a sequentially complete topological vector space regularly ordered by a normal, closed, generating cone, then $E(\mathfrak{T}_0)$ is a barreled space.

In Section 1 of Chapter 4 we shall identify another interesting class of spaces to which (1.7) can be applied to conclude that the members of this class are barreled for the order topology.

The following concept will be useful in obtaining an important inductive limit characterization of the order topology.

1.10 Definition. A subset H of the positive cone K in an ordered vector space E **exhausts** K if, for each $x \in K$, there are $h \in H$ and $\lambda > 0$ such that $x \leq \lambda h$.

Of course, if E is an ordered vector space with an order unit e, then the set consisting of e alone certainly exhausts the cone in E.

Also, the cone in every ordered vector space contains an exhausting subset, namely, the cone itself. Examples of ordered vector spaces without order units that contain countable exhausting subsets are provided by the space φ of sequences of real numbers with only finitely many nonzero components (see (1.6) of Chapter 1) and the space $\mathscr{K}(X)$ of all real-valued, continuous functions with compact support in a σ-compact, locally compact Hausdorff space X (see (4.20) of Chapter 2).

1.11 Proposition. Suppose that E is an almost Archimedean ordered vector space and that H is a subset of the positive cone K in E that exhausts K. For each $h \in H$, h is an order unit in the linear subspace $E_h = \bigcup_{n=1}^{\infty} n[-h, h]$ of E and the order topology $\mathfrak{T}_0^{(h)}$ on E_h is generated by a norm. The order topology $\mathfrak{T}_0$ on E is the inductive topology with respect to the family $\{E_h(\mathfrak{T}_0^{(h)}) : h \in H\}$ of linear subspaces of E.

Proof. Obviously, h is an order unit in E_h, and (1.4) implies that the order topology $\mathfrak{T}_0^{(h)}$ on E_h is generated by Minkowski functional p_h of $[-h, h]$, which is a norm on E_h. If V is a convex, circled subset of E that absorbs each order bounded set and if $h \in H$, then $V \cap E_h$ certainly absorbs $[-h, h]$; hence, the canonical embedding mapping $g_h : E_h(\mathfrak{T}_0^{(h)}) \to E(\mathfrak{T}_0)$ is continuous. On the other hand, if $\mathfrak{T}$ is any locally convex topology on E for which each embedding mapping $g_h : E_h(\mathfrak{T}_0^{(h)}) \to E(\mathfrak{T})$ is continuous and if V is a convex circled neighborhood of θ for $\mathfrak{T}$, then we can conclude that V is a neighborhood of θ for $\mathfrak{T}_0$ if we can show that V absorbs each order interval of the form $[\theta, h]$ for $h \in H$. (For if B is an order bounded set, then $B \subset [x, y] = x + [\theta, y - x] \subset x + [\theta, \lambda h]$ for suitable $h \in H$ and $\lambda > 0$.) But, for each $h \in H$, $[\theta, h]$ is $\mathfrak{T}_0^{(h)}$ bounded in E_h; hence, $[\theta, h]$ is $\mathfrak{T}$-bounded in $E(\mathfrak{T})$ since g_h is $\mathfrak{T}$-continuous. Therefore, V absorbs $[\theta, h]$. It follows that $\mathfrak{T}_0$ is the inductive topology with respect to the family $\{E_h(\mathfrak{T}_0^{(h)}) : h \in H\}$.

1.12 Corollary. If E is a regularly ordered vector space, then $E(\mathfrak{T}_0)$ is a bornological locally convex space.

Proof. Since E is regularly ordered, $\mathfrak{T}_0$ is a Hausdorff topology by (1.3). But, if a locally convex space is equipped with the inductive topology with respect to a family of bornological spaces, then it is also bornological; hence, $E(\mathfrak{T}_o)$ is a bornological space.

1.13 Proposition. If E is an ordered vector space and T is an order bounded linear mapping of $E(\mathfrak{T}_o)$ into a locally convex space $F(\mathfrak{O})$ in which every order bounded set is $\mathfrak{O}$-bounded, then T is continuous.

Proof. If V is a convex, circled neighborhood of θ in $F(\mathfrak{O})$, then $T^{-1}(V)$ is a convex, circled set that absorbs all order bounded sets. Therefore, $T^{-1}(V)$ is a neighborhood of θ for $\mathfrak{T}_o$; that is, T is continuous.

1.14 Corollary. If E, F are ordered vector spaces and if T is an order bounded linear mapping of E into F, then T is continuous for the respective order topologies on E and F.

1.15 Corollary. If E is an ordered vector space, the dual of E for the order topology coincides with the space E^b of order bounded linear functionals on E.

1.16 Proposition. If E is a regularly ordered vector space and $\mathfrak{T}$ is a locally convex topology on E, then the following assertions are equivalent:

a. $\mathfrak{T}$ is the order topology on E.

b. $\mathfrak{T}$ is the Mackey topology $\tau(E, E')$ and $E' = E^b$.

In addition, if E has the decomposition property, then (*a*) and (*b*) are equivalent to the statement:

c. $\mathfrak{T}$ is the finest locally convex topology on E for which the cone K in E is normal.

Proof. The equivalence of (*a*) and (*b*) follows immediately from (1.12) and (1.15). Suppose that E has the decomposition property and that $\mathfrak{T}$ coincides with the order topology on E. Then there is a neighborhood basis $\mathscr{W}$ of θ consisting of convex, circled sets W such that $V = W \cap (K - K)$ is the convex circled hull of $\left\{ \bigcup_{h \in H} \lambda_h [-h, h] \right\}$ (where H is a subset of K that exhausts K and $\lambda_h > 0$). If $y \in W$ and

$\theta \leq x \leq y$, then $y \in V$ and

$$y = \sum_{k=1}^{n} \beta_{h_k} z_{h_k}; \qquad \sum_{k=1}^{n} |\beta_{h_k}| \leq 1; \qquad z_{h_k} \in \lambda_{h_k}[-h_k, h_k].$$

But then $\theta \leq x \leq \sum_{k=1}^{n} |\beta_{h_k}| \lambda_{h_k} h_k$; hence,

$$x = \sum_{k=1}^{n} |\beta_{h_k}| x_{h_k}$$

where $\theta \leq x_{h_k} \leq \lambda_{h_k} h_k$ since E has the decomposition property. Therefore, $x \in W$; hence, K is normal for $\mathfrak{T}_0$ by (1.3) of Chapter 2. The fact that (a) implies (c) now follows from (1.3).

Conversely, if (c) is satisfied, then $\mathfrak{T}_0$ is finer than $\mathfrak{T}$ by (1.3). On the other hand, $\mathfrak{T}$ is finer than $\mathfrak{T}_0$ since the cone K is normal for $\mathfrak{T}_0$ if E has the decomposition property.

The following proposition shows that (1.16) can be sharpened considerably if the underlying ordered vector space is a vector lattice.

1.17 Proposition. If E is a regularly ordered vector lattice equipped with a locally convex topology $\mathfrak{T}$, the following assertions are equivalent:

a. $\mathfrak{T}$ coincides with the order topology $\mathfrak{T}_0$ on E.
b. $\mathfrak{T}$ is the finest topology on E for which E is a locally convex lattice.
c. $\mathfrak{T}$ is the finest locally convex topology on E for which every continuous linear functional is order bounded and every positive linear functional is continuous.
d. $E(\mathfrak{T})$ is a locally convex lattice, $\mathfrak{T}$ is the Mackey topology $\tau(E, E')$ and every positive linear functional on E is continuous.

Proof. If H is an exhausting subset of the positive cone in E and if $h \in H$, then $E_h = \bigcup_{n=1}^{\infty} n[-h, h]$ is a lattice ideal in E. Therefore, (4.16) of Chapter 2, (1.11) and (1.16) show that (a) is equivalent to (b) and that (a) implies (d).

If (a) holds, then $E(\mathfrak{T})' = E^b = E^+$ and $\mathfrak{T} = \tau(E, E^b)$ by (1.16); therefore, (c) is satisfied. On the other hand, (c) implies that

$E(\mathfrak{T})' = E^b$ and $\tau(E, E') = \mathfrak{T}$; hence, $\mathfrak{T} = \mathfrak{T}_o$ by (1.16). Finally, (d) implies that $E(\mathfrak{T})' = E^b$ and $\mathfrak{T} = \tau(E, E')$; consequently, (d) implies (a).

The following result shows that the order structure completely determines the topology in a wide and interesting class of locally convex lattices.

1.18 Proposition. If $E(\mathfrak{T})$ is a bornological locally convex lattice ordered by a sequentially complete cone K, then $\mathfrak{T}$ coincides with the order topology on E.

Proof. (4.13) of Chapter 2 shows that K is a strict b-cone; hence, (2.17) of Chapter 2 implies that every positive linear functional on $E(\mathfrak{T})$ is continuous. The fact that $E(\mathfrak{T})$ is bornological implies that $\mathfrak{T} = \tau(E, E')$. Therefore, $\mathfrak{T} = \mathfrak{T}_o$ by (1.17).

1.19 Corollary. If $E(\mathfrak{T})$ is a complete metrizable locally convex lattice, then $\mathfrak{T}$ coincides with the order topology on E.

The following simple example shows that the topology of a complete locally convex lattice is not determined by the order structure of the space.

1.20 Example. If $C[a, b]$ is the vector space of all continuous, real-valued functions on the closed interval $[a, b]$ $(a \neq b)$, and if $C[a, b]$ is ordered by the cone of non-negative functions on $[a, b]$, then $C[a, b]$ is a Banach lattice for the norm

$$\|f\| = \sup \{|f(t)| : a \leq t \leq b\}.$$

However, if $\mathscr{C}$ is the class of all compact, countable subsets of $[a, b]$, the space $C[a, b]$ is easily seen to be a complete locally convex lattice for the topology generated by the seminorms

$$p_C(f) = \sup \{|f(t)| : t \in C\} \qquad (C \in \mathscr{C}).$$

Since these topologies are distinct, we see that the topology of a complete locally convex lattice is not determined by the order structure.

1.21 Notes. The order topology was studied independently by Namioka [1] and Schaefer [2], and most of the results that we have presented here can be found, either explicitly or implicitly, in these papers. (It should be noted that Namioka refers to the order topology as "the order bound topology $\mathfrak{T}_b$".)

In Section 1 of Chapter 4, we shall relate the order topology to relative uniform convergence in a vector lattice. The properties of the order topology will also be employed in Section 2 of Chapter 4 in connection with the description of the "order completion" of a vector lattice.

Other papers related to the subject matter of this section: Goffman [2], Weston [3]. (Also, see the references in (1.27) and (2.9) of Chapter 4.)

§2. THE TOPOLOGY OF UNIFORM CONVERGENCE ON ORDER BOUNDED SETS

Suppose that $\langle E, F \rangle$ is a dual system with respect to the bilinear functional $(x, y) \to \langle x, y \rangle$. If K is a cone in E and if $\mathfrak{S}_0$ is the class of all order bounded subsets of E, then F is a topological vector space for the $\mathfrak{S}_0$-topology if and only if the following condition is satisfied:

(O) For each $y \in F$, the linear functional g_y defined for each $x \in E$ by $g_y(x) = \langle x, y \rangle$ is an order bounded linear functional on E.

If we make the usual identification of F with the linear subspace $\{g_y : y \in F\}$ of E^*, then condition (O) simply requires the inclusion of F in E^b. When condition (O) is satisfied, the resulting topology on F will be denoted by $o(F, E)$ and we shall say that $o(F, E)$ is the **topology on F of uniform convergence on the order bounded subsets of E.**

Condition (O) is not very restrictive; for example:

(a) If $E(\mathfrak{T})$ is a locally convex space ordered by a $\sigma(E, E')$-normal cone and $F = E'$, then (O) is satisfied by (1.21) of Chapter 2.

(b) If $F(\mathfrak{D})$ is a locally convex space ordered by a generating cone H, if $\mathfrak{D}$ is consistent with the dual system $\langle E, F \rangle$, and if K is the dual cone of H, then it is clear that $H \subset E^b$; hence, condition (O) is satisfied.

(c)   If λ is a sequence space and if λ, $\lambda^{\times}$ are ordered by their respective cones of sequences with non-negative components, then $\lambda^{\times} \subset \lambda^{b}$, and $\lambda \subset (\lambda^{\times})^{b}$ if the cone in λ is generating. If $\langle \Lambda, \Lambda^{\times} \rangle$ is a dual system of Köthe function spaces, then $\Lambda^{\times} \subset \Lambda^{b}$ and $\Lambda \subset (\Lambda^{\times})^{b}$ for the usual order on Λ and $\Lambda^{\times}$ (see (1.6) of Chapter 1).

Before we proceed to the description of the basic properties of the topology $o(F, E)$ of uniform convergence on the order bounded sets in E, we shall identify this topology for a number of specific choices of E and F.

2.1   Examples.   a.   Suppose that E is an almost Archimedean ordered vector space with an order unit e, then, as we have seen in (1.4), the order topology $\mathfrak{T}_{0}$ on E is generated by the norm:

$$\|x\| = \inf \{\alpha > 0 : x \in \alpha[-e, e]\}, \qquad (*)$$

and the cone in E is normal for $\mathfrak{T}_{0}$. Therefore, if $F = E(\mathfrak{T}_{0})'$, then $F = E^{b}$. Since every order interval in E is contained in a suitable multiple of $[-e, e]$, the topology $o(F, E)$ coincides with the topology generated by the dual norm

$$\|y\| = \sup \{|\langle x, y \rangle| : \|x\| \le 1\}$$

in F for the norm $(*)$ generating $\mathfrak{T}_{0}$ on E.

In particular, if E is the space $C(X)$ of continuous real-valued functions on a compact Hausdorff space X ordered by the cone of functions in $C(X)$ that are non-negative on X, then $F = E(\mathfrak{T}_{0})'$ coincides with the space $\mathcal{M}(X)$ of Radon measures on X and $o(\mathcal{M}(X), C(X))$ is generated by the norm

$$\|\mu\| = \sup \{\textstyle\int_{X} f \, d\mu : \|f\| \le 1\}.$$

Since $\mathcal{M}(X)$ is a Banach lattice for this norm and the order generated by the cone of positive Radon measures, the order topology $\mathfrak{T}_{0}$ on $\mathcal{M}(X)$ coincides with $o(\mathcal{M}(X), C(X))$.

As further special cases, we note that if $E = \ell^{\infty}$ (resp. $E = L_{\mu}^{\infty}(X)$) in its usual order (see (1.6) of Chapter 1) and if $F = \ell^{1}$ (resp. $F = L_{\mu}^{1}(X)$), then $o(F, E)$ is the topology generated by the norm

$$\|x\| = \sum_{n=1}^{\infty} |x_{n}| \qquad (\text{resp. } \|f\| = \textstyle\int_{X} |f| \, d\mu).$$

The first example presented above shows that the topology $o(F, E)$ need not be consistent with the dual system $\langle E, F \rangle$. The preceding considerations also show that if E is an almost Archimedean ordered vector space with an order unit and if $F \subset E^b$, then $o(F, E)$ is a normable topology. On the other hand, it is not difficult to show that E has an order unit if $o(F, E)$ is normable and the cone K in E is $\sigma(E, F)$-closed and generating.

b. Suppose that λ is a sequence space in which the cone of sequences with non-negative components is generating. In the theory of the dual system $\langle \lambda, \lambda^\times \rangle$, a significant role is played by the so-called **normal topology** on λ which is generated by the following family of seminorms

$$p_u(x) = \sum_{n=1}^\infty |x_n u_n| \qquad (u \in \lambda^\times).$$

Since the order interval $[-u, u]$ is a solid subset of $\lambda^\times$, it follows that

$$p_u(x) = \sup \{ |\langle x, v \rangle| : v \in [-u, u] \}$$

for all $u \geq \theta$ in $\lambda^\times$. Hence, since the cone in $\lambda^\times$ is generating, the normal topology on λ coincides with $o(\lambda, \lambda^\times)$. In view of 2(4) in §30 of Köthe [1], the topology $o(\lambda, \lambda^\times)$ is always consistent with the dual system $\langle \lambda, \lambda^\times \rangle$.

Similarly, if Λ is a Köthe function space and $\Lambda^\times$ is its Köthe dual, the topology $o(\Lambda, \Lambda^\times)$ is generated by the seminorms

$$p_g(f) = \int_X |fg| \, d\mu \qquad (g \in \Lambda^\times).$$

c. Suppose that $\langle E, F \rangle$ is a dual system, that $F \subset E^b$, that the cone K in E generates E, and that K contains a countable subset H that exhausts K (see (1.10)), then it is clear that $o(F, E)$ is metrizable since the class consisting of all intersections of finite subclasses of

$$\left\{ \frac{1}{n} [-h, h]^\circ : h \in H, n = 1, 2, \ldots \right\}$$

is a neighborhood basis of θ for $o(F, E)$. On the other hand, it is not difficult to show that if $o(F, E)$ is metrizable and if K is a $\sigma(E, F)$-closed, generating cone, then K contains a countable set that exhausts K.

In particular, the cone of non-negative functions in the space $\mathcal{K}(X)$ of all continuous, real-valued functions with compact support in a σ-compact, locally compact Hausdorff space X contains a countable exhausting subset. In fact, if $\{C_n\}$ is an increasing sequence of open sets such that $\bar{C}_n$ is a compact subset of C_{n+1} for each n, and $X = \bigcup_{n=1}^{\infty} \bar{C}_n$, then any sequence $\{h_n\}$ of continuous functions on X such that $0 \le h_n(t) \le 1$ for all $t \in X$ and

$$h_n(t) = \begin{cases} 0 & \text{if } t \notin C_{n+1} \\ 1 & \text{if } t \in C_n \end{cases}$$

is surely a countable exhausting subset of the cone. If U_n is the unit ball for the norm

$$\|f\|_n = \sup \{|f(t)| : t \in \bar{C}_n\}$$

on the linear subspace $\mathcal{K}(X, \bar{C}_n)$ consisting of all functions in $\mathcal{K}(X)$ with support in $\bar{C}_n$, then $[-h_{n-1}, h_{n-1}] \subset U_n \subset [-h_n, h_n]$. Therefore, the topology $o(\mathcal{M}(X), \mathcal{K}(X))$ on the space $\mathcal{M}(X)$ of Radon measures on X is metrizable, and a sequence $\{\mu_m\}$ of Radon measures on X converges to θ for $o(\mathcal{M}(X), \mathcal{K}(X))$ if and only if the sequence of restrictions to each $\mathcal{K}(X, \bar{C}_n)$ converges to θ in the dual norm topology in $\mathcal{K}(X, \bar{C}_n)'$. Thus, $o(\mathcal{M}(X), \mathcal{K}(X))$ coincides with the so-called "strong topology" on $\mathcal{M}(X)$ (see Exercise 4 of §2, Chapter III in Bourbaki [2]).

We shall now go on to a discussion of the basic properties of the topology of uniform convergence on order bounded sets.

2.2 Proposition. If $\langle E, F \rangle$ is a dual system, if E is ordered by a generating cone K, and if $F \subset E^b$, then K is a strict $\mathfrak{S}_0$-cone for the class $\mathfrak{S}_0$ of all order bounded subsets of E and the dual cone K' of K is normal in F for $o(F, E)$.

Proof. Since K is generating, the class $\{[-x, x] : x \in K\}$ is a fundamental system for $\mathfrak{S}_0$. If $x \in K$ and $z \in [-x, x]$, then

$$z = \tfrac{1}{2}(z + x) - \tfrac{1}{2}(x - z) \in [\theta, x] - [\theta, x];$$

hence, $[-x, x] \subset K \cap [-x, x] - K \cap [-x, x]$. Consequently, K is a strict $\mathfrak{S}_0$-cone.

The fact that K is generating implies that the dual wedge K' of K is a cone in F. Since the family of seminorms

$$p_x(y) = \sup \{|\langle z, y \rangle| : z \in [-x, x]\} \qquad (x \in K)$$

generates $o(F, E)$, it follows from (1.5) of Chapter 2 that K' is normal for $o(F, E)$.

In (2.1)(a), we observed that the topology $o(F, E)$ need not be consistent with the dual system $\langle E, F \rangle$ in general. We shall now establish some sufficient conditions for the consistency of this topology.

2.3 Proposition. If E is a vector space ordered by a cone K, if $F \subset E^b$, and if E is a full subset of the algebraic dual F^* of F, then $o(F, E)$ is consistent with the dual system $\langle E, F \rangle$.

Proof. Since $F \subset E^b$, the order intervals in E are $\sigma(E, F)$-bounded and, therefore, precompact for $\sigma(E, F)$. But E is a full subspace of F^*; hence, each order interval in E is an order interval in F^*. Moreover, since the wedge $(K')^*$ is $\sigma(F^*, F)$-closed in F^*, these order intervals are $\sigma(F^*, F)$-closed. In view of the fact that the completion of E for $\sigma(E, F)$ is F^* equipped with $\sigma(F^*, F)$ (see Exercise 11 in §1 of Chapter IV in Bourbaki [1]), it follows that each order interval in E is $\sigma(E, F)$-compact. Therefore, by virtue of the Mackey-Arens Theorem, $o(F, E)$ is consistent with the dual system $\langle E, F \rangle$.

2.4 Corollary. If E is a locally convex space ordered by a closed, generating cone K and if E' is a full subspace of either the algebraic dual E^* of E or the order dual E^+ of E, then $o(E, E')$ is consistent with the dual system $\langle E, E' \rangle$.

Proof. The cone $K^* = \{f \in E^* : f(x) \geq 0 \text{ for all } x \in K\}$ orders E^+ as well as E^*; hence, if E' is a full subspace of E^+, it is also a full subspace of E^*. Therefore, it is only necessary to establish the result in case E' is a full subspace of E^*.

In view of the fact that K is $\sigma(E, F)$-closed and generating, it follows that $E \subset (E')^b$ (for the order on E' generated by the dual cone K' of K) and $K = (K')'$. Therefore, we can apply (2.3) with $F = E$ and $E = E'$ to obtain the desired result.

2.5 Corollary. If E is a regularly ordered vector space ordered by a generating cone, then $o(E, E^+)$ is consistent with the dual system $\langle E, E^+ \rangle$.

Proof. Since E is a regularly ordered vector space, $\langle E, E^+ \rangle$ is a dual system for the bilinear functional defined for $x \in E, f \in E^+$ by $\langle x, f \rangle = f(x)$. The $\sigma(E, E^+)$-closure of K in E is a closed generating cone; hence, the result follows from (2.4).

2.6 Corollary. If $E(\mathfrak{X})$ is a locally convex lattice, then $o(E, E')$ is consistent with $\langle E, E' \rangle$.

Proof. This result is an immediate consequence of (4.17) of Chapter 2 and (2.4).

2.7 Proposition. Suppose that E is an almost Archimedean ordered vector space with an order unit e, and that E is a full subspace of $(E^+)^+$, then E is reflexive for the order topology.

Proof. The Minkowski functional p_e of the order interval $[-e, e]$ is a norm on E generating the order topology (see (1.4)) and $E(\mathfrak{X}_o)' = E^+$ (see 1.21) of Chapter 2 and (1.15). Since E is a full subspace of $(E^+)^+$, it is a full subspace of $(E^+)^*$; hence, $o(E^+, E)$ is consistent with $\langle E, E^+ \rangle$ by (2.3). But then $[-e, e]$ is $\sigma(E, E^+)$-relatively compact; consequently, $E(\mathfrak{X}_o)$ is reflexive.

Though we shall not present the details here, it can be shown that, under quite general conditions, the topology of uniform convergence on order bounded sets is preserved in the formation of topological products and locally convex sums (see (1.4) and (1.5) in the author's paper [1]). It can also be shown by example that this topology is not always preserved in the formation of quotient spaces.

The following result, together with (1.17), shows that, in a sense, the topology of uniform convergence on order bounded sets and the order topology are at opposite extremes of an interesting range of topologies on a vector lattice.

2.8 Proposition. Suppose that $\langle E, F \rangle$ is a dual system, that E is a vector lattice ordered by a cone K, and that the dual cone K' of K generates F. If $\mathfrak{X}$ is any topology on E that is finer than $\sigma(E, F)$ and if the lattice operations in E are continuous for $\mathfrak{X}$, then $\mathfrak{X}$ is finer than $o(E, F)$. If K is $\sigma(E, F)$-closed, if F^b is a lattice, and if E is a sublattice of F^b, then the lattice operations in E are continuous for $o(E, F)$.

Proof. $E \subset F^b$ and $\{[-y, y]^\circ : y \in K'\}$ is a neighborhood basis of θ for $o(E, F)$ since K and K' are generating. If y_0 is any element of K', then

$$U = \{x \in E : \langle x, y_0 \rangle \le 1\}$$

is a neighborhood of θ for $\mathfrak{T}$ since $\mathfrak{T}$ is finer than $\sigma(E, F)$. In view of the fact that the lattice operations in $E(\mathfrak{T})$ are continuous, there is a neighborhood V of θ for $\mathfrak{T}$ such that $|x| \in U$ whenever $x \in V$. But then, if $y \in [-y_0 y_0]$ and $x \in V$, it follows that

$$\langle x, y \rangle = \langle x^+, y \rangle - \langle x^-, y \rangle \le \langle x^+, y_0 \rangle + \langle x^-, y_0 \rangle$$
$$= \langle |x|, y_0 \rangle \le 1,$$

since $|x| \in U$. Therefore, $V \subset [-y_0, y_0]^\circ$; hence, $\mathfrak{T}$ is finer than $o(E, F)$.

If K is $\sigma(E, F)$-closed, then $K = (K')'$; hence, K is normal for $o(E, F)$ by (2.2). Therefore, in view of (4.5) of Chapter 2, the second assertion of the proposition will follow if we can establish the $o(E, F)$-continuity of the mapping $x \to x^+$ at θ. Suppose $\{x_\alpha : \alpha \in I\}$ is a net that converges to θ for $o(E, F)$ and let y_0 be an arbitrary element of K'. Choose $\alpha_0 \in I$ so that $x_\alpha \in [-y_0, y_0]^\circ$ for all $\alpha \ge \alpha_0$, then

$$\langle x_\alpha^+, y \rangle \le \langle x_\alpha^+, y_0 \rangle = \sup \{\langle x_\alpha, z \rangle : z \in [\theta, y_0]\}$$
$$\le \sup \{\langle x_\alpha, z \rangle : z \in [-y_0, y_0]\} \le 1$$

for all $\alpha \ge \alpha_0$ and all $y \in [-y_0, y_0]$ since E is a sublattice of F^b. Therefore, $\{x_\alpha^+\}$ converges to θ for $o(E, F)$, which implies the desired result.

2.9 Corollary. If $E(\mathfrak{T})$ is a locally convex lattice, then $o(E, E')$ is coarser than $\mathfrak{T}$ and $E(o(E, E'))$ is a locally convex lattice.

Proof. The assertion is an immediate consequence of (4.17) of Chapter 2 and (2.8).

2.10 Corollary. Suppose that $\langle E, F \rangle$ is a dual system, that E is a vector lattice ordered by a cone K, and that the dual cone K' of K generates F. If there is an order interval in F that is not $\sigma(F, E)$-compact, then there does not exist a topology on E consistent with $\langle E, F \rangle$ for which the lattice operations are continuous.

Proof. This result is an immediate consequence of (2.8) and the Mackey-Arens Theorem.

2.11 Example. As a simple application of (2.10), we note that there does not exist a topology on ℓ^1 consistent with the dual system $\langle \ell^1, (c) \rangle$ for which the lattice operations are continuous. In fact, the unit ball U in (c) corresponding to the norm

$$\|x\| = \sup_n \{|x_n|\}$$

is not $\sigma((c), \ell^1)$-compact, yet U coincides with the order interval $[-e, e]$ (where $e_n = 1$ for all n). Moreover, (2.9) implies that the topology $o(\ell^1, (c))$, that is, the topology generated by the norm

$$\|y\| = \sum_{n=1}^{\infty} |y_n| \qquad y = (y_n) \in \ell^1$$

is the only topology on ℓ^1 consistent with the dual system $\langle \ell^1, \ell^\infty \rangle$ for which the lattice operations are continuous.

The second observation in the preceding example can be formalized as follows:

2.12 Proposition. If E is a regularly ordered vector lattice, then each of the following conditions implies that $o(E, E^+)$ coincides with the order topology and that $o(E, E^+)$ is the only topology finer than $\sigma(E, E^+)$ for which E is a locally convex lattice:

a. Each convex, $\sigma(E^+, E)$-compact subset of E^+ is order bounded.
b. E^+ contains an order unit.
c. The cone K^* in E^+ contains a countable exhausting subset.

Proof. E is a locally convex lattice for $\mathfrak{T}_o$ (see (1.17)); hence, K is $\mathfrak{T}_o$-closed and $E(\mathfrak{T}_o)' = E^+$. Therefore, by (2.9), $o(E, E^+)$ is consistent with the dual system $\langle E, E^+ \rangle$ and $o(E, E^+)$ is coarser than $\mathfrak{T}_o$. However, each of the conditions stated in the proposition implies that $o(E, E^+) = \tau(E, E^+)$. In fact, $o(E, E^+)$ is normable if (b) is satisfied and metrizable if (c) is satisfied (see (2.1)). Consequently, $o(E, E^+)$ coincides with the order topology if any one of these conditions is satisfied. The remainder of the assertion follows from (2.8) and (1.17).

Proposition (2.8) also yields the following conclusions concerning the continuity of the lattice operations for the weak topology.

2.13 Proposition.   Suppose that $\langle E, F \rangle$ is a dual system, that E is a vector lattice ordered by a cone K, and that the dual cone K' of K generates F. Then if the lattice operations in E are continuous for $\sigma(E, F)$, each order interval in F is contained in a finite dimensional subspace of F. In addition, if F contains an order unit, then E and F are finite dimensional spaces.

Proof.   If the lattice operations in E are continuous for $\sigma(E, F)$, then $\sigma(E, F) = o(E, F)$ by (2.8). It follows that each order interval in F is equicontinuous for $\sigma(E, F)$, that is, each order interval in F is contained in a finite dimensional subspace of F. Therefore, if F contains an order unit, F must be a finite dimensional space; consequently, E is also a finite dimensional space.

2.14 Proposition.   If E is a vector lattice which is normable and has a normal positive cone K, then the lattice operations in E are continuous for the weak topology if and only if E is a finite dimensional space.

Proof.   Suppose that the lattice operations in E are continuous for $\sigma(E, E')$, but that E is not a finite dimensional space. Since K is normal, the dual cone K' of K generates E' by (1.21) of Chapter 2. Define a sequence $\{y_n\}$ in K' as follows: Choose $y_1 \in K'$ so that $\|y_1\| = 1$, where $y \to \|y\|$ is a norm on E' that generates the strong topology $\beta(E', E)$. Since the lattice operations in E are continuous for $\sigma(E, E')$, the order interval $[-y_1, y_1]$ spans a finite dimensional subspace of E' by (2.13). Hence, there is an element y_2 in K' such that $\|y_2\| = 1$ and $\{y_1, y_2\}$ is a linearly independent set. Again, (2.13) implies that $[-y_1, y_1] \cup [-y_2, y_2]$ does not span E'. After y_{k-1} has been chosen, select $y_k \in K'$ such that $\|y_k\| = 1$ and

$$y_k \notin \text{linear hull} \left\{ \bigcup_{n=1}^{k-1} [-y_n, y_n] \right\}.$$

The sequence

$$\left\{ \sum_{n=1}^{m} \frac{1}{2^n} y_n : m = 1, 2, 3, \ldots \right\}$$

is a Cauchy sequence in E' for $\beta(E', E)$; hence, there is a $y \in K'$ such that

$$y = \sum_{n=1}^{\infty} \frac{1}{2^n} y_n.$$

Since the linear hull of $[-y, y]$ contains $[-y_n, y_n]$ for all n, the order interval $[-y, y]$ is not contained in a finite dimensional subspace. This contradicts the conclusion of (2.13); hence, E must be a finite dimensional space. Since the converse is obvious, the proof is complete.

It is obvious that the preceding proof can easily be adapted to a more general setting. For example, if $\langle E, F \rangle$ is a dual system of the sort described in (2.13) and if there is a topology on F for which F is a complete metrizable topological vector space and K' is closed, then the lattice operations in E are $\sigma(E, F)$-continuous if and only if E is finite dimensional.

The following result is a counterpart to (2.14) for Köthe sequence spaces.

2.15 Proposition. If λ is a lattice ordered sequence space, the lattice operations in λ are continuous for $\sigma(\lambda, \lambda^{\times})$ if and only if $\lambda^{\times} = \varphi$.

Proof. If the lattice operations in λ are continuous for $\sigma(\lambda, \lambda^{\times})$, suppose that there is a $u \in \lambda^{\times}$ such that $u \notin \varphi$ and $u \geq \theta$. Then, there is a sequence $\{n_k\}$ of positive integers such that $u_{n_k} \neq 0$ for all k. Define a sequence $\{v^{(k)}\}$ in $\lambda^{\times}$ as follows:

$$v_n^{(k)} = \begin{cases} u_n & \text{if } n \leq n_k \\ 0 & \text{if } n > n_k \end{cases}$$

then $v^{(k)} \in [-u, u]$ for all k, and $\{v^{(k)} : k = 1, 2, \ldots\}$ is a linearly independent set. These conclusions contradict (2.13); hence, it follows that $\lambda^{\times} \subset \varphi$. Since $\varphi \subset \lambda^{\times}$, we conclude that $\lambda^{\times} = \varphi$.

On the other hand, it is not difficult to verify that every order interval in φ is contained in the convex, circled hull of a finite subset of φ; hence, if $\lambda^{\times} = \varphi$, $o(\lambda, \lambda^{\times})$ and $\sigma(\lambda, \lambda^{\times})$ coincide; therefore, the lattice operations in λ are $\sigma(\lambda, \lambda^{\times})$-continuous by (2.8).

The preceding result shows that the only perfect sequence space λ with the property that the lattice operations are continuous for $\sigma(\lambda, \lambda^{\times})$ is the space ω. In contrast to this situation, we can establish the following result.

2.16 Proposition.   If λ is a lattice ordered sequence space, then the lattice operations in λ are sequentially continuous for $\sigma(\lambda, \lambda^{\times})$.

Proof. Suppose that $\{x^{(n)}\}$ is a sequence in λ that converges to $x^{(0)} \in \lambda$ for $\sigma(\lambda, \lambda^{\times})$; then this sequence converges to the same limit for $\sigma(\lambda^{\times\times}, \lambda^{\times})$. But $\lambda^{\times\times}$ is a perfect sequence space; hence, $\lambda^{\times\times}$ equipped with $\sigma(\lambda^{\times\times}, \lambda^{\times})$ is the projective limit of the family of sequence spaces $\{\lambda_u : u \in \lambda^{\times}; u \geq \theta\}$, where each

$$\lambda_u = \left\{ x \in \omega : \sum_{n=1}^{\infty} |x_n u_n| < +\infty \right\}$$

is order and topologically isomorphic to $\ell^1(\sigma(\ell^1, \ell^{\infty}))$, $\omega(\sigma(\omega, \varphi))$, or the product of these two spaces. (See §30 in Köthe [1] for details concerning this representation.) Therefore, $\{|x^{(n)}|\}$ converges to $|x^{(0)}|$ in λ_u for $\sigma(\lambda_u, \lambda_u^{\times})$ for each $u \in \lambda^{\times}$ since the lattice operations in $\omega(\sigma(\omega, \varphi))$ and $\ell^1(\sigma(\ell^1, \ell^{\infty}))$ are sequentially continuous by (2.15) and the equivalence of norm and weak convergence for sequences in ℓ^1. It follows that $\{|x^{(n)}|\}$ converges to $|x^{(0)}|$ for $\sigma(\lambda^{\times\times}, \lambda^{\times})$ (see §19,10 in Köthe [1]; consequently, the lattice operations in λ are sequentially continuous for $\sigma(\lambda, \lambda^{\times})$ because $\sigma(\lambda^{\times\times}, \lambda^{\times})$ induces $\sigma(\lambda, \lambda^{\times})$ on λ.

2.17 Corollary.   The topology $\sigma(\lambda, \lambda^{\times})$ on a lattice ordered sequence space λ is metrizable if and only if $\lambda^{\times} = \varphi$.

Proof. The necessity is an immediate consequence of (2.15) and (2.16). On the other hand, if $\lambda^{\times} = \varphi$, then $\lambda^{\times\times} = \omega$. Hence, since $\sigma(\omega, \varphi)$ is a metrizable topology that induces $\sigma(\lambda, \varphi)$ on λ, $\sigma(\lambda, \varphi)$ is also metrizable.

It should be noted that the analog to (2.16) for Köthe function spaces is not valid (see (4.12) of Chapter 2).

2.18 Notes. The results established in this section can be found in the author's papers [1] (see Sections I, II) and [3]. Gordon [1] also studied the topology of uniform convergence on order bounded sets, though in a more restricted setting. In Chapter 4, we shall make use of the properties of this topology to answer certain questions concerning the topological structure of bands and the order properties of continuous linear mappings.

Komura-Koshi [1] establish some interesting facts about the topology of uniform convergence on order bounded sets for nuclear spaces; in particular, they show that this topology coincides with the given topology in any nuclear locally convex lattice. Pietsch [2] also makes use of the topology $o(E, F)$ in his investigation concerning summability in vector lattices. In this connection, see also Amemiya [3]. (1.27) and (3.19) of Chapter 4 contain further references related to the subject matter of this section.

Chapter Four

Selected Topics in the
Theory of Ordered
Topological Vector Spaces

We shall now complement the basic theory of ordered topological vector spaces developed in the preceding chapters with a discussion of some special topics in the theory. The latter portion of Section 2 makes some use of the concepts introduced in Section 1; apart from this, the sections of this chapter are quite independent of one another.

§1. RELATIONS BETWEEN ORDER COMPLETE-NESS AND TOPOLOGICAL COMPLETENESS IN ORDERED TOPOLOGICAL VECTOR SPACES

Some of the deepest results in the theory of ordered topological vector spaces are concerned with providing suitable answers to questions of the following sort:

a. Under what conditions is an order complete topological vector space necessarily topologically complete?

b. What conclusions can be drawn concerning order completeness and the structure of bands from the properties of the topology in a topological vector lattice?

c. When is it possible to "complete" an ordered vector space in an order theoretic sense?

This section is devoted to an exposition of some of the theory that has been developed in this direction. We shall begin with a discussion of the circle of problems raised by question (a).

1.1 Definitions. A topological vector lattice $E(\mathfrak{T})$ is **locally order complete** if there is a neighborhood basis of θ for $\mathfrak{T}$ consisting of solid, order complete sets. An ordered topological vector space $E(\mathfrak{T})$ is **boundedly order complete** if every $\mathfrak{T}$-bounded, directed $(\leq)$ subset has a supremum.

Note that if $E(\mathfrak{T})$ is a locally order complete vector lattice, then E is order complete. Also, if $E(\mathfrak{T})$ is a boundedly order complete vector lattice ordered by a normal cone, then E is order complete.

1.2 Examples. a. Suppose that Λ is a Köthe function space and that $\Lambda^{\times}$ is the Köthe dual of Λ (see (1.6) of Chapter 1). If $\mathfrak{S}$ is a class of $\sigma(\Lambda^{\times}, \Lambda)$-bounded, solid subsets of $\Lambda^{\times}$ such that $\mathfrak{S}$ is directed by inclusion and $\Lambda^{\times} = \cup\{S : S \in \mathfrak{S}\}$, then the $\mathfrak{S}$-topology on Λ is generated by the class $\mathscr{W}$ of positive multiples of the polars for $\langle \Lambda, \Lambda^{\times} \rangle$ of the sets in $\mathfrak{S}$. It is clear from (4.4) of Chapter 2 that the sets in $\mathscr{W}$ are solid; moreover, standard results from measure theory imply that these sets are order complete and that Λ is boundedly order complete for the $\mathfrak{S}$-topology (see Goffman [1] for details).

b. A simple example of an order complete Banach lattice that is not boundedly order complete is provided by the space (c_0) of null sequences of real numbers, ordered by the cone K of sequence with non-negative components, and equipped with the norm

$$\|x\| = \sup_{n}\{|x_n|\}$$

The space $C[0, 1]$ of continuous, real-valued functions on the unit interval, ordered by the cone of non-negative functions, and equipped with the topology generated by the norm

$$\|f\| = \int_a^b |f(t)| \, dt$$

is not locally order complete. This is most easily verified by making use of the proposition that follows.

1.3 Proposition. If $E(\mathfrak{X})$ is a locally order complete vector lattice, then each order interval in E is topologically complete.

Proof. We shall first establish the result for the case in which $\mathfrak{X}$ is a metrizable topology. Choose a countable neighborhood basis $\mathscr{W} = \{W_n : n = 1, 2, \ldots\}$ of θ for $\mathfrak{X}$ such that each W_n is a solid, order complete set and $W_{n+1} + W_{n+1} \subset W_n$ for all n. To show that a given order interval $[u, v]$ is complete, it is sufficient to prove that each sequence $\{x_n\}$ in $[u, v]$ with the property:

$$x_{n+1} - x_n \in W_{n+1} \qquad n = 1, 2, \ldots$$

converges to an element x of $[u, v]$. For each pair p, q of positive integers such that $p \le q$, it is true that

$$\sup \{x_n : p \le n \le q\} - x_p$$
$$= \sup \{x_n - x_p : p \le n \le q\}$$
$$\le \sup \{|x_n - x_p| : p \le n \le q\}$$
$$\le \sum_{n=p}^{q-1} |x_{n+1} - x_n| \in W_{p+1} + W_{p+2} + \cdots + W_q \subset W_p.$$

In view of the fact that $\sup \{x_n : p \le n \le q\} \le v$ for all p, q, we conclude that

$$y_p = \sup \{x_n : n \ge p\} \in x_p + W_p \qquad p = 1, 2, \ldots$$

since W_p is order complete for each p. A similar argument shows that

$$z_p = \inf \{x_n : n \ge p\} \in x_p + W_p \qquad p = 1, 2, \ldots$$

Since the sequence $\{z_p\}$ is monotone increasing and bounded above by v while $\{y_p\}$ is monotone decreasing and bounded below by u, $y = \inf \{y_p\}$, and $z = \sup \{z_p\}$ exist, and $y - z \in W_n$ for all n. But then $y = z$ since $\mathfrak{X}$ is a Hausdorff topology. Hence, $\{x_n\}$ converges to y for $\mathfrak{X}$ since $y_p \ge y \ge z_p$ for all p. $y \in [u, v]$ since the cone in $E(\mathfrak{X})$

is closed by (4.7) and (4.13) in Chapter 2. Therefore, each order interval in $E(\mathfrak{T})$ is topologically complete if $\mathfrak{T}$ is a metrizable topology.

Let us now consider the general case, that is, the case when $\mathfrak{T}$ is not necessarily metrizable. If $\mathscr{W} = \{W_\alpha : \alpha \in A\}$ is a neighborhood basis of θ for $\mathfrak{T}$ consisting of solid, order complete sets, define Ω to be the class of all countable collections $\omega = \{W_{\alpha_n} : n = 1, 2, \ldots\}$ of sets in $\mathscr{W}$ such that ω is a neighborhood basis of θ in E for a topology $\mathfrak{T}_\omega$ for which $E(\mathfrak{T}_\omega)$ is a (not necessarily Hausdorff) topological vector space. The class Ω is nonempty and directed by inclusion. If $\alpha \in A$, define $W_\alpha^{(0)} = \bigcap_{\lambda > 0} \lambda W_\alpha$, then

$$N_0 = \cap \{W_\alpha^{(0)} : W_\alpha \in \mathscr{W}\}; \; N_\omega = \cap \{W_\alpha^{(0)} : W_\alpha \in \omega\} \qquad (\omega \in \Omega)$$

are bands in E since the elements of $\mathscr{W}$ are order complete and solid sets.

Define P_ω to be the projection of E onto the complementary band $N_\omega^\perp$ of N_ω that vanishes on N_ω, and let P_0 be the corresponding projection of E onto $N_0^\perp$, then the following results are easily verified:

a. If $\omega_1 \subset \omega_2$, then $P_{\omega_1} \leq P_{\omega_2}$ and $P_{\omega_1} \circ P_{\omega_2} = P_{\omega_1}$.
b. $0 \leq P_\omega \leq P_0 \leq I$ where I is the identity mapping on E.
c. $P_0 = I$ if and only if $\mathfrak{T}$ is a Hausdorff topology.
d. P_0, P_ω are continuous linear operators on $E(\mathfrak{T})$.
e. $P_0 = \sup \{P_\omega : \omega \in \Omega\}$.

To show that every order interval in $E(\mathfrak{T})$ is topologically complete, it suffices to consider intervals of the form $[\theta, v]$ for $v \geq \theta$ since

$$[u, v] = u + [\theta, v - u]$$

and since translation is uniformly continuous on $E(\mathfrak{T})$. If $\{x_\alpha : \alpha \in I\}$ is a Cauchy net in $[\theta, v]$ and $\omega \in \Omega$ then $\{P_\omega(x_\alpha) : \alpha \in I\}$ is a Cauchy net in $N_\omega^\perp$ for the topology $\mathfrak{T}_\omega^\perp$ induced on $N_\omega^\perp$ by $\mathfrak{T}_\omega$. Since $\mathfrak{T}_\omega^\perp$ is a metrizable topology, $\{P_\omega(x_\alpha) : \alpha \in I\}$ converges to an element $x_\omega \in [\theta, P_\omega v]$ for the topology $\mathfrak{T}_\omega^\perp$.

If $\omega_2 \supset \omega_1$, then the $\mathfrak{T}_{\omega_2}^\perp$-limit of $\{P_{\omega_1}(x_\alpha) : \alpha \in I\}$ is x_{ω_1} since $\{P_{\omega_1}(x_\alpha) : \alpha \in I\}$ has a unique $\mathfrak{T}_{\omega_2}^\perp$-limit in $N_{\omega_1}^\perp$. Moreover, $x_{\omega_1} \in [\theta, v]$, since the positive cone in $N_{\omega_1}^\perp$ is closed for the topology induced by

$\mathfrak{T}_{\omega_2}$. By virtue of (a), the set $\{x_\omega : \omega \in \Omega\}$ is directed ($\leq$) and majorized by v. Define $u = \sup \{x_\omega : \omega \in \Omega\}$. Now, if $\omega_2 \supset \omega_1$, then

$$P_{\omega_1}(x_{\omega_2}) = P_{\omega_1}(\mathfrak{T}_{\omega_1}^{\perp}\text{-limit } \{P_{\omega_2}(x_\alpha) : \alpha \in I\})$$
$$= \mathfrak{T}_{\omega_2}^{\perp}\text{-limit } \{(P_{\omega_1}P_{\omega_2}(x_\alpha)) : \alpha \in I\}$$
$$= \mathfrak{T}_{\omega_2}^{\perp}\text{-limit } \{P_{\omega_1}(x_\alpha) : \alpha \in I\} = x_{\omega_1}.$$

Hence, for each fixed $\omega_1 \in \Omega$, it follows that

$$P_{\omega_1}u = \sup \{P_{\omega_1}x_\omega : \omega \in \Omega\} = \sup \{P_{\omega_1}x_\omega : \omega \supset \omega_1\} = x_{\omega_1}.$$

If $\omega \in \Omega$, then u is a cluster point of $\{x_\alpha : \alpha \in I\}$ for $\mathfrak{T}_\omega$ if and only if $P_\omega u$ is a cluster point of $\{P_\omega x_\alpha : \alpha \in I\}$ for $\mathfrak{T}_\omega^{\perp}$ since P_ω is a continuous projection of $E(\mathfrak{T}_\omega)$ onto $N_\omega^{\perp}(\mathfrak{T}_\omega^{\perp})$ that vanishes on N_ω. But $P_\omega u = x_\omega = \mathfrak{T}_\omega^{\perp}$-limit of $\{P_\omega x_\alpha : \alpha \in I\}$; hence, u is a $\mathfrak{T}_\omega$-cluster point of the net $\{x_\alpha : \alpha \in I\}$ for each $\omega \in \Omega$. Therefore, $\{x_\alpha : \alpha \in I\}$ converges to u for the topology $\mathfrak{T}_\omega$; that is, each order interval in $E(\mathfrak{T})$ is complete.

1.4 Corollary. Every locally order complete locally convex lattice $E(\mathfrak{T})$ is a barreled space for the order topology. In addition, if E contains an order unit e, then $E(\mathfrak{T}_0)$ is a Banach space for the norm topology generated by the Minkowski functional of $[-e, e]$.

Proof. The first assertion is an immediate consequence of (1.8) of Chapter 3 and (1.3), while the second assertion follows from the fact that the unit ball $[-e, e]$ for $\mathfrak{T}_0$ is complete for the topology $\mathfrak{T}$ which is coarser than $\mathfrak{T}_0$.

1.5 Proposition (*Nakano*). If $E(\mathfrak{T})$ is a locally order complete, boundedly order complete vector lattice, then $E(\mathfrak{T})$ is topologically complete.

Proof. For the moment, let us make the added assumption that $\mathfrak{T}$ is a Hausdorff topology. If $\{x_\alpha : \alpha \in I\}$ is a Cauchy net in $E(\mathfrak{T})$, then $\{x_\alpha^+ : \alpha \in I\}$ is a Cauchy net since $E(\mathfrak{T})$ is a topological vector lattice. If we can show that $\{x_\alpha^+ : \alpha \in I\}$ converges in $E(\mathfrak{T})$, it will follow that $\{x_\alpha : \alpha \in I\}$ converges in $E(\mathfrak{T})$ as well. Suppose that x is an element of the positive cone K in E, then $\{(x_\alpha^+) \cap x : \alpha \in I\}$ is a Cauchy net in the order interval $[\theta, x]$. Hence, since $[\theta, x]$ is complete by (1.3), the net $\{(x_\alpha^+) \cap x : \alpha \in I\}$ converges for $\mathfrak{T}$ to some element a_x in $[\theta, x]$.

We shall now show that $\{a_x : x \geq \theta\}$ is a $\mathfrak{T}$-bounded set. To this end, suppose that $\mathscr{W} = \{W_\beta : \beta \in B\}$ is a neighborhood basis of θ for $\mathfrak{T}$ consisting of solid, order complete sets. Then, if W_β is a given element of $\mathscr{W}$ choose $\beta' \in B$ so that $W_{\beta'} + W_{\beta'} + W_{\beta'} \subset W_\beta$. Since $\{x_\alpha^+ : \alpha \in I\}$ is a Cauchy net for $\mathfrak{T}$, there is an $\alpha_0 \in I$ such that

$$x_\alpha^+ - x_{\alpha'}^+ \in W_{\beta'} \qquad \text{for all } \alpha \geq \alpha_0, \alpha' \geq \alpha_0.$$

Choose $\lambda_0 \geq 1$ so that $x_{\alpha_0}^+ \in \lambda_0 W_{\beta'}$, then $x_\alpha^+ \in \lambda_0(W_{\beta'} + W_{\beta'})$ for $\alpha \geq \alpha_0$. Also, since $\{(x_\alpha^+) \cap x : \alpha \in I\}$ converges to a_x for $\mathfrak{T}$, there is an $\alpha_1 \subset I$ such that $(x_\alpha^+) \cap x \subset a_x + W_{\beta'}$ for all $\alpha \geq \alpha_1$ and such that $\alpha_1 \geq \alpha_0$. But then, since $W_{\beta'}$ is solid, $\{a_x : x \geq 0\} \subset \lambda_0 W_\beta$, that is $\{a_x : x \geq \theta\}$ is a $\mathfrak{T}$-bounded set.

The set $\{a_x : x \geq \theta\}$ is directed $(\leq)$ by the ordering on the cone K; hence, the supremum a of this set exists in E since $E(\mathfrak{T})$ is boundedly order complete. Also, in view of the fact that the lattice operations in $E(\mathfrak{T})$ are continuous, it is true that

$$a_y \cap x = a_x \cap y$$

for all x, y in the cone K; hence, $a \cap x = \sup \{a_y \cap x : y \geq \theta\} = a_x$ for all $x \geq \theta$. If $W_\beta \in \mathscr{W}$, choose $W_{\beta'}$ so that $W_{\beta'} + W_{\beta'} \subset W_\beta$, and then select $\alpha_0 \in I$ so that $x_\alpha^+ - x_{\alpha'}^+ \in W_{\beta'}$ for all $\alpha \geq \alpha_0, \alpha' \geq \alpha_0$. If $\alpha_1 \geq \alpha_0$ and $x_1 = x_{\alpha_1}^+ \cup a$, then there is an $\alpha_2 \in I$ such that $(x_\alpha^+) \cap x_1 \in a + W_{\beta'}$ for all $\alpha \geq \alpha_2$ since $a_{x_1} = a \cap x_1 = a \cap (x_{\alpha_1}^+ \cup a) = (a \cup x_{\alpha_1}^+) \cup a = a$. It follows that, if $\alpha \geq \alpha_1, \alpha \geq \alpha_2$, then

$$|x_{\alpha_1}^+ - (x_\alpha^+ \cap x_1)| = |x_{\alpha_1}^+ \cap x_1 - x_\alpha^+ \cap x_1| \leq |x_{\alpha_1}^+ - x_\alpha^+|$$

Hence, $x_{\alpha_1}^+ = \{x_{\alpha_1}^+ - x_\alpha^+ \cap x_1\} + x^+ \cap x_1 \in a + W$ if $\alpha_1 \geq \alpha_0$. Therefore, $\{x_\alpha^+ : \alpha \in I\}$ converges to a for $\mathfrak{T}$; that is, $E(\mathfrak{T})$ is complete.

If $E(\mathfrak{T})$ is not a Hausdorff space and if $N_0 = \bigcap_{\beta \in B} W_\beta^{(0)}$ where $W_\beta^{(0)} = \bigcap_{\lambda > 0} \lambda W_\beta$ for each $\beta \in B$, then N_0 is a band in E since $E(\mathfrak{T})$ is locally order complete. Moreover, the topology induced by $\mathfrak{T}$ on the complementary band $N_0^\perp$ of N_0 is a Hausdorff topology for which $N_0^\perp$ is locally order complete and boundedly order complete. Since the projection P_0 of E onto $N_0^\perp$ that vanishes on N_0 is continuous, it maps each Cauchy net $\{x_\alpha : \alpha \in I\}$ in $E(\mathfrak{T})$ into a Cauchy net in $N_0^\perp$. Hence, $\{P_0(x_\alpha) : \alpha \in I\}$ converges to some element a_0 in $N_0^\perp$ by the first part of the proof. Since P_0 is continuous and vanishes on N_0, it follows that $\{x_\alpha : \alpha \in I\}$ converges to a_0 for $\mathfrak{T}$.

1.6 Corollary. If $E(\mathfrak{T})$ is a locally convex lattice with the property that the filter of sections of each directed $(\leq)$, $\mathfrak{T}$-bounded subset converges in $E(\mathfrak{T})$, then $E(\mathfrak{T})$ is complete.

Proof. In view of (1.5), it is enough to show that $E(\mathfrak{T})$ is locally order complete and boundedly order complete. Since $E(\mathfrak{T})$ is a locally convex lattice, the cone in E is closed and normal, and there is a neighborhood basis $\mathscr{W}$ of θ consisting of closed, solid sets. Therefore, if $W \in \mathscr{W}$ and D is a directed $(\leq)$ subset of W that is majorized in E, then every section S_x $(x \in D)$ of D is bounded. Consequently, the filter $\mathfrak{F}(D)$ of sections of D converges to an element $x_0 \in W$, and $x_0 = \sup(D)$ by (3.1) of Chapter 2. It follows that $E(\mathfrak{T})$ is locally order complete. The fact that $E(\mathfrak{T})$ is boundedly order complete is an immediate consequence of (3.1) of Chapter 2.

1.7 Examples. a. We have already observed in (1.2) that a Köthe function space Λ is locally order complete and boundedly order complete for any $\mathfrak{S}$-topology $\mathfrak{T}_\mathfrak{S}$ on Λ corresponding to a directed class $\mathfrak{S}$ of $\sigma(\Lambda^\times, \Lambda)$-bounded, solid, subset of $\Lambda^\times$. Therefore, $\Lambda(\mathfrak{T}_\mathfrak{S})$ is topologically complete by (1.5). In particular, this result implies the classical completeness theorem for the Lebesgue spaces.

b. In connection with (1.6), it should be noted that the filter of sections of a directed $(\leq)$ $\mathfrak{T}$-bounded set need not converge in a locally order complete, boundedly order complete lattice $E(\mathfrak{T})$. An example to support this remark is provided by (3.3) of Chapter 2.

c. By making use of (1.3) and the properties of the topology of uniform convergence on order bounded sets, it is possible to give a short proof of an interesting result due to Dixmier providing a necessary and sufficient condition for $C(X)$ to be a dual space. Before we formulate this result explicitly, let us recall the following definitions: A compact Hausdorff space X is **hyperstonian** if it is extremally disconnected and the normal measures on X separate points of $C(X)$. (A **normal measure** on X is a Radon measure μ such that $\mu(f_\alpha) \to \mu(f)$ whenever $\{f_\alpha : \alpha \in I\}$ is a directed $(\leq)$ subset of $C(X)$ with supremum f.)

Proposition. The space $C(X)$ of all continuous real valued functions on a compact Hausdorff space X is the strong dual of a Banach lattice if and only if X is hyperstonian.

Proof.† Let $F = C(X)$ and let E be the vector space of all normal measures on X, then $\langle E, F \rangle$ is a dual system if the normal measures on X separate points in $C(X)$. If E is equipped with the norm topology induced by F', then E is an L-space. To show that F is the dual of E for this topology, it is sufficient to show that the order interval $[-e, e]$ (where e is the function that is identically equal to 1 on X) is $\sigma(F, E)$-compact. To this end, we first note that the topology $o(F, E)$ is consistent with $\langle E, F \rangle$ by (2.3) of Chapter 3; in fact, E is a band in F^b. Since $o(F, E)$ is generated by the family of seminorms

$$f \to \mu(|f|) \qquad 0 \le \mu \in E,$$

the canonical embedding of F into $G = \prod\{L^1(\mu) : \theta \le \mu \in E\}$ is a homeomorphism $\big($for $o(F, E)\big)$ of F onto a linear subspace of G. F is locally order complete for $o(F, E)$; hence, the order interval $[-e, e]$ is complete for the uniform structure induced by $o(F, E)$. Therefore, the image of $[-e, e]$ in G is complete, hence closed in G. Consequently, the image of $[-e, e]$ is weakly closed in G and contained in the weakly compact set $\prod\{[-e_\mu, e_\mu] : \theta \le \mu \in E]$ in G $\big($where e_μ is the canonical image of e in $L^1(\mu)\big)$. It follows that $[-e, e]$ is $\sigma(F, E)$-compact. On the other hand, if $C(X)$ is the dual of a Banach lattice E, the elements of E determine normal measures on E; hence, the proof is complete.

We shall now identify some interesting classes of locally convex lattices that satisfy one or both of the main hypotheses of (1.5).

1.8 Proposition. If $E(\mathfrak{T})$ is a locally convex lattice, then E' is locally order complete for the strong topology $\beta(E', E)$. In addition if $E(\mathfrak{T})$ is a barreled space, then E' is boundedly order complete for $\beta(E', E)$.

Proof. In view of (4.17) of Chapter 2, the first assertion will be established if we can show that the polar B° of each $\sigma(E, E')$-bounded,

---

† This proof, which is due to H. Schaefer, was communicated to me by him in a conversation in 1965.

solid subset of E is an order complete subset of E'. If D is a directed ($\leq$) subset of B° that is majorized in E', then $y_0 = \sup(D)$ is defined on the cone in E by

$$y_0(x) = \sup\{y(x) : y \in D\}.$$

Therefore, since the cone in E is generating, it follows that y_0 is in the $\sigma(E', E)$-closure of D. But B° is $\sigma(E', E)$-closed; hence, $y_0 = \sup(D) \in B^\circ$. Therefore, B° is an order complete subset of E'.

Suppose that $E(\mathfrak{T})$ is a barreled space and that D is a $\beta(E', E)$-bounded, directed ($\leq$) subset of E'. Then, since each $\beta(E', E)$-bounded subset of E' is $\sigma(E', E)$-relatively compact, D has a $\sigma(E', E)$-cluster point y_0. It is clear that $y_0(x) = \sup\{y(x) : y \in D\}$ for $x \geq \theta$; hence, y_0 is the supremum of D in E'. Therefore, $E'(\beta(E', E))$ is boundedly order complete.

The following results are immediate consequences of (1.4) (1.5), and (1.8).

1.9   Corollary.   If $E(\mathfrak{T})$ is a locally order complete vector lattice, then E^+ is locally order complete, boundedly order complete, and topologically complete for the strong topology $\beta(E^+, E)$.

1.10   Corollary.   If $E(\mathfrak{T})$ is a barreled locally convex lattice, then E' is complete for $\beta(E', E)$.

1.11   Corollary.   Every reflexive locally convex lattice is locally order complete and topologically complete.

The last corollary is particularly interesting in view of the fact that Komura [1] has shown that there are reflexive locally convex spaces that are not topologically complete.

1.12   Proposition.   Suppose that $E(\mathfrak{T})$ is a metrizable locally convex space ordered by a strict b-cone K, and suppose that $\mathfrak{T}$ is coarser than the order topology on E. If each monotone increasing, topologically bounded sequence in $E(\mathfrak{T})$ has a supremum, then $E(\mathfrak{T})$ is topologically complete.

Proof.   Suppose that $\{p_n : n = 1, 2, \ldots\}$ is a countable family of seminorms generating $\mathfrak{T}$ such that $p_n(x) \leq p_{n+1}(x)$ for all $x \in E$ and all positive integers n. Given a Cauchy sequence in $E(\mathfrak{X})$, choose a subsequence $\{x_n\}$ such that

$$p_n(x_{n+1} - x_n) \le \frac{1}{2^{2n}} \qquad n = 1, 2, \ldots$$

Define $w_n = 2^n(x_{n+1} - x_n)$ for each positive integer n, then $\{2^n w_n : n = 1, 2, \ldots\}$ is a $\mathfrak{X}$-bounded sequence since

$$p_{n_0}(2^n w_n) \le p_n(2^n w_n) \le 1$$

for $n \ge n_0$. Therefore, since K is a strict b-cone, there exist sequences $\{u_n\}$, $\{v_n\}$ in K such that $w_n = u_n - v_n$ for all positive integers n, and such that $\{2^n u_n\}$, $\{2^n v_n\}$ are topologically bounded sequences. It follows that the monotone increasing sequences

$$\left\{ \sum_{n=1}^{k} u_n : k = 1, 2, \ldots \right\}, \qquad \left\{ \sum_{n=1}^{k} v_n : k = 1, 2, \ldots \right\} \qquad (*)$$

are topologically bounded. Define u and v to be the respective suprema of the sequences in $(*)$. Then, the linear hull M of the order interval $[-(u + v), (u + v)]$ contains both of these sequences; moreover, $(u + v)$ is an order unit in M. If we define

$$y_k = \sum_{n=1}^{k} \frac{1}{2^n} u_n, \qquad z_k = \sum_{n=1}^{k} \frac{1}{2^n} v_n, \qquad (**)$$

then $\{y_k\}$ and $\{z_k\}$ are Cauchy sequences in M for the order topology on M, since, for example,

$$\theta \le y_{k+j} - y_k = \sum_{n=k+1}^{k+j} \frac{1}{2^n} u_n \le \frac{1}{2^{k+1}} \sum_{n=k+1}^{k+j} u_n \le \frac{1}{2^{k+1}} u$$

for all positive integers k, j. Now $M(\mathfrak{X}_0)$ is complete by (1.4); hence, the sequences $(**)$ converge in $M(\mathfrak{X}_0)$ to elements y, z, respectively. But the order topology on E induces a coarser topology on M than the order topology on M; hence, the sequences $(**)$ converge to y, z, respectively for the given topology $\mathfrak{X}$. Since $x_{k+1} = x_1 + y_k - z_k$, we conclude that $\{x_k\}$ converges to $x_1 + y - z$ for $\mathfrak{X}$. Therefore, $E(\mathfrak{X})$ is topologically complete.

We shall now turn our attention to matters related to the second question posed at the beginning of this section, namely: What conclusions can be drawn concerning order completeness and the structure of bands from the properties of the topology in a topological vector lattice? We shall see that the topology of uniform convergence on order bounded sets plays a fundamental role in these considerations.

1.13 Proposition. Suppose that $\langle E, F \rangle$ is a dual system, that E is ordered by a generating cone K. that F is ordered by the dual cone K' of K, and that $F \subset E^b$. If F is complete for o(F, E), then F is an order complete set, and a directed $(\leq)$ subset D of F has a supremum in F if and only if the filter $\mathfrak{F}(D)$ of sections of D contains a $\sigma(F, E)$-bounded section; moreover, when sup (D) exists, then $\mathfrak{F}(D)$ converges to sup (D) for o(F, E).

Proof. Suppose that D is a directed $(\leq)$ subset of F that is majorized by $y_0 \in F$, then the filter $\mathfrak{F}(D)$ contains an order interval. Since K generates E, each order interval in F is a $\sigma(F, E)$-bounded set; therefore, $\mathfrak{F}(D)$ contains a $\sigma(F, E)$-bounded set.

On the other hand, if the filter $\mathfrak{F}(D)$ of sections of a directed $(\leq)$ subset D contains a $\sigma(F, E)$-bounded section S, then, to show that D has a supremum, we can assume that $S \subset K'$ without loss in generality. In view of the fact that F is complete and K' is closed for o(F, E), it suffices to show that $\mathfrak{F}(D)$ is a Cauchy filter by (3.1) of Chapter 2. If $x_0 \in K$ and $\lambda_0 = \sup\{\langle x_0, y\rangle : y \in S\}$, choose $y_0 \in S$ so that $\lambda_0 - \langle x_0, y\rangle \leq \frac{1}{2}$ for all y in the section $S_{y_0} = \{z \in S : z \geq y_0\}$. Then, if y_1, y_2 are elements of S_{y_0} and if $w \in [-x_0, x_0]$,

$$|\langle w, y_1 - y_2\rangle| \leq |\langle w, y_1 - y_0\rangle| + |\langle w, y_0 - y_2\rangle|$$
$$\leq \langle x_0, y_1 - y_0\rangle + \langle x_0, y_2 - y_0\rangle$$
$$\leq \lambda_0 - \langle x_0, y_0\rangle + \lambda_0 - \langle x_0, y_0\rangle \leq 1;$$

that is, $S_{y_0} - S_{y_0} \subset [-x_0, x_0]^\circ$. Hence, since the cone K generates E, it follows that $\mathfrak{F}(D)$ is a Cauchy filter in E. The remaining assertions of the proposition follow quickly from this conclusion.

1.14 Proposition. Suppose that $\langle E, F \rangle$ is a dual system, that E is a vector lattice ordered by a cone K, that F is ordered by the dual cone K' of K, and that $F \subset E^b$. If F is complete for o(F, E), then F is boundedly order complete for o(F, E). In addition, if F is a sublattice of E^b, then F is locally order complete for o(F, E).

Proof. The first assertion is an immediate consequence of (1.13). To prove the second assertion, we note that, if $x \in K$, then a directed ($\leq$) subset D of $[-x, x]^\circ$ that is majorized in F contains a $\sigma(F, E)$-bounded set since $\mathfrak{F}(D)$ contains order intervals. Therefore, by (1.13), the supremum y_0 of D exists and $\mathfrak{F}(D)$ converges to y_0 for o(F, E). Since $[-x, x]^\circ$ is o(F, E)-closed, we conclude that $y_0 \in [-x, x]^\circ$, that is, F is locally order complete for o(F, E).

In contrast to the situation described in (3.3) of Chapter 2, we can establish the following result for the topology of uniform convergence on order bounded sets.

1.15 Proposition. If $\langle E, F \rangle$ is a dual system, if E is a vector lattice, and if F is an order complete sublattice of E^b, then the filter $\mathfrak{F}(D)$ of sections of any majorized, directed ($\leq$) subset of F converges to sup (D) for o(F, E). F is locally order complete for o(F, E). B is a band in F if and only if B is an o(F, E)-closed lattice ideal in F.

Proof. To prove the first assertion, suppose that $y_0 = \sup (D)$ and let x_0 be an arbitrary element of the cone in E. Since $\langle x_0, y_0 \rangle = \sup \{\langle x_0, y \rangle : y \in D\}$, we can choose $y_1 \in D$ so that $\langle x_0, y_0 - y_1 \rangle \leq 1$. Then if $x \in [-x_0, x_0]$ and $y \in S_{y_1} = \{z \in D : z \geq y_1\}$, we obtain

$$\langle x, y_0 - y \rangle \leq \langle x_0, y_0 - y \rangle \leq \langle x_0, y_0 - y_1 \rangle \leq 1;$$

hence, the section S_{y_1} of D is contained in $y_0 + [-x_0, x_0]^\circ$. Therefore, $\mathfrak{F}(D)$ converges to sup (D) for o(F, E). It follows immediately that F is locally order complete for o(F, E) since there is a neighborhood basis of θ for o(F, E) consisting of o(F, E)-closed solid sets by (2.8) of Chapter 3.

If B is an o(F, E)-closed lattice ideal in F and if D is a directed ($\leq$) subset of B that is majorized in F, then sup (D) $\in B$ since the filter $\mathfrak{F}(D)$ of sections of D converges to sup (D) for o(F, E). Therefore, B is a band in F.

On the other hand, if B is a band in F, then B is certainly a lattice ideal in F. If P is the projection of F onto B that vanishes on the complementary band $B^\perp$ of B, then P is o(F, E)-continuous since F

is a locally convex lattice for $o(F, E)$ by (2.8) of Chapter 3. Since $B = (I - P)^{-1}(\theta)$, it follows that B is $o(F, E)$-closed.

The preceding result enables us to establish the following characterization of the band generated by a lattice ideal.

1.16 Proposition. If $\langle E, F \rangle$ is a dual system, if E is a vector lattice, and if F is an order complete sublattice of E^b, then the $o(F, E)$-closure $\overline{M}$ of a lattice ideal M in F coincides with the band $(M^\perp)^\perp$ generated by M in F.

Proof. If M is a lattice ideal in F, the closure $\overline{M}$ of M for $o(F, E)$ is a lattice ideal in F by (2.8) of Chapter 3 and (4.8) of Chapter 2. Proposition (1.15) implies that $\overline{M} \supset (M^\perp)^\perp$ since $(M^\perp)^\perp$ is the intersection of all bands in F that contain M. On the other hand, $(M^\perp)^\perp$ is a band in F; hence, it is $o(F, E)$-closed by (1.15). Therefore, $(M^\perp)^\perp \supset \overline{M}$, which completes the proof.

1.17 Proposition. If $\langle E, F \rangle$ is a dual system, if E is a vector lattice, and if F is a lattice ideal in E^b, then the band in E^b generated by F coincides with the $o(F, E)$-completion of F.

Proof. E^b is locally order complete for $o(E^b, E)$ by virtue of (1.15). We assert that E^b is boundedly order complete for this topology. In fact, if D is an $o(E^b, E)$-bounded, directed ($\leq$) subset of E^b, then $\sup \{\langle x_0, y \rangle : y \in D\}$ exists for each $x_0 \geq \theta$ in E. Consequently, $\sup (D)$ exists in E^b, that is, E^b is boundedly order complete for $o(E^b, E)$. It follows from (1.5) that E^b is complete for $o(E^b, E)$.

The topology $o(E^b, E)$ induces $o(F, E)$ on F; hence, the $o(F, E)$-completion of F coincides with the closure $\overline{F}$ of F in E^b for $o(E^b, E)$. By virtue of (1.16), $\overline{F}$ is the band $(F^\perp)^\perp$ generated by F in E^b.

1.18 Example. Suppose that F is the vector space (c_0) of null sequences of real numbers and that $E = \ell^1$ is the vector space of summable sequences of real numbers. Since ℓ^1 is a complete, metrizable locally convex lattice for the topology generated by the norm

$$\|x\| = \sum_{n=1}^{\infty} |x_n|, \qquad (*)$$

it follows that E^b can be identified with the vector space ℓ^∞ of all bounded sequences of real numbers $\left(\text{see } (1.19) \text{ of Chapter 3}\right)$. (c_0) is obviously a lattice ideal in ℓ^∞, but (c_0) is not a band in ℓ^∞ $\left(\text{see } (4.2)\right.$

of Chapter 1). Therefore, (c_0) is not complete for the topology $o((c_0), \ell^1)$; in particular, $o((c_0), \ell^1)$ is strictly coarser than the topology generated by $\|u\| = \sup_n |u_n|$, and strictly finer than the weak topology $\sigma(c_0), \ell^1)$ (see (2.15) and (2.8) of Chapter 3). Finally, we note that, if $z \in \ell^\infty$ and if $|z| \cap |x| = \theta$ for all $x \in (c_0)$, then $z = \theta$. Consequently, the band in ℓ^∞ generated by (c_0) coincides with ℓ^∞. It follows from (1.17) that the completion of (c_0) for $o((c_0), \ell^1)$ can be identified with ℓ^∞ equipped with $o(\ell^\infty, \ell^1)$.

The final portion of this section will be devoted to an exposition of some of the theory related to the subject of the third question posed at the beginning of this section, namely: When is it possible to "complete" an ordered vector space in an order theoretic sense? More specifically, we wish to construct an order complete vector lattice $\hat{E}$ corresponding to a given ordered vector space E in such a way that $\hat{E}$ may be regarded as the "order completion" of E. Of course, the answer to the question of whether a given ordered vector space has such a completion depends basically on the relationship that E is required to bear to $\hat{E}$.

The first construction for an order completion that we shall present here is valid for any Archimedean ordered vector space. It represents a straightforward generalization of the Dedekind procedure for completing the rational number system.

The second type of order completion that we shall discuss applies to a more restricted class of spaces than the class of Archimedean ordered vector spaces considered above. However, it has the advantage of providing an order completion that is more concrete and tractable than that provided by the Dedekind procedure mentioned above.

1.19 Proposition. Suppose that E is an Archimedean ordered vector space equipped with a generating cone K. There exist an order complete vector lattice $\hat{E}$ and a one-to-one linear mapping φ of E into $\hat{E}$ with the following properties:

a. For each $x \in E$, $x \geq \theta$ in E if and only if $\varphi(x) \geq \theta$ in $\hat{E}$.

b. If A is a subset of E for which the supremum (resp. infimum) of A

exists in E, then $\varphi(\sup (A)) = \sup \{\varphi(x) : x \in A\}$ (resp. $\varphi(\inf (A))$
$= \inf \{\varphi(x) : x \in A\})$.

c. If $\hat{y} \in \hat{E}$, there is a subset A of E such that $\hat{y} = \inf \{\varphi(x) : x \in A\}$.

Moreover, if E_1 is an order complete vector lattice and if φ_1 is a one-to-one linear mapping of E into E_1 with properties (a), (b), (c), then there is a one-to-one linear mapping ψ of E_1 onto $\hat{E}$ such that $y_1 \geq \theta$ in E_1 if and only if $\psi(y_1) \geq \theta$ in $\hat{E}$.

Proof. Suppose that A, B are minorized subsets of E. Define $A \leq B$ to mean that every lower bound for A is also a lower bound for B, and define the **cut** (A) **determined by A** to be

$$(A) = \bigcup_{A \leq B} B.$$

The following properties of cuts are easily established, especially if they are proved in the order presented below:

1. $A_1 \leq A_2$ if and only if $(A_1) \supset (A_2)$.
2. $A_1 \leq A_2$ and $A_2 \leq A_1$ if and only if $(A_1) = (A_2)$.
3. $((A)) = (A)$.
4. $(a) \leq A$ if and only if a is a lower bound of A.
5. Given two cuts (A_1), (A_2), there is a $c \in E$ such that $(c) \leq (A_1)$, $(c) \leq (A_2)$.
6. If $A_1 \leq A_2$ and if A_3 is any minorized subset of E, then $A_1 + A_3 \leq A_2 + A_3$.
7. If $A_1 \leq A_2$ and $A_3 \leq A_4$, then $A_1 + A_3 \leq A_2 + A_4$.
8. If $(A_1) = (A_2)$ and $(A_3) = (A_4)$, then $(A_1 + A_3) = (A_2 + A_4)$.
9. If $A_1 \leq A_2$, then $\alpha A_1 \leq \alpha A_2$ for all $\alpha \geq 0$.
10. If $(A_1) = (A_2)$, then $(\alpha A_1) = (\alpha A_2)$ for all $\alpha \geq 0$.

Define $\hat{E}$ to be the collection of all cuts determined by subsets of E. If (A_1), (A_2) are elements of $\hat{E}$, define the sum $(A_1) \hat{+} (A_2)$ to be the cut determined by the set $A_1 + A_2$. By virtue of (8), the sum is well defined; moreover, it is clear that this binary operation on $\hat{E}$ is commutative and associative. Also, if θ is the zero element of E, the cut (θ) obviously has the property that $(A) \hat{+} (\theta) = (A)$ for each cut (A) determined by a subset A of E. We shall now establish the existence of the "negative cut" corresponding to a given cut (A) in

$\hat{E}$. Define $B = \{-x : (x) \leq A\}$, then $x + y \geq \theta$ for all $x \in A$, $y \in B$; hence, $(A) \,\hat{+}\, (B) \geq (\theta)$. On the other hand, if $a \leq x + y$ for all $x \in A$, $y \in B$, then, for any $y \in B$, we have $a - y \leq x$ for each $x \in A$, that is, $(a - y) \leq A$ for all $y \in B$. Therefore, if $y \in B$, then $y - a \in B$. By induction, it follows that $y - na \in B$ whenever $y \in B$ and n is any positive integer. We conclude that

$$a \leq \frac{1}{n} \{x + y\} \qquad n = 1, 2, \ldots$$

for all $x \in A$, $y \in B$; hence, $a \leq \theta$ since E is Archimedean. Therefore, $(A) \,\hat{+}\, (B) \leq (\theta)$; hence, (2) implies that (B) is a cut with the property that $(A) \,\hat{+}\, (B) = (\theta)$. The fact that (B) is the only cut that satisfies this equation follows, as usual, from the commutativity and associativity of the sum. We shall employ the symbol $-(A)$ to denote this unique element (B).

Scalar multiplication in $\hat{E}$ is defined as follows: If $(A) \in \hat{E}$ and $\alpha \geq 0$, define

$$\alpha(A) = (\{\alpha x : x \in A\});$$

for $\alpha < 0$, define $\alpha(A)$ to be the cut $\{-\alpha\}\{-(A)\}$. Then, $\alpha(A)$ is well defined for each real number α by (10); moreover, it is an easy matter to verify the following relations:

$$\alpha\{(A_1) \,\hat{+}\, (A_2)\} = \alpha(A_1) \,\hat{+}\, \alpha(A_2).$$

$$\alpha\{\beta(A)\} = \alpha\beta(A).$$

$$1(A) = (A).$$

To complete the proof that $\hat{E}$ is a vector space, it is only necessary to show that

$$\{\alpha + \beta\}(A) = \alpha(A) \,\hat{+}\, \beta(A) \qquad (*)$$

for all real numbers α, β and all cuts $(A) \in \hat{E}$. By definition of the relation $\leq$ and the operation of addition,

$$\alpha(A) \,\hat{+}\, \beta(A) \leq \{\alpha + \beta\}(A)$$

for all $\alpha \geq 0$, $\beta \geq 0$. In particular,

$$\alpha\{-(A)\} \,\hat{+}\, \beta\{-(A)\} \geq \{\alpha + \beta\}\{-(A)\}$$

for all non-negative real numbers α, β. Using the relation $\{-\alpha\}\{-(A)\}$ $= \alpha(A)$ for $\alpha < 0$, and the group properties of addition, we can establish (*).

The relation $\leq$ defines an order on $\hat{E}$ with respect to which $\hat{E}$ is an ordered vector space by (2), (6), and (9). Moreover, the cone $\hat{K} = \{(A) \in \hat{E} : (A) \geq (\theta)\}$ is generating by (5). If $\{(A_\alpha) : \alpha \in I\}$ is a subset of $\hat{E}$ with the property that, for some $(A) \in \hat{E}$, $(A_\alpha) \geq (A)$ for all $\alpha \in I$, then it is easy to verify that the cut determined by $\bigcup_{\alpha \in I} A_\alpha$ is the infimum of $\{(A_\alpha) : \alpha \in I\}$. We conclude that $\hat{E}$ is an order complete vector lattice.

Define the mapping φ of E into $\hat{E}$ by

$$\varphi(a) = \text{the cut determined by } \{a\} = (a),$$

then, in view of (2) and the definitions of the linear and order structures in $\hat{E}$, it is clear that φ is a one-to-one, linear mapping with properties (a), (b), (c).

If E_1 is an order complete vector lattice and φ_1 is a one-to-one, linear mapping of E into E_1 with properties (a), (b), (c), then, given $a_1 \in E_1$, choose subsets A, B of E such that

$$a_1 = \inf \{\varphi_1(x) : x \in A\} = \sup \{\varphi_1(y) : y \in B\}.$$

Consequently, $\theta = \inf \{\varphi_1(x - y) : x \in A, y \in B\}$; hence,

$$\theta = \inf \{x - y : x \in A, y \in B\}.$$

But then, $\theta = \inf \{\varphi(x - y) : x \in A, y \in B\}$; therefore, there is an $\hat{a} \in \hat{E}$ such that

$$\hat{a} = \inf \{\varphi(x) : x \in A\} = \sup \{\varphi(y) : y \in B\}.$$

If ψ is the mapping of E_1 into $\hat{E}$ defined at $a_1 \in E_1$ by $\psi(a_1) = \hat{a}$, then ψ is a one-to-one, linear mapping of E_1 onto $\hat{E}$ with the property that $a_1 \geq \theta$ if and only if $\psi(a_1) \geq \theta$. (This assertion can be verified by making use for (c) for E_1 and $\hat{E}$.) This completes the proof of the proposition.

1.20 Definition. If E is an Archimedean ordered vector space ordered by a generating cone, the (essentially unique) order complete vector lattice $\hat{E}$ associated with E in (1.19) is called the **cut completion** of E.

For the sake of convenience, we shall ordinarily identify E with the linear subspace $\varphi(E)$ of $\hat{E}$.

Our next result indicates the topological character of the cut completion for an interesting class of locally convex lattices.

1.21 Proposition. Suppose that $E(\mathfrak{T})$ is a locally convex lattice with the property that $\{x_\alpha : \alpha \in I\}$ converges to θ for $\mathfrak{T}$ whenever $\{x_\alpha : \alpha \in I\}$ is a monotone decreasing net such that $\theta = \inf \{x_\alpha : \alpha \in I\}$. Then there is a locally convex topology $\hat{\mathfrak{T}}$ on the cut completion $\hat{E}$ of E such that $\hat{\mathfrak{T}}$ induces $\mathfrak{T}$ on E, $E(\mathfrak{T})$ is dense in $\hat{E}(\hat{\mathfrak{T}})$, and $\hat{E}(\hat{\mathfrak{T}})$ is a locally convex lattice.

Proof. Suppose that $\{p_\beta : \beta \in B\}$ is a family of seminorms generating the topology $\mathfrak{T}$ such that $|x| \leq |y|$ implies $p_\beta(x) \leq p_\beta(y)$ for all $\beta \in B$. If $\hat{x} \in \hat{E}$, there is a subset A of the cone K in E such that $|\hat{x}| = \sup \{A\}$ by $(1.19)(c)$. Without loss in generality, we can assume that $A = \{x_\alpha : \alpha \in I\}$ is an increasing net in K where I has the same cardinality as a neighborhood basis of θ in $E(\mathfrak{T})$. Define

$$\hat{p}_\beta(\hat{x}) = \sup_{\alpha \in I} p_\beta(x_\alpha) \qquad (\beta \in B),$$

then each $\hat{p}_\beta$ is independent of the particular choice of a monotone increasing net $\{x_\alpha : \alpha \in I\}$ with supremum $|\hat{x}|$, since $\{p_\beta(z_\alpha) : \alpha \in I\}$ converges to 0 for each net $\{z_\alpha : \alpha \in I\}$ that decreases to θ. Each $\hat{p}_\beta$ is a seminorm on $\hat{E}$, $\hat{p}_\beta(x) = p_\beta(x)$ if $x \in E$, and $\hat{p}_\beta(\hat{x}) \leq \hat{p}_\beta(\hat{y})$ whenever $|\hat{x}| \leq |\hat{y}|$. Therefore, the family $\{\hat{p}_\beta : \beta \in B\}$ generates a topology $\hat{\mathfrak{T}}$ on $\hat{E}$ such that $\hat{E}(\hat{\mathfrak{T}})$ is a locally convex lattice and $\hat{\mathfrak{T}}$ induces $\mathfrak{T}$ on E. The fact that E is dense in $\hat{E}(\hat{\mathfrak{T}})$ follows from $(1.19)(c)$.

We refer the reader to the notes at the end of this section for references to papers that study the cut completion of some concrete ordered vector spaces.

The remainder of this section will be devoted to a description of an alternate procedure for "order completing" an ordered vector space. The starting point for this development is the following homomorphism theorem:

1.22 Proposition. Suppose that E is an ordered vector space with the decomposition property and that F is a lattice ideal in the order dual E^+ of E. The canonical mapping φ of E into F^+ is linear, and preserves the suprema and infima of finite sets in E, whenever these suprema or infima exist in E.

Proof. The proof given in (4.17) of Chapter 2 for the particular case in which $F = E'$ immediately carries over to this more general setting.

If E is a regularly ordered vector space with the decomposition property and if the cone K in E generates E, then (1.22) implies that the canonical map φ of E into E^{++} is an isomorphism of E into E^{++} with the property that $\varphi(x) \vee \varphi(y) = \varphi(x \vee y)$ (resp. $\varphi(x) \wedge \varphi(y) = \varphi(x \wedge y)$) whenever $x \vee y$ (resp. $x \wedge y$) exists in E. Now E^{++} is a vector lattice and the intersection of any family of sublattices of E^{++} is again a sublattice of E^{++}. Hence, we can define the vector lattice $\tilde{E}$ generated by E to be the smallest sublattice of E^{++} containing $\varphi(E)$; that is, $\tilde{E}$ is the intersection of all sublattices of E^{++} containing $\varphi(E)$. It can be shown that if M is any other regularly ordered vector lattice such that E is isomorphic to a linear subspace of M, then $\tilde{E}$ is also isomorphic to a linear subspace of M (see (13.6) in Schaefer [4] for details). Hence, $\tilde{E}$ represents a "minimal" extension of E to a vector lattice.

Since E^{++} is also an order complete vector lattice, it might be hoped that the canonical mapping φ could also be used to construct a minimal order complete extension of E as well. However, this is not always possible since φ may not preserve the infima (resp. suprema) of minorized (resp. majorized) subsets of E, even when E is an order complete vector lattice to begin with.

1.23 Example. The vector space ℓ^∞ of all bounded sequences of real numbers, ordered by the cone of sequences in ℓ^∞ with nonnegative components, is an order complete vector lattice (see (1.6) of Chapter 1). The sequence $\{x^{(n)}\}$ in ℓ^∞ defined by

$$x_m^{(n)} = \inf \left\{ 1, \frac{n}{m} \right\} \qquad m, n = 1, 2, \ldots$$

is a monotone increasing sequence with the supremum $e = (e_n) \in \ell^\infty$ (where $e_n = 1$ for all n). However, we shall now show that e is not the supremum of $\{x^{(n)}\}$ when ℓ^∞ is canonically embedded in the order complete lattice $(\ell^{\infty})^{++}$. In fact, if $e = \sup_{n} \{x^{(n)}\}$ in $(\ell^{\infty})^{++}$, then $f(e) = \sup_{n} \{f(x^{(n)})\}$ for each positive linear functional f on ℓ^{∞}. Since each positive linear functional on ℓ^{∞} is continuous for the topology generated by the norm $\|x\| = \sup_{n} |x_n|$ (see (2.17)(a) in Chapter 2), and each continuous linear functional on ℓ^{∞} is the difference of two positive continuous linear functionals (see (1.21) of Chapter 2), it follows that $\{x^{(n)}\}$ converges to e for the weak topology $\sigma(\ell^{\infty}, (\ell^{\infty})')$ determined by this norm. Therefore, $\{x^{(n)}\}$ converges to e for the norm topology by (3.4) of Chapter 2, contrary to the relation $\|e - x^{(n)}\| = 1$ for all n. Consequently, e is not the supremum of $\{x^{(n)}\}$ in $(\ell^{\infty})^{++}$.

In the light of this example, we introduce the following additional restriction on an ordered vector space to enable us to construct the order completion in the order bidual.

1.24 Definition. A regularly ordered vector space E with the decomposition property ordered by a generating cone is **minimal** if the canonical mapping φ of E into E^{++} has the property that $\varphi(\sup(A)) = \sup\varphi(A)$ (resp. $\varphi(\inf(A)) = \inf\varphi(A)$) whenever $\sup(A)$ (resp. $\inf(A)$) exists for a subset A of E.

1.25 Proposition. Suppose that E is a minimal ordered vector space, then the cut completion $\hat{E}$ of E can be identified with the order complete vector lattice in E^{++} generated by the canonical image $\varphi(E)$ of E in E^{++}; that is, $\hat{E}$ is essentially the intersection of all order complete sublattices of E^{++} that contain $\varphi(E)$.

Proof. Define E_1 to be the intersection of all order complete sublattices of E^{++} that contain $\varphi(E)$. Then E_1 is an order complete vector lattice that obviously satisfies (a) and (b) of (1.19). The mapping $(A) \leftrightarrow \varphi(A)$ establishes a one-to-one correspondence between the collection of all cuts in E and the collection of all cuts in $\varphi(E)$. Since E_1 is an order complete vector lattice, it can be identified with its cut completion by (1.19). Hence, the cut completion $\hat{E}$ of E may be regarded to be a subset of E_1. On the other hand, $\hat{E}$ is an order complete vector lattice containing $\varphi(E)$; hence, E_1 is a subset of $\hat{E}$. We conclude that the cut completion of E can be identified with E_1.

The following result provides a useful test for minimality of an ordered vector space.

1.26 Proposition. If E is a regularly ordered vector lattice, then the following assertions are equivalent:

a. E is minimal.

b. The filter $\mathfrak{F}(D)$ of sections of each directed ($\leq$) subset D of E that has a supremum $x_0 \in E$ converges to x_0 for the order topology $\mathfrak{T}_o$ on E.

c. $\mathfrak{T}_o$ is the finest locally convex topology $\mathfrak{T}$ on E for which each order convergent net converges to its order limit for $\mathfrak{T}$.

d. Each order convergent net in E converges to its order limit for $\mathfrak{T}_o$.

Proof. If E is minimal and if D is a directed ($\leq$) subset of E with a supremum $x_0 \in E$, then

$$f(x_0) = \sup \{f(x) : x \in D\}$$

for each positive linear functional f on E (see Equation (10) in Section 2 of Chapter 1). Therefore, $\mathfrak{F}(D)$ converges to x_0 for $\sigma(E, E^+)$. But the cone K in E is normal for the order topology $\mathfrak{T}_o$ by (1.16) of Chapter 3; hence, $\mathfrak{F}(D)$ converges to x_0 for $\mathfrak{T}_o$ (see (3.4) of Chapter 2).

Now suppose that condition (b) is satisfied and that $\{x_\alpha : \alpha \in I\}$ is a net in E that order converges to $x_0 \in E$. Choose a monotone decreasing net $\{y_\alpha : \alpha \in I\}$ such that $\inf\{y_\alpha : \alpha \in I\} = \theta$ and $|x_\alpha - x_0| \leq y_\alpha$ for all $\alpha \in I$. By virtue of (b), $\{y_\alpha : \alpha \in I\}$ converges to θ for $\mathfrak{T}_o$; hence, $\{x_\alpha : \alpha \in I\}$ converges to x_0 for $\mathfrak{T}_o$ since $E(\mathfrak{T}_o)$ is a locally convex lattice by (1.17) of Chapter 3. Suppose that $\mathfrak{T}$ is any other locally convex topology on E with the property that every order convergent net in $E(\mathfrak{T})$ converges to its order limit for $\mathfrak{T}$. If $h \geq 0$, consider the linear subspace $E_h = \bigcup_{n=1}^{\infty} n[-h, h]$ used in providing the inductive topology characterization of $\mathfrak{T}_o$ given in (1.11) of Chapter 3. Since the sequence $\left\{\frac{1}{k} h : k = 1, 2, \ldots\right\}$ order converges to θ, the canonical mapping of $E_h(\mathfrak{T}_o^{(h)})$ into $E(\mathfrak{T})$ is continuous. Therefore, $\mathfrak{T}_o$ is finer than $\mathfrak{T}$ by definition of the inductive topology.

Since it is obvious that (c) implies (d), let us suppose that (d) is satisfied. If $D = \{x_\alpha : \alpha \in I\}$ is a directed ($\le$) subset of E with a supremum x_0 in E, then $\{x_\alpha : \alpha \in I\}$, regarded as a net directed by D, order converges to x_0. Therefore, this net converges to x_0 for $\mathfrak{X}_0$. Since each positive linear functional on E is continuous for $\mathfrak{X}_0$ (see (1.17) of Chapter 3), it follows that

$$f(x_0) = \sup \{f(x) : x \in D\}$$

for each positive linear functional on E. Therefore, $x_0 = \sup (D)$ in E^{++}, which completes the proof.

   1.27 Notes. The fundamental results (1.3) and (1.5) are due to Nakano [3], though the proof that we have presented for (1.3) includes a clarification, due to Schaefer [5], of the original proof. Goffman [1] observed that Nakano's theorem could be used to establish the completeness of Köthe function spaces for an interesting class of topologies (see (1.7)(*a*)). (1.12) is a generalization due to Schaefer [4] of a theorem of Amemiya [1]. Propositions (1.13) to (1.18) can be found in the author's paper [2].

   The cut completion of an ordered vector space (see (1.19)) is discussed in Nakano [4]. Dilworth [1] proved that the cut completion of the vector lattice $C(X)$ of all continuous, real valued functions on a compact Hausdorff space X can be represented as the order complete vector lattice of all continuous, real valued functions on the Stone space Y associated with the Boolean algebra of regularly open sets in X (see Theorem (6.1)). He also obtained a different representation in terms of normal, upper semicontinuous functions on X, but this alternate representation is not a vector lattice for the usual linear operations for functions. Nakano and Shimogaki [1] proved that the cut completion of $C(X)$ can be represented as the order complete vector lattice of all normal quasi-continuous functions on X, two such functions f and g being identified if

$$\overline{\lim_{x \to a}} f(x) = \overline{\lim_{x \to a}} g(x)$$

for each $a \in X$. (A function is quasi-continuous if and only if it is continuous on the complement of a set of first category in X.) Recently, Johnson and Mack [1] obtained necessary and sufficient conditions on a completely regular space X in order that the cut completion of $C(X)$ be representable as a $C(Y)$ for a suitable choice of Y.

Other papers related to the subject matter of this section: Amemiya [2], Halperin-Luxemburg [1], Vladimirov [1] and Yamamuro [1].

§2. TOPOLOGICAL PROPERTIES OF ORDER CONVERGENCE

In Section 5 of Chapter 1, we introduced two basic modes of order convergence based on the order structure of an ordered vector space. We observed that almost everywhere convergence and convergence in measure are special instances of order convergence and order *-convergence, respectively. In this section, we shall establish an intimate relation between relative uniform convergence and convergence for the order topology. We shall also establish some sufficient topological conditions for an ordered vector space to enjoy the diagonal property or to be order separable. As we have seen in Section 5 of Chapter 1, these properties are fundamental to a number of considerations concerning order convergence.

2.1 Proposition. Suppose that E is a vector lattice with an order unit e and that $\{x_n\}$ is a sequence in E. Then the following assertions are equivalent:

a. $\{x_n\}$ is convergent to x_0 for the order topology $\mathfrak{T}_o$ on E.
b. $\{x_n\}$ is relatively uniformly convergent to x_0.
c. $\{x_n\}$ is relatively uniformly *-convergent to x_0.

Proof. It is obviously sufficient to establish the result for the case in which $x_0 = \theta$. If $\{x_n\}$ converges to θ for $\mathfrak{T}_o$, then there is an integer n_1 such that $x_n \in [-e, e]$ for all $n \geq n_1$. After the integer n_{k-1} has been chosen, select $n_k > n_{k-1}$ so that $x_n \in \frac{1}{k}[-e, e]$ for all $n \geq n_k$.

(These choices are possible since $\frac{1}{k}[-e, e]$ is a $\mathfrak{T}_o$-neighborhood of θ for each k.) If we choose $\lambda > 0$ so that $x_n \in \lambda[-e, e]$ for $n = 1, \ldots,$

$n_1 - 1$ and if we define $\lambda_n > 0$ as follows:

$$\lambda_n = \begin{cases} \lambda & \text{if } n = 1, \ldots, n_1 - 1 \\ \dfrac{1}{k} & \text{if } n_k \leq n < n_{k+1} \end{cases} \quad k = 1, 2, \ldots$$

then $|x_n| \leq \lambda_n e$ for all n and $\{\lambda_n\}$ decreases to 0. Therefore, $\{x_n\}$ is relatively uniformly convergent to θ. It is clear that if a sequence $\{x_n\}$ converges relatively uniformly to θ, then $\{x_n\}$ converges to θ for $\mathfrak{T}_o$ since each neighborhood of θ for $\mathfrak{T}_o$ absorbs order intervals. Consequently, (a) is equivalent to (b). Since topological convergence always has the star property (see the remarks after (5.2) of Chapter 1), the equivalence of (a) and (b) implies the equivalence of (a) and (c).

2.2 Proposition. If $E(\mathfrak{T})$ is an Archimedean vector lattice and a topological vector space, the following assertions are equivalent:

a. $\mathfrak{T}$ coincides with the order topology $\mathfrak{T}_o$.
b. $\mathfrak{T}$ is the finest locally convex topology $\mathfrak{T}'$ on E for which each relatively uniformly *-convergent sequence converges to its order limit for $\mathfrak{T}'$.
c. $\mathfrak{T}$ is the finest locally convex topology $\mathfrak{T}'$ on E for which each relatively uniformly convergent sequence converges to its order limit for $\mathfrak{T}'$.

Proof. In view of the fact that topological convergence has the star property, it is clear that (b) and (c) are equivalent.

Suppose that $\mathfrak{T}$ coincides with the order topology $\mathfrak{T}_o$ on E, then $\mathfrak{T}$ is the inductive topology with respect to the family $\{E_h(\mathfrak{T}_o^{(h)}) : h \geq \theta\}$ of linear subspaces of E (see (1.11) of Chapter 3). The element h is an order unit in $E_h = \bigcup_{k=1}^{\infty} k[-h, h]$; hence, by (2.1), relative uniform convergence, relative uniform *-convergence, and $\mathfrak{T}_o^{(h)}$-convergence all coincide for sequences in E_h. If $\{x_n\}$ is a sequence in E that converges relatively uniformly to $x_0 \in E$, then there is an $h \geq \theta$ such that $\{x_n\} \subset E_h$, $x_0 \in E_h$, and $\{x_n\}$ converges relatively uniformly to x_0 in E_h. Since $\mathfrak{T}$ induces a coarser topology on E_h than $\mathfrak{T}_o^{(h)}$, it follows that $\{x_n\}$ converges to x_0 for $\mathfrak{T}$. Also, if $\mathfrak{T}'$ is any other locally convex topology on E with the property that relative uniform convergence implies convergence for $\mathfrak{T}'$, then $\mathfrak{T}'$ is coarser than $\mathfrak{T}$ by (2.1) since $\mathfrak{T}$ is the finest locally convex topology on E for which the canonical embedding mapping of $E_h(\mathfrak{T}_0^{(h)})$ into E is continuous for each $h \geq \theta$. Therefore, we conclude that (a) implies (c).

On the other hand, if $\mathfrak{T}$ satisfies condition (c), then $\mathfrak{T}$ induces a coarser topology on E_h than $\mathfrak{T}_0^{(h)}$ by (2.1); hence, $\mathfrak{T}$ is coarser than the order topology on E. Since each relatively uniformly convergent sequence converges for $\mathfrak{T}_0^{(h)}$ in some E_h, it is also $\mathfrak{T}_0$-convergent. Therefore, in view of the fact that $\mathfrak{T}$ satisfies (c), we conclude that $\mathfrak{T}_0$ is coarser than $\mathfrak{T}$. Consequently, $\mathfrak{T}_0 = \mathfrak{T}$, which completes the proof.

2.3 Corollary. The following assertions concerning a linear functional f on an Archimedean vector lattice E are equivalent:

a. f is continuous for the order topology on E.

b. f is order bounded.

c. $\{f(x_n)\}$ converges to 0 whenever $\{x_n\}$ is a sequence in E that is relatively uniformly convergent to θ.

d. $\{f(x_n)\}$ converges to 0 whenever $\{x_n\}$ is a sequence in E that is relatively uniformly *-convergent to θ.

Proof. The equivalence of (a) and (b) was established in (1.15) of Chapter 3. (a) implies (c) by (2.2). If f is not order bounded, there is an $x \geq \theta$ such that $|f(x_n)| > n$ for some sequence $\{x_n\} \subset [-x, x]$. But then $\left\{\dfrac{1}{n} x_n\right\}$ is relatively uniformly convergent to θ, yet $\left|f\left(\dfrac{1}{n} x_n\right)\right| > 1$. Therefore, (c) implies (b). Since the equivalence of (c) and (d) is obvious, the proof is complete.

The following result identifies topological convergence and relative uniform *-convergence for an important class of ordered topological vector spaces.

2.4 Proposition. If $E(\mathfrak{T})$ is a complete metrizable topological vector lattice, then a sequence $\{x_n\}$ in E converges to $x_0 \in E$ for $\mathfrak{T}$ if and only if $\{x_n\}$ is relatively uniformly *-convergent to x_0.

Proof. Suppose that $\{x_n\}$ is relatively uniformly convergent to x_0. Choose $u \geq \theta$ and a sequence $\{\lambda_n\}$ of positive real numbers decreasing to 0 such that $|x_n - x_0| \leq \lambda_n u$ for all n. Given a solid neighborhood U of θ for $\mathfrak{T}$, choose $\lambda_0 > 0$ so that $\lambda_0 u \in U$, and then select a positive integer n_0 such that $\lambda_n \leq \lambda_0$ for all $n \geq n_0$. Since $|x_n - x_0| \leq \lambda_n u \leq \lambda_0 u$ for $n \geq n_0$, it follows that $x_n - x_0 \in U$ for $n \geq n_0$. Therefore, $\{x_n\}$ converges to x_0 for $\mathfrak{T}$. From this fact, it is easy to conclude that relative uniform $*$-convergence implies convergence for $\mathfrak{T}$.

On the other hand, suppose that $\{x_n\}$ converges to θ for $\mathfrak{T}$ and let $\{y_n\}$ be a given subsequence of $\{x_n\}$. We shall now show that there is a subsequence $\{y_{n_k}\}$ of $\{y_n\}$ that is relatively uniformly convergent to θ. Choose a countable neighborhood basis $\mathscr{W} = \{W_n : n = 1, 2, \ldots\}$ of θ for $\mathfrak{T}$ such that $W_{n+1} + W_{n+1} \subset W_n$ for each n. Since the lattice operations in $F(\mathfrak{T})$ are continuous, the sequence $\{|y_n|\}$ converges to θ for $\mathfrak{T}$. Therefore, there is a subsequence $\{y_{n_k}\}$ of $\{y_n\}$ such that $k|y_{n_k}| \in W_k$ for each k. It follows that

$$\left\{ \sum_{k=1}^{m} k|y_{n_k}| : m = 1, 2, \ldots \right\} \qquad (*)$$

is a Cauchy sequence in $E(\mathfrak{T})$ since

$$\sum_{k=m+1}^{m+p} k|y_{n_k}| \in W_{m+1} + \cdots + W_{m+p} \subset W_m$$

for all m, p. Therefore, there is an element $y \in E$ such that the sequence $(*)$ converges to y for $\mathfrak{T}$. It is clear that $|y_{n_k}| \leq \frac{1}{k} y$ for all k; hence, $\{y_{n_k}\}$ converges relatively uniformly to θ. It follows that $\{x_n\}$ is relatively uniformly $*$-convergent to θ, which completes the proof of the proposition.

The preceding result shows that the topology of a complete metrizable topological vector lattice $E(\mathfrak{T})$ is completely determined by the order structure. In fact, the closure $\bar{A}$ of a subset A of E for $\mathfrak{T}$ is given by

$$\bar{A} = \left\{ x \in E : x \text{ is the limit of a relatively uniformly} \right.$$
$$\left. *\text{-convergent sequence } \{x_n\} \subset A \right\} \qquad (\dagger)$$

However, $(\dagger)$ cannot be used to define a closure operator on an arbitrary vector lattice as the following example shows.

2.5   Example. (Roberts [2].) Define E to be the vector space of all continuous, real-valued functions f on the non-negative real axis such that, for some real numbers α, β and some natural numbers m, $|f(t)| \leq \alpha t^m + \beta$ for all $t \geq 0$, E is a vector lattice for the order determined by the cone K of non-negative functions in E. For each pair of natural numbers m and n, define the function f_{mn} as follows:

$$f_{mn}(t) = \frac{1}{m} t^n + \frac{1}{n} \qquad (t \geq 0).$$

Then $\left| f_{mn}(t) - \dfrac{1}{n} \right| \leq \dfrac{1}{m} t^n$ for all m, n; hence, the sequence

$$\{ f_{mn} : m = 1, 2, \ldots \}$$

converges relatively uniformly to the function f_n defined by

$$f_n(t) = \frac{1}{n} \qquad (t \geq 0).$$

Since $\{f_n\}$ is obviously relatively uniformly convergent to θ, it follows that $\theta \in \bar{\bar{A}}$ where $A = \{ f_{mn} : m, n = 1, 2, \ldots \}$, yet $\theta \notin \bar{A}$. In fact, no sequence in A that involves infinitely many distinct choices for the index n can be relatively uniformly convergent since such a sequence is not even order bounded in E. Therefore, $\bar{\bar{A}} \neq \bar{A}$, that is, (†) does not define a closure operator in E.

Of course, if a vector lattice E has the diagonal property and is σ-order complete, then relative uniform convergence is equivalent to order convergence by (5.9) of Chapter 1. Therefore, (†) defines a closure operator by (5.6) of Chapter 1.

Our next objective will be to establish convenient tests for the diagonal property and order separability in topological vector lattices.

2.6   Proposition. If $E(\mathfrak{T})$ is a metrizable, σ-order complete vector lattice ordered by a normal cone K and if $\{y_k\}$ converges to θ for $\mathfrak{T}$ whenever $\{y_k\}$ is a sequence in E that decreases to θ, then E is order separable. In addition, if $E(\mathfrak{T})$ is a complete or boundedly order complete topological vector lattice, then E has the diagonal property.

Proof. Suppose that $\mathscr{W} = \{ W_n : n = 1, 2, \ldots \}$ is a countable neighborhood basis of θ for $\mathfrak{T}$ consisting of full, circled sets W_n such that $W_{n+1} + W_{n+1} \subset W_n$ for all n. Define p_n to be the Minkowski functional of W_n and let $\{x_\alpha : \alpha \in I\}$ be a monotone decreasing net in the cone. We shall show that

$$\inf_\alpha \left\{ \sup_{\beta \geq \alpha} p_n(x_\alpha - x_\beta) \right\} = 0 \qquad (*)$$

for all n. In fact, let us suppose to the contrary that there exist a natural number n_0 and an $\varepsilon_0 > 0$ such that

$$\inf_\alpha \left\{ \sup_{\beta \geq \alpha} p_{n_0}(x_\alpha - x_\beta) \right\} > \varepsilon_0$$

Choose a monotone decreasing sequence $\{x_{\alpha_k}\}$ such that

$$p_{n_0}(x_{\alpha_k} - x_{\alpha_{k+1}}) > \varepsilon_0$$

and define $x_0 = \inf\{x_{\alpha_k} : k = 1, 2, \ldots\}$. Then $\{x_{\alpha_k} - x_0 : k = 1, 2, \ldots\}$ decreases to θ, yet

$$p_{n_0}(x_{\alpha_k} - x_0) \geq p_{n_0}(x_{\alpha_k} - x_{\alpha_{k+1}}) > \varepsilon_0$$

since W_{n_0} is full. This contradicts the hypothesis; consequently, $(*)$ must hold.

By virtue of $(*)$, we can choose $\alpha_n \in I$ so that

$$\sup_{\beta \geq \alpha_n} p_n(x_{\alpha_n} - x_\beta) \leq \frac{1}{n} \qquad n = 1, 2, \ldots$$

Define $x_0 = \inf_n \{x_{\alpha_n}\}$, then

$$p_n(x_{\alpha_n} - x_0 \cap x_\alpha) \leq \frac{1}{n} \qquad n = 1, 2, \ldots \qquad (**)$$

for all α, since $\sup_k \{x_{\alpha_n} - x_\alpha \cap x_{\alpha_k}\} = x_{\alpha_n} - x_0 \cap x_\alpha$ and $p_n(x_{\alpha_n} - x_{\alpha_k} \cap x_\alpha) \leq \frac{1}{n}$ for $k \geq n$. It follows from $(**)$ that

$$p_n(x_0 - x_0 \cap x_\alpha) \leq \frac{1}{n} \qquad n = 1, 2, \ldots$$

for all α. Therefore, $x_0 = x_0 \cap x_\alpha$ since $\mathfrak{T}$ is a Hausdorff topology, that is, $\inf_k \{x_{\alpha_k}\} = x_0 = \inf_\alpha \{x_\alpha\}$. From this conclusion, it is an easy matter to deduce that E is order separable.

To prove the second assertion of the proposition let us first suppose that $\{y^{(n)}\}$ is sequence in $E(\mathfrak{T})$ that decreases to θ and that, for each positive integer k, the sequence $\{y^{(k,n)}\}$ decreases to $y^{(n)}$. Choose a countable neighborhood basis $\mathscr{V} = \{V_n : n = 1, 2, \ldots\}$ of θ for $\mathfrak{T}$ consisting of full, open sets V_n with the following properties:

$$y^{(n)} \in V_n; \quad \overline{V}_{n+1} \subset V_n \qquad n = 1, 2, \ldots$$

The sequence $\{y^{(k,1)} - y^{(1)}\}$ decreases to θ; hence, $\{y^{(k,1)} - y^{(1)}\}$ converges to θ for $\mathfrak{T}$. Since V_1 is open and $y^{(1)} \in V_1$, there is an integer k_1 such that $y^{(k_1,1)} \in V_1$. The fact that $\{y^{(k,2)}\}$ decreases to $y^{(2)}$ and $\sup\{y^{(k_1,1)}, y^{(k,2)}\}$ decreases to $\sup\{y^{(k_1,1)}, y^{(2)}\} = y^{(k_1,1)}$ implies that there is an integer $k_2 > k_1$ such that

$$\sup\{y^{(k_1,1)}, y^{(k_2,2)}\} \in V_1; \; y^{(k_2,2)} \in V_2$$

since V_1, V_2 are open.

Proceeding inductively, we can select $k_n > k_{n-1}$ such that

$$\sup\{y^{(k_p,p)}, \ldots, y^{(k_n,n)}\} \in V_p \qquad (1 \le p \le n - 1)$$

and

$$y^{(k_n,n)} \in V_n.$$

Therefore,

$$\sup\{y^{(k_m,m)}, \ldots, y^{(k_{m+p}, m+p)}\} \in V_m \text{ for } m, p = 1, 2, \ldots$$

Define $z^{(n)} = \sup\{y^{(k_1,1)}, \ldots, y^{(k_n,n)}\}$ for each positive integer n, then

$$z^{(n+p)} - z^{(n)} \le \sup\{y^{(k_n,n)}, \ldots, y^{(k_{n+p}, n+p)}\} \in V_n$$

for all p; hence, $\{z^{(n)}\}$ is a $\mathfrak{T}$-bounded Cauchy sequence. But $\{z^{(n)}\}$ is monotone increasing and $E(\mathfrak{T})$ is boundedly order complete or topologically complete; hence, it follows that

$$s_n = \sup\{y^{(k_p,p)} : p \ge n\}$$

exists in E for each n. Also, since $\sup\{y^{(k_n,n)}, \ldots, y^{(k_{n+p}, n+p)}\}$ increases to s_n, it is true that $s_n \in \overline{V}_n \subset V_{n-1}$. Therefore, $\{s_n\}$ converges to θ for $\mathfrak{T}$. The cone K in $E(\mathfrak{T})$ is closed by (4.13) of Chapter 2; hence, $\theta = \inf\{s_n\}$ by (3.2) of Chapter 2. We conclude that $\{y^{(k_n,n)} : n = 1, 2, \ldots\}$ order converges to θ.

Now suppose that $\{y^{(n)}\}$ is an arbitrary sequence in E that order converges to θ and that, for each positive integer n, $\{y^{(k,n)}\}$ decreases to $y^{(n)}$. Define

$$\bar{y}^{(n)} = \sup\,\{y^{(k)} : k \geq n\}$$

and

$$\bar{y}^{(k,n)} = \sup\,\{\bar{y}^{(n)}, y^{(k,n)}\},$$

then $\{\bar{y}^{(n)}\}$ decreases to θ and $\{\bar{y}^{(k,n)}\}$ decreases to $\bar{y}^{(n)}$ for each n. Therefore, according to the last step in the proof, one can find a strictly increasing sequence $\{k_n\}$ of positive integers such that $\{\bar{y}^{(k_n,n)}\}$ order converges to θ. However, $y^{(n)} \leq y^{(k_n,n)} \leq \bar{y}^{(k_n,n)}$; hence, $\{y^{(k_n,n)}\}$ order converges to θ.

Next, suppose that $\{y^{(n)}\}$ order converges to $y \in E$ and that $\{y^{(k,n)}\}$ decreases to $y^{(n)}$ for each n. Then, $\{y^{(n)} - y\}$ order converges to θ and $\{y^{(k,n)} - y\}$ decreases to $y^{(n)} - y$. Therefore, by the preceding step in the proof, there is a strictly increasing sequence $\{k_n\}$ of positive integers such that $\{y^{(k_n,n)}\}$ order converges to y.

If $y^{(k,n)}$ order converges to $y^{(n)}$ for each n and $y^{(n)}$ order converges to y, define

$$z^{(k,n)} = \sup\,\{y^{(m,n)} : m \geq n\}; \qquad w^{(k,n)} = \inf\,\{y^{(m,n)} : m \geq n\}.$$

Then, $\{z^{(k,n)}\}$ decreases to $y^{(n)}$ and $\{w^{(k,n)}\}$ increases to $y^{(n)}$ for each n. By making use of the conclusion drawn in the preceding step in the proof, we deduce the existence of strictly increasing sequences $\{p_n\}$, $\{q_n\}$ such that $\{z^{(p_n,n)}\}$ and $\{w^{(q_n,n)}\}$ order converge to y. If we choose a strictly increasing sequence $\{k_n\}$ such that $k_n > p_n$, $k_n > q_n$ for each n, then $\{y^{(k_n,n)}\}$ order converges to y since

$$z^{(p_n,n)} \geq z^{(k_n,n)} \geq y^{(k_n,n)} \geq w^{(k_n,n)} \geq w^{(q_n,n)}$$

for each n, which completes the proof of the proposition.

2.7   Example.   If X is a locally compact, σ-compact Hausdorff space and μ is a positive Radon measure on X, then, if $p \geq 1$, the space $L_\mu^p(X)$ (see (1.2)) satisfies all the conditions imposed on E in (2.6). Therefore, $L_\mu^p(X)$ is order separable and has the diagonal property.

2.8   Notes.   The results relating relative uniform convergence to convergence for the order topology are essentially contained in Section 6 of the author's paper [1] and also in Gordon [2]. (2.4) is a simple generalization, due to the author, of Theorem 9 of Chapter 15 in Birkhoff [2]. The basic techniques employed in that part of the proof of (2.6) dealing with the diagonal property are due to Kantorovitch [2] (see Satz 34). In his fundamental papers [2] and [3], Kantorovitch made extensive use of a restriction on σ-order complete vector lattices which he referred to as "regularity". Orihara [1] proved that the requirement of regularity is equivalent to a slight strengthening of the combined restrictions of order separability and the diagonal property.

§3. ORDER PROPERTIES OF SPACES OF CONTINUOUS LINEAR MAPPINGS

As we have already seen in Section 2 of Chapter 1, a natural order structure exists on various classes of linear mappings acting from one ordered vector space into another, namely, the order structure determined by the cone of positive linear mappings. The main objective of this section is to study the rudiments of this structure for classes of linear mappings that are defined by topological conditions, for example, the class of all continuous linear mappings, or the class of all compact linear mappings.

If $E(\mathfrak{T})$ and $F(\mathfrak{O})$ are ordered topological vector spaces, the set $\mathscr{K}$ of positive continuous linear mappings of $E(\mathfrak{T})$ into $F(\mathfrak{O})$ is a wedge in the vector space $\mathscr{L}(E, F)$ of all continuous linear mappings of $E(\mathfrak{T})$ into $F(\mathfrak{O})$. If the linear hull $K - K$ of the cone K in E is dense in $E(\mathfrak{T})$, $\mathscr{K}$ is a cone in $\mathscr{L}(E, F)$. Thus, in this case, $\mathscr{L}(E, F)$ is also an ordered vector space for the order determined by $\mathscr{K}$, and it is natural to investigate the extent to which the order structures of E and F influence that of $\mathscr{L}(E, F)$.

3.1   Proposition.   If $E(\mathfrak{T})$ and $F(\mathfrak{O})$ are topological vector lattices and if $F(\mathfrak{O})$ is an order complete vector lattice, then the supremum (resp. infimum) of every majorized (resp. minorized) subset of $\mathscr{L}(E, F)$ exists in $\mathscr{L}(E, F)$.

Proof. It is obviously sufficient to prove that if $\{T_\alpha : \alpha \in I\}$ is a subset of $\mathscr{L}(E, F)$ that is majorized by an element $T_0 \in \mathscr{L}(E, F)$, then the supremum of this set exists in $\mathscr{L}(E, F)$. Suppose that x is an element of the cone K in E and that

$$x = \sum_{k=1}^{n} x_k \qquad x_k \in K$$

then,

$$\sum_{k=1}^{n} T_{\alpha_k} x_k \leq \sum_{k=1}^{n} T_0 x_k = T_0 x$$

for any choice $\alpha_k \in I$ $(k = 1, 2 \ldots, n)$. Therefore, since $F(\mathfrak{D})$ is an order complete vector lattice, we conclude that, for each $x \in K$, the supremum Sx of the set

$$\left\{ \sum_{k=1}^{n} T_{\alpha_k} x_k : x = \sum_{k=1}^{n} x_k ; x_k \in K ; \alpha_k \in I \right\}$$

exists in $F(\mathfrak{D})$. As we have already noted in the remarks preceding (2.3) in Chapter 1, the mapping S of K into F that is defined to have the value Sx at $x \in K$ can be extended to a linear mapping S of E into F. Moreover, it is clear that if we can show that S is in $\mathscr{L}(E, F)$, then S is the supremum of the set $\{T_\alpha : \alpha \in I\}$ in $\mathscr{L}(E, F)$. To establish the fact that S is in $\mathscr{L}(E, F)$, we first observe that $(T_0 - T_{\alpha_0})x \geq (T_0 - S)x \geq \theta$ for any $x \in K$ and any fixed $\alpha_0 \in I$. Therefore, since T_0 and T_{α_0} are continuous linear mappings, and since $E(\mathfrak{T})$, $F(\mathfrak{D})$ are topological vector lattices, the relation

$$|(T_0 - S)x| \leq (T_0 - T_{\alpha_0})|x| \qquad (x \in E)$$

implies that $T_0 - S \in \mathscr{L}(E, F)$. Consequently, $S \in \mathscr{L}(E, F)$ which completes the proof.

3.2 Corollary. If $E(\mathfrak{T})$ and $F(\mathfrak{D})$ are topological vector lattices and if $F(\mathfrak{D})$ is order complete, then the linear hull $\mathscr{K} - \mathscr{K}$ of the cone $\mathscr{K}$ in $\mathscr{L}(E, F)$ is an order complete vector lattice.

Under the hypotheses stated in (3.1) it is not necessarily true that the cone $\mathscr{K}$ generates $\mathscr{L}(E, F)$; in particular, $\mathscr{L}(E, F)$ need not be a vector lattice.

3.3   *Examples.*   a. Consider the infinite matrix $A = (a_{pq})$ defined by

$$a_{pq} = \begin{cases} \dfrac{1}{p-q} & \text{if } p \neq q \\ 0 & \text{if } p = q \end{cases}$$

Hilbert has shown that A is a matrix transformation on ℓ^2 into itself (see, for example p. 236 in Hardy-Littlewood-Polya [1]). Hence, A is a continuous linear operator on ℓ^2 if ℓ^2 is equipped with the norm: $\|x\| = \left(\sum_{n=1}^{\infty} |x_n|^2 \right)^{1/2}$. However, if x and y are the elements of ℓ^2 defined by

$$x_p = y_p = \frac{1}{\sqrt{p} \log p} \quad (p > 1); \qquad x_1 = y_1 = y_2$$

then

$$\sum_{p=1}^{\infty} \sum_{q=1}^{\infty} |a_{pq}| x_p y_q = +\infty. \tag{*}$$

We shall now use (*) to show that A is not an order bounded linear operator on ℓ^2 (for the order on ℓ^2 determined by the cone of all elements of ℓ^2 with non-negative components).

Define $z = (z_p) \in \ell^2$ by

$$z_p = \sum_{q=1}^{\infty} |a_{pq}| y_q$$

and set

$$u_q^{(p)} = (\text{sign } a_{pq}) y_q.$$

Then $u^{(p)} = (u_q^{(p)}) \in [-y, y]$ for all p, and

$$z_p = \sum_{q=1}^{\infty} a_{pq} u_q^{(p)} = (Au^{(p)})_p.$$

Suppose, contrary to our assertion, that A is an order bounded linear operator on ℓ^2. Then there is a $u \geq \theta$ such that $Au^{(p)} \in [-u, u]$ for each positive integer p. It follows that

$$-\langle u, v \rangle \leq \langle Au^{(p)}, v \rangle \leq \langle u, v \rangle$$

for all $v \geq \theta$ in ℓ^2; in particular, if we take v to be the unit vector $e^{(p)}$, we obtain the relation

$$z_p = |z_p| = |(Au^{(p)})_p| \leq u_p$$

for each p. But then

$$\sum_{p=1}^{\infty} \sum_{q=1}^{\infty} |a_{pq}| y_q x_p = \sum_{p=1}^{\infty} z_p x_p \leq \sum_{p=1}^{\infty} u_p x_p < +\infty$$

since x, u are elements of ℓ^2. This contradicts (∗); hence, A is not an order bounded linear operator on ℓ^2.

Now if A could be written as the difference of two positive (continuous) linear operators on ℓ^2, then A would be order bounded. Therefore, the cone $\mathcal{K}$ of positive continuous linear operators on ℓ^2 does not generate $\mathcal{L}(\ell^2, \ell^2)$.

In view of (5.15) and (5.16) of Chapter 1, it is true that $L^b(\ell^2, \ell^2) = L^{so}(\ell^2, \ell^2)$. Hence, A also provides an example of a continuous linear operator on ℓ^2 that is not sequentially order continuous. Moreover, (5.9) of Chapter 1 and (2.4) show that each continuous linear operator on ℓ^2 is sequentially order ∗-continuous. Therefore, A is an order ∗-continuous linear operator that is not order bounded (cf. (5.15) of Chapter 1).

b. Suppose that Ω is the union of a disjoint sequence $\{\Omega_n\}$ of sets where each Ω_n consists of 2^n points x_{ni}, $i = 1, 2, \ldots, 2^n$. Define an infinite matrix $A = (a_{ij})$ in the following way: The matrix A_1 of the first two rows and columns of A is

$$A_1 = \begin{pmatrix} +1 & +1 \\ +1 & -1 \end{pmatrix}$$

After the matrix A_{n-1} of the first 2^{n-1} rows and columns of A has been defined, define A_n by the following block array:

$$A_n = \begin{pmatrix} A_{n-1} & A_{n-1} \\ A_{n-1} & -A_{n-1} \end{pmatrix}$$

An induction argument can be used to verify that

$$\sum_{i=1}^{2^n} a_{ik} a_{ip} = 2^n \delta_{kp} \qquad (*)$$

whenever $1 \leq k, p \leq 2^n$.

Suppose that m is the measure that assigns a unit mass to each point of Ω and that m_n is the restriction of that measure to Ω_n. If f_n is in $L^2(\Omega_n, m_n)$ and $f_n(x_{nk}) = b_k$, then f_n can be identified with the 2^n-tuple $(b_1, \ldots, b_{2^k})$. In order to define a linear operator T_n on $L^2(\Omega_n, m_n)$, it is only necessary to specify its values on the characteristic functions e_{nk} of the points x_{nk} $(k = 1, 2, \ldots, 2^n)$; hence, set

$$T_n e_{nk} = 2^{-n/2} \sum_{i=1}^{2^n} a_{ik} e_{ni}.$$

Then, if $f = (b_1, \ldots, b_{2^n}) \in L^2(\Omega_n, m_n)$, it follows from (∗) that

$$\|T_n f\|^2 = 2^{-n} \sum_{i=1}^{2^n} \left(\sum_{k=1}^{2^n} a_{ik} b_k \right)^2$$

$$= 2^{-n} \sum_{i=1}^{2^n} \left(\sum_{k=1}^{2^n} a_{ik}^2 b_k^2 + 2 \sum_{p \neq q} a_{ip} a_{iq} b_p b_q \right) = \sum_{k=1}^{2^n} b_k^2 = \|f\|^2.$$

Therefore, $\|T_n\| = 1$. Since Ω_n is finite, the operator $|T_n|$ exists and is continuous on $L^2(\Omega_n, m_n)$; moreover,

$$|T_n|(e_{nk}) = 2^{-n/2} \sum_{i=1}^{2^n} e_{ni}.$$

A direct computation shows that $\||T_n|f\| \leq 2^{n/2}\|f\|$ for each f in $L^2(\Omega_n, m_n)$. On the other hand, if e is the function that is identically equal to 1 on Ω_n, then $\||T_n|e\| = 2^{n/2}\|e\|$; hence, the L^2-norm of $|T_n|$ is precisely $2^{n/2}$.

If $f \in L^2(\Omega, m)$ and f_n denotes the restriction of f to Ω_n, then $f_n \in L^2(\Omega_n, m_n)$. Hence, we can "piece together" an operator T on $L^2(\Omega, m)$ by

$$Tf = \sum_{n=1}^{\infty} T_n f_n.$$

T is a continuous linear operator on $L^2(\Omega, m)$. In fact, if $f \in L^2(\Omega, m)$ then

$$\|f\|^2 = \sum_{n=1}^{\infty} \|f_n\|^2 \geq \sum_{n=1}^{\infty} \|T_n f_n\|^2 = \|Tf\|^2;$$

hence, $\|T\| \leq 1$. However, since $\||T_n|\| = 2^{n/2}$, the absolute value $|T|$ of T does not exist in the space of continuous linear operators on $L^2(\Omega, m)$.

A simple modification of the preceding construction shows that the class of compact operators on $L^2(\Omega, m)$ is not a lattice either. Specifically, if we set $S_n = 2^{-n/2}T_n$, then

$$\|S_n\| = 2^{-n/2} \qquad \||S_n|\| = 1.$$

The operator $S = \sum_{n=1}^{\infty} S_n$ is compact, since the partial sums of the series defining S are compact operators that converge to S in norm. The operator $|S|$ is continuous but not compact (as can be seen by considering the image under $|S|$ of the sequence of characteristic functions $\{1_{\Omega_n}\}$.

Of course, if the vector space $\mathscr{L}(E, F)$ of all continuous linear mappings of an ordered topological vector space $E(\mathfrak{T})$ into an ordered topological vector space $F(\mathfrak{D})$ is a vector lattice, then the cone $\mathscr{K}$ of positive continuous linear mappings of E into F generates $\mathscr{L}(E, F)$ since each $T \in \mathscr{L}(E, F)$ can be written as $T = T^+ - T^-$. However, the following result shows that the converse is also valid for a wide class of spaces.

3.4 Proposition. Suppose that $E(\mathfrak{T})$ is a topological vector lattice and that $F(\mathfrak{D})$ is an order complete topological vector lattice. If the cone $\mathscr{K}$ in $\mathscr{L}(E, F)$ is a generating cone, then $\mathscr{L}(E, F)$ is a lattice ideal in the order complete vector lattice $L^b(E, F)$ of order bounded linear mappings of E into F.

Proof. Since $\mathscr{K}$ generates $\mathscr{L}(E, F)$, it is true that $\mathscr{L}(E, F) \subset L^b(E, F)$; moreover, $L^b(E, F)$ is an order complete vector lattice by (2.3) of Chapter 1. Suppose that $T \in \mathscr{L}(E, F)$, $S \in L^b(E, F)$, and $|S| \leq |T|$. Choose T_1, T_2 in $\mathscr{K}$ so that $T = T_1 - T_2$, then

$$-(T_1 + T_2) \leq S \leq (T_1 + T_2);$$

hence, $|S| \leq T_1 + T_2$. Note that if $\{x_\alpha : \alpha \in I\}$ is a net in $E(\mathfrak{T})$ that converges to θ, then $\{|x_\alpha| : \alpha \in I\}$ also converges to θ for $\mathfrak{T}$ since $E(\mathfrak{T})$ is a topological vector lattice. Since T_1, T_2 are continuous, it follows that $\{|S||x_\alpha| : \alpha \in I\}$ converges to θ for $\mathfrak{D}$. In view of the fact that $|Sx| \leq |S||x|$ for all $x \in E$, it follows that $\{Sx_\alpha : \alpha \in I\}$ converges to θ for $\mathfrak{D}$ since $F(\mathfrak{D})$ is a topological vector lattice. Therefore, S is continuous, that is, $\mathscr{L}(E, F)$ is a lattice ideal in $L^b(E, F)$.

3.5 Corollary. If $E(\mathfrak{T})$, $F(\mathfrak{O})$ are topological vector lattices, if F is an order complete vector lattice, and if the cone $\mathscr{K}$ in $\mathscr{L}(E, F)$ is a generating cone, then $\mathscr{L}(E, F)$ is an order complete vector lattice.

We shall now present a number of sufficient conditions for the cone $\mathscr{K}$ in $\mathscr{L}(E, F)$ to be generating (and therefore, in view of (3.5), for $\mathscr{L}(E, F)$ to be an order complete vector lattice).

3.6 Proposition. Suppose that E is a vector lattice and that F is an order complete vector lattice containing an order unit e. Then, the vector space $\mathscr{L}(E, F)$ of all linear mappings of E into F that are continuous for the respective order topologies on E and F is an order complete vector lattice.

Proof. Suppose $T \in \mathscr{L}(E, F)$, then, since the order interval $[-e, e]$ is a neighborhood of θ for the order topology on F, there is a neighborhood V of θ for the order topology on E such that $T(V) \subset [-e, e]$. If B is an order bounded set in E, there is an $\alpha > 0$ such that $B \subset \alpha V$. Therefore, $T(B) \subset [-\alpha e, \alpha e]$; consequently, T is an order bounded linear mapping. It follows that there exist positive linear mappings T_1, T_2 of E into F such that $T = T_1 - T_2$. Since every positive linear mapping is continuous for the respective order topologies on E and F (see (1.14) of Chapter 3), it follows that the cone in $\mathscr{L}(E, F)$ is a generating cone. The assertion now follows from (3.5).

3.7 Corollary. If $E(\mathfrak{T})$ is a sequentially complete, bornological locally convex lattice and if $F(\mathfrak{O})$ is an order complete vector lattice ordered by a normal cone with a nonempty interior, then $\mathscr{L}(E, F)$ is an order complete vector lattice.

Proof. This result is an immediate consequence of (1.4) and (1.18) of Chapter 3 and (3.6).

In view of the remarks in (4.23) of Chapter 2, the restrictions imposed on $F(\mathfrak{O})$ in (3.7) force this space to be isomorphic to the space $C(X)$ of continuous, real-valued functions on an extremally disconnected, compact Hausdorff space X (see (1.3)).

3.8 Proposition. Suppose that E is a normed vector lattice such that the norm is additive on the cone and suppose that $F(\mathfrak{O})$ is a locally convex lattice in which the filter of sections of each directed ($\leq$), $\mathfrak{O}$-bounded set D converges to sup (D) for $\mathfrak{O}$. Then $\mathscr{L}(E, F)$ is an order complete vector lattice.

Proof. Suppose that p is an $\mathfrak{O}$-continuous seminorm on F with the property that $p(y_1) \leq p(y_2)$ whenever $|y_1| \leq |y_2|$. Define the seminorm P on $\mathscr{L}(E, F)$ as follows:

$$P(T) = \sup \{p(Tx) : \|x\| \leq 1\}.$$

Suppose that $T \in \mathscr{L}(E, F)$, that $x \geq \theta$, and that $x = \sum_{i=1}^{n} x_i$ where $x_i \geq \theta$ for each i. Then

$$p\left(\sum_{i=1}^{n} |Tx_i|\right) \leq \sum_{i=1}^{n} p(|Tx_i|) = \sum_{i=1}^{n} p(Tx_i) \leq \sum_{i=1}^{n} P(T)\|x_i\| = P(T)\|x\| ; \; (*)$$

hence, the set

$$\left\{\sum_{i=1}^{n} |Tx_i| : x = \sum_{i=1}^{n} x_i; x_i \geq \theta\right\}$$

is $\mathfrak{O}$-bounded. Since this set is also directed ($\leq$), its supremum

$$|T|x = \sup \left\{\sum_{i=1}^{n} |Tx_i| : x = \sum_{i=1}^{n} x_i; x_i \geq \theta\right\}$$

exists for each $x \geq \theta$. Therefore, according to the remarks preceding (2.4) in Chapter 1, $|T|$ exists in $L^b(E, F)$. Moreover, $|T|$ is continuous by virtue of ($*$) and the hypothesis concerning directed ($\leq$) sets. The assertion now follows from (3.5).

Of course, an (L)-space satisfies the restriction imposed on E in the preceding proposition while the hypotheses on F are satisfied in Köthe function spaces for an interesting class of topologies. Therefore, in particular, the vector space of all continuous linear mappings of $L_\mu^1(X)$ into $L_\mu^p(X)$ for $p \geq 1$ is an order complete vector lattice (see (1.2) of Chapter 4).

For sequence spaces, we can establish the following sufficient conditions.

3.9 Proposition. Suppose that λ and μ are sequence spaces equipped with their respective weak topologies determined by their Köthe duals and ordered by their respective cones of sequences with nonnegative components. Each of the following conditions implies that $\mathscr{L}(\lambda, \mu)$ is an order complete vector lattice:

a. λ is an arbitrary perfect sequence space and μ is (c_0), ℓ^∞, or ω.

b. μ is an arbitrary perfect sequence space and λ is ℓ^1 or φ.

Proof. As we have already observed in (2.2) of Chapter 1, the space $\mathscr{L}(\lambda, \mu)$ can be identified with the vector space of all matrix transformations of λ into μ. Under this identification, the cone $\mathscr{K}$ of positive continuous linear mappings of λ into μ corresponds to the cone of matrix transformations with non-negative entries.

Suppose that λ is perfect and that μ is (c_0) or ℓ^∞. If $A \in \mathscr{L}(\lambda, \mu)$, then A is represented by an infinite matrix (a_{ij}). Define $a^{(i)} = (a_{ij} : j = 1, 2, \ldots)$ then $a^{(i)} \in \lambda^\times$ by condition (MT − 1) on matrix transformations (see (2.2) of Chapter 1). Condition (MT − 2) on matrix transformations implies that $(\langle x, a^{(i)} \rangle : i = 1, 2, \ldots)$ is an element of μ for each $x \in \lambda$. If $\mu = \ell^\infty$, this implies that $\{a^{(i)} : i = 1, 2, \ldots\}$ is a $\sigma(\lambda^\times, \lambda)$-bounded set. If $\mu = (c_0)$, this implies that $\{|a^{(i)}| : i = 1, 2, \ldots\}$ is $\sigma(\lambda^\times, \lambda)$-convergent since the lattice operations in $\lambda^\times$ are $\sigma(\lambda^\times, \lambda)$-sequentially continuous by (2.16) of Chapter 3. In either case, the matrix $(|a_{ij}|)$ satisfies conditions (MT − 1) and (MT − 2) for a matrix transformation since

$$\langle x, |a^{(i)}| \rangle = \sum_{j=1}^{\infty} |a_{ij}| x_j \qquad (i = 1, 2, \ldots)$$

for each $x \in \lambda$. Therefore, $|A|$ exists in $\mathscr{L}(\lambda, \mu)$; consequently, $\mathscr{L}(\lambda, \mu)$ is an order complete vector lattice by (3.5).

If λ is perfect and $\mu = \omega$, then $\mathscr{L}(\lambda, \mu)$ is clearly an order complete vector lattice in view of the fact that $\mathscr{L}(\lambda, \mu)$ coincides with the vector space of matrix transformations of λ into μ.

If λ and μ are perfect sequence spaces, then $B \in \mathscr{L}(\mu^\times, \lambda^\times)$ if and only if B is represented by the transpose of a matrix representing an element of $\mathscr{L}(\lambda, \mu)$. Since $(\ell^\infty)^\times = \ell^1$ and $\omega^\times = \varphi$, it follows that $\mathscr{L}(\ell^1, \mu)$ and $\mathscr{L}(\varphi, \mu)$ are order complete vector lattices for any perfect sequence space μ.

The following result will enable us to obtain a sufficient condition for the cone $\mathscr{K}$ to be a generating cone in $\mathscr{L}(E, F)$ when E is nuclear.

3.10 Proposition. If $E_1(\mathfrak{T}_1)$ is a locally convex space ordered by a normal cone K_1 and if $E_2(\mathfrak{T}_2)$ is a quasicomplete locally convex space ordered by a closed strict b-cone K_2, then each nuclear mapping of E_1 into E_2 can be expressed as the difference of two positive nuclear mappings of E_1 into E_2.

Proof. If T is a nuclear mapping of E_1 into E_2, then there exist an equicontinuous sequence $\{f_n\}$ in E_1', a sequence $\{\lambda_n\}$ in ℓ^1, and a bounded sequence $\{y_n\}$ in E_2 such that

$$Tx = \sum_{n=1}^{\infty} \lambda_n f_n(x) y_n \qquad (*)$$

for each $x \in E_1$. Choose a convex, circled neighborhood V of θ such that $|f_n(z)| \leq 1$ for all $z \in V$ and all n. If $E_V = E_1/p^{-1}(0)$ where p denotes the Minkowski functional of V, then p induces a norm $\| \cdot \|$ on E_V, each f_n induces a linear functional $\bar{f}_n$ on E_V that is continuous for this norm, and the canonical image K_V of the cone K_1 in E_1 is normal for the norm topology on E_V. Therefore, by (1.22) of Chapter 2, there exist positive, continuous linear functionals $\bar{h}_n, \bar{g}_n$ on E_V such that: $\bar{f}_n = \bar{h}_n - \bar{g}_n$ for each n, $\bar{h}_n, \bar{g}_n$ define positive linear functionals h_n, g_n on E_1 and for some constant k, $|h_n(z)| \leq$ k, $|g_n(z)| \leq$ k for all $z \in V$ and all n. Also, since K_2 is a strict b-cone in E_2, we can write $y_n = u_n - v_n$ where $\{u_n\}, \{v_n\}$ are bounded sequences in K_2. If we replace y_n by $u_n - v_n$ and f_n by $h_n - g_n$ in $(*)$, we can regroup terms to obtain a representation of T of the required sort.

3.11 Corollary. If $E(\mathfrak{T})$ is a nuclear space ordered by a normal cone K and if F is an order complete Banach lattice, then the cone $\mathcal{K}$ in $\mathcal{L}(E, F)$ generates $\mathcal{L}(E, F)$.

The following result will be useful in determining the lattice properties of spaces of weakly continuous linear mappings.

3.12 Proposition. Suppose that $\langle E_1, F_1 \rangle$, $\langle E_2, F_2 \rangle$ are dual systems, and E_1, E_2 are ordered by generating cones K_1, K_2 that are normal for the weak topologies $\sigma(E_1, F_1)$, $\sigma(E_2, F_2)$, respectively, then a weakly continuous linear mapping T is continuous for $o(E_1, F_1)$ and $o(E_2, F_2)$ if and only if the adjoint T' of T is an order bounded linear mapping of F_2 into F_1.

Proof. Since K_1, K_2 are weakly normal, K_1', K_2' generate F_1, F_2, respectively; moreover, $E_1 \subset F_1^b$ and $E_2 \subset F_2^b$ since K_1, K_2 generate E_1, E_2, respectively. If T is continuous for $o(E_1, F_1)$ and $o(E_2, F_2)$ and if $y \in K_2'$, there is an $x \in K_1'$ such that

$$T([-x, x]^\circ) \subset [-y, y]^\circ$$

by definition of the topology of uniform convergence on order bounded sets. Since K_1', K_2' are weakly closed, the order intervals $[-x, x]$, $[-y, y]$ are weakly closed, convex sets containing θ. Therefore, by the Bipolar Theorem, $T'([-y, y]) \subset [-x, x]$. Consequently, T' is an order bounded linear mapping since K_1', K_2' generate F_1, F_2, respectively.

On the other hand, if T' is an order bounded linear mapping of F_2 into F_1 and if V is a given $o(E_2, F_2)$-neighborhood of θ in E_2, there is a $y \in K_2'$ such that $[-y, y]^\circ \subset V$. Choose $x \in K_1'$ so that $T'([-y, y]) \subset [-x, x]$. But then $T([-x, x]^\circ) \subset [-y, y]^\circ \subset V$; that is, T is continuous for $o(E_1, F_1)$ and $o(E_2, F_2)$.

3.13 Proposition. Suppose that $E(\mathfrak{T})$, $F(\mathfrak{S})$ are locally convex lattices and that every positive linear functional on F' is continuous for $\tau(F', F)$. Then, the following assertions are equivalent:

a.   The class $\mathscr{L}_\sigma(E, F)$ of all weakly continuous linear mappings of E into F is a vector lattice.

b.   Each weakly continuous linear mapping of E into F is continuous for $o(E, E')$ and $o(F, F')$.

Proof.   Since E, F are locally convex lattices, it follows that E', F' are order complete vector lattices (see (4.17) of Chapter 2) and $E \subset (E')^b$, $F \subset (F')^b$. If (a) is satisfied and T is weakly continuous, then $T = T^+ - T^-$ where T^+, T^- are positive, weakly continuous linear mappings of E into F. The adjoint mappings $(T^+)', (T^-)'$ are also positive; hence, $(T^+)', (T^-)'$ are order bounded linear mappings. But then (3.12) implies that T^+, T^- are continuous for $o(E, E')$ and $o(F, F')$; consequently, condition (b) is satisfied.

On the other hand, suppose that (b) holds. Then, if $T \in \mathscr{L}_\sigma(E, F)$, it follows from (3.12) that T' is an order bounded linear mapping of

F' into E'. Therefore, the positive part S of T' exists in $L^b(F', E')$ and

$$Sy = \sup \{T'z : \theta \leq z \leq y\}$$

for each $y \geq \theta$ in F'. If $x \in E$ and $x \geq \theta$, then

$$(S^*x)(y) = (Sy)(x) \geq 0$$

for all y in F' such that $y \geq \theta$. Therefore, $y \to (S^*x)(y)$ defines a positive linear functional on F' that is continuous for $\tau(F', F)$; it follows that the algebraic adjoint S^* of S maps E into F. Consequently, S is weakly continuous; that is, the positive part of each element of $\mathscr{L}_\sigma(E, F)$ exists in $\mathscr{L}_\sigma(E, F)$.

In (3.3)(b), we observed that there is a compact linear operator T on $L^2(\Omega, m)$ such that

a. $|T|$ exists as a continuous linear operator on $L^2(\Omega, m)$.

b. $|T|$ is not compact.

The following assertion provides a sufficient condition for the compactness of the absolute value of each compact linear mapping.

3.14 Proposition. Suppose that $E(\mathfrak{T})$ is a locally convex lattice and that F is a Banach lattice with an order unit. Then, the compact linear mappings of E into F constitute a vector lattice.

Proof. Suppose that T is a compact linear mapping of E into F. Choose a solid neighborhood V of θ such that $T(V)$ is relatively compact in F. For each $y \geq \theta$ such that $y \in V$, it is true that the set $\{Tx : |x| \leq y\}$ is contained in $T(V)$. Therefore, by (3.10) of Chapter 2, it follows that the supremum of this set exists for each $y \geq \theta$. If we define

$$|T|y = \sup \{Tx : |x| \leq y\}$$

for each $y \geq \theta$, then, according to the remarks preceding (2.4) in Chapter 1, $|T|$ exists in $L^b(E, F)$. To prove that T is compact, it is only necessary to observe that

$$\{\sup \{Tx : |x| \leq y\} : y \in V, y \geq \theta\}$$

is relatively compact (see (3.10) of Chapter 2), that is, $|T|$ maps the neighborhood V of θ into a relatively compact set.

It is clear from the proof of (3.14) that the compact linear mappings of E into F form a vector lattice if E and F are locally convex lattices and F has the following properties:

a. Each relatively compact subset of F has a supremum in F.
b. If C is a relatively compact subset of F, then $\{\sup(S) : S \subset C\}$ is relatively compact in F.

As we have seen in (3.11) of Chapter 2, there are spaces with these two properties that do not contain order units.

The remainder of this section will be devoted to a description of some of the topological properties of the order in $\mathscr{L}(E, F)$.

3.15 Proposition. If $E_1(\mathfrak{T}_1)$ is a locally convex space ordered by an $\mathfrak{S}$-cone K_1 and if $E_2(\mathfrak{T}_2)$ is a locally convex space ordered by a normal cone K_2, then the cone $\mathscr{K}$ of positive, continuous linear mappings of $E_1(\mathfrak{T}_1)$ into $E_2(\mathfrak{T}_2)$ is normal for the $\mathfrak{S}$-topology on $\mathscr{L}(E, F)$.

Proof. Since K_1 is an $\mathfrak{S}$-cone in $E_1(\mathfrak{T}_1)$, the class $\mathfrak{S}' = \{\overline{\Gamma(S \cap K_1)} : S \in \mathfrak{S}\}$ (where $\Gamma(B)$ denotes the convex, circled hull of B) is a fundamental system for $\mathfrak{S}$ (see the remarks following (1.11) of Chapter 2). The fact that K_2 is normal in $E_2(\mathfrak{T}_2)$ implies that there is a family $\{p_\alpha : \alpha \in A\}$ of seminorms generating $\mathfrak{T}_2$ such that $p_\alpha(y_1) \leq p_\alpha(y_2)$ whenever $\alpha \in A$ and $\theta \leq y_1 \leq y_2$. Now, if $T \in \mathscr{L}(E, F)$

$$\sup\{p_\alpha(Tx) : x \in \overline{\Gamma(S \cap K_1)}\} = \sup\{p_\alpha(Tx) : x \in S \cap K_1\}$$

for each $\alpha \in A$. Therefore, the family of seminorms:

$$P_{\alpha S}(T) = \sup\{p_\alpha(Tx) : x \in S \cap K_1\} \qquad (S \in \mathfrak{S}, \alpha \in A)$$

generates the $\mathfrak{S}$-topology on $\mathscr{L}(E, F)$. Since it is clear that $P_{\alpha,S}(T_1) \leq P_{\alpha,S}(T_2)$ for all $\alpha \in A$, $S \in \mathfrak{S}$ whenever $0 \leq T_1 \leq T_2$, we conclude that the cone $\mathscr{K}$ in $\mathscr{L}(E, F)$ is normal for the $\mathfrak{S}$-topology.

3.16 Proposition. If $E_1(\mathfrak{T}_1)$ is a locally convex space ordered by a weakly normal cone K_1 and if $E_2(\mathfrak{T}_2)$ is a locally convex space ordered by a generating cone K_2, then the linear hull $\mathscr{K} - \mathscr{K}$ of the cone $\mathscr{K}$ in $\mathscr{L}(E_1, E_2)$ is dense in $\mathscr{L}(E_1, E_2)$ for the topology of pointwise convergence.

Proof. The dual of $\mathscr{L}(E_1, E_2)$ for the topology of pointwise convergence is algebraically isomorphic to $E_1 \otimes E_2'$; the isomorphism in question associates the linear functional

$$T \to \langle Tx, y' \rangle$$

with the element $x \otimes y'$ of $E_1 \otimes E_2'$. (See Prop. 11 of §2, Chap. IV in Bourbaki [1]). Each element $x' \otimes y \in E_1' \otimes E_2$ determines an element $T_{x',y} \in \mathscr{L}(E_1, E_2)$ defined by

$$T_{x',y}(x) = \langle x, x' \rangle y \qquad (x \in E_1).$$

Moreover, $T_{x',y} \in \mathscr{K}$ whenever $x' \in K_1'$, $y \in K_2$. If $x_0 \in K_1$, $y_0' \in K_2'$ and $x_0 \otimes y_0'$ vanishes on each $T \in \mathscr{K}$, then, in particular,

$$(x_0 \otimes y_0')(T_{x',y}) = \langle x_0, x' \rangle \langle y, y_0' \rangle = 0$$

for all $x' \in K_1'$, $y \in K_2$. Hence, since $E_1' = K_1' - K_1'$ and $E_2 = K_2 - K_2$, it follows that $x_0 = \theta$ or $y_0' = \theta$. Therefore, $\mathscr{K}$ is dense for the topology of pointwise convergence on $\mathscr{L}(E_1, E_2)$.

3.17 Proposition. Suppose that $E_1(\mathfrak{T}_1)$ is a barreled space ordered by a generating cone K_1 and that $E_2(\mathfrak{T}_2)$ is a semireflexive space ordered by a normal closed cone K_2. If $\mathscr{H}$ is a directed ($\le$) subset of $\mathscr{L}(E_1, E_2)$ which satisfies one of the following conditions:

a. $\mathscr{H}$ is majorized in $\mathscr{L}(E_1, E_2)$.

b. Some section of $\mathscr{H}$ is bounded for the topology of pointwise convergence.

then the filter $\mathfrak{F}(\mathscr{H})$ of sections of $\mathscr{H}$ converges to an element $T_0 \in \mathscr{L}(E_1, E_2)$ uniformly on each precompact subset of E_1 and $T_0 = \sup(\mathscr{H})$.

Proof. The cone $\mathscr{K}$ of positive, continuous linear mappings of E_1 into E_2 is normal for the topology of pointwise convergence by (3.15). Hence, every order bounded subset of $\mathscr{L}(E_1, E_2)$ is bounded for the topology of pointwise convergence. Therefore, if $\mathscr{H}$ satisfies (a), it also satisfies (b). If (b) holds and $x \in K_1$, the set

$$\mathscr{H}_x = \{Tx : T \in \mathscr{H}\}$$

is a directed ($\le$) subset of E_2 that contains an $\mathfrak{T}_2$-bounded section. Consequently, by (3.7) of Chapter 2, the filter $\mathfrak{F}(\mathscr{H}_x)$ of sections of

$\mathscr{H}_x$ converges to some element y_x of $E_2(\mathfrak{T}_2)$. If we define a mapping T_0 of K_1 into E_2 by setting

$$T_0 x = y_x \qquad (x \in K_1),$$

then T_0 can be extended to a linear mapping T_0 of E_1 into E_2, and $\mathfrak{F}(\mathscr{H}_x)$ converges to $T_0 x$ for each $x \in E_1$. It follows from the Banach-Steinhaus Theorem that $T_0 \in \mathscr{L}(E_1, E_2)$ and that $\mathfrak{F}(\mathscr{H})$ converges to T_0 uniformly on each precompact subset of E_1. It remains to be shown that $T_0 = \sup(\mathscr{H})$. In view of (3.1) of Chapter 2, it is sufficient to show that $\mathscr{K}$ is closed in $\mathscr{L}(E_1, E_2)$ for the topology of pointwise convergence. But, for each $x \in E_1$, the mapping $f_x : \mathscr{L}(E_1, E_2) \to E_2(\mathfrak{T}_2)$ defined by

$$f_x(T) = Tx$$

is continuous for the topology of pointwise convergence on $\mathscr{L}(E_1, E_2)$. Hence, since K_2 is closed and

$$\mathscr{K} = \bigcap_{x \in K_1} f_x^{-1}(K_2),$$

it follows that $\mathscr{K}$ is closed for the topology of pointwise convergence.

3.18 Corollary. If $E(\mathfrak{T})$ is a reflexive locally convex space ordered by a normal b-cone K, then each pointwise bounded, monotone increasing sequence $\{T_n\}$ of continuous linear operators on $E(\mathfrak{T})$ converges to a continuous linear operator T_0 uniformly on each compact subset of $E(\mathfrak{T})$.

Proof. The closure $\bar{K}$ of K is a normal, closed, strict b-cone by (1.6) and (1.15) of Chapter 2, and $\{T_n\}$ is a monotone sequence for the order structure on E determined by $\bar{K}$. Therefore, (3.17) can be applied to $E(\mathfrak{T})$ ordered by $\bar{K}$ to obtain the desired result.

3.19 Notes. Kantorovitch [3] made the first systematic study of the order structure of spaces of linear mappings. Example (3.2)(a) can be found in the author's joint paper with Sherbert [1]. That paper contains a number of other results concerning continuous linear mappings on sequence spaces including sufficient conditions for the vector spaces of continuous or order continuous linear mappings to be bands in the order complete vector lattice of all order bounded linear mappings. These results yield rather strong operator decompositions (see Proposition 2.10, Corollary (2.12) and the example that follows (2.12)). Example (3.2)(b) is due to Krengel [1], [2]; moreover, (3.6), (3.8), and (3.14) represent simple generalizations of results found in his papers. (3.9), and (3.13) are taken from the author's papers [1], [4]; (3.10), (3.15), (3.16), and (3.17) are due to Schaefer [3].

§4. SPECIAL POINTS AND SUBSETS OF THE CONE

This section is devoted to a discussion of some of the basic properties of certain distinguished points and subsets of the cone in an ordered vector space.

As we have seen in (1.10) of Chapter 2, normal cones with non-empty interiors cannot occur in non-normable topological vector spaces. Moreover, since any interior element of the cone is obviously an order unit, it follows from the remarks made in (4.23) of Chapter 2 that any Banach lattice in which the cone has a nonempty interior can be renormed with an equivalent norm for which the given lattice is an abstract M-space with a unit element. Consequently, the class of ordered topological vector spaces possessing cones with nonempty interiors is not very broad.

A number of authors have introduced concepts weaker than that of an interior point to describe "interior-like" elements of the cone for spaces in which the interior of the cone may be empty. The definitions selected by these authors were deteremined by the particular class of problems they were considering at the time. For example, Schaefer [6], [7] employed the notion of a quasi-interior point (see below) as a replacement for interior points in his studies of the spectral properties of positive operators.

Our first objective in this section will be to establish relationships between the three types of "interior-like" elements of a cone that seem to be most significant in the theory of ordered vector spaces.

4.1 Definitions. An element x_0 of the positive cone K in an ordered topological vector space $E(\mathfrak{T})$ is a **quasi-interior point** of K if the linear hull of the order interval $[\theta, x_0]$ is dense in $E(\mathfrak{T})$. An element $x_0 \in K$ is a **nonsupport point** of K if each closed hyperplane H that supports K and passes through x_0 contains K. An element x_0 of K is a **weak order unit** if, for each $y \in K$ such that $y \neq \theta$, there is a $z \in K$ such that $z \neq \theta$ and $z \le x_0, z \le y$.

Observe that the definition of weak order unit given here agrees with that introduced in (4.23) of Chapter 2 when the underlying space is a vector lattice.

4.2 Proposition. Consider the following assertions concerning an element x_0 in the positive cone K of an ordered topological vector space $E(\mathfrak{T})$: (1) x_0 is a quasi-interior point of K, (2) x_0 is a nonsupport point of K, (3) x_0 is a weak order unit. Then:

a. (1) implies (2) in general.
b. If $E(\mathfrak{T})$ is a topological vector lattice, then (1) implies (3).
c. (2) implies (3) if E is an order complete vector lattice that is regularly ordered and if every positive linear functional on $E(\mathfrak{T})$ is continuous; moreover, if E is also minimal, then (2) is equivalent to (3).
d. (3) implies (1) if E is regularly ordered, E is a full subset of E^{++}, and $\mathfrak{T}$ is coarser than the order topology on E.

Proof. (a) follows immediately from the fact that if H is a closed hyperplane of support to K then

$$H = \{x \in E : f(x) = 0\}$$

for some nonzero, continuous, positive linear functional f on E ($\mathfrak{T}$).

To prove (b), suppose that x_0 is a quasi-interior point of K and that $\inf\{x_0, |y|\} = \theta$ for some $y \in E$. Then $y \perp z$ for all $z \in [\theta, x_0]$; hence, y is disjoint from each element of the closure of the linear hull of $[\theta, x_0]$ since the lattice operations in $E(\mathfrak{T})$ are continuous. Therefore, $y = \theta$, that is, x_0 is a weak order unit.

Now suppose that the conditions imposed in the first assertion of (c) are satisfied by E and let x_0 be a nonsupport point of K. Define M to be the band generated by x_0; then, if $M \neq E$, there is a nonzero positive linear functional f_0 on $M^\perp$ since $M^\perp$ is regularly ordered. It follows that there is a nonzero positive linear functional f on E that vanishes on M. This contradicts the fact that x_0 is a nonsupport of K since every positive linear functional on $E(\mathfrak{T})$ is continuous. Therefore, $M = E$, that is, x_0 is a weak order unit in E. On the other hand, if E is minimal and x_0 is a weak order unit, then the band generated by x_0 is E. Therefore, to conclude that x_0 is a nonsupport point of K, it would suffice to show that if $y \in K$ and if f is a positive linear functional on E for which $f(y) = 0$, then f vanishes on the band M in E generated by y. According to (4.9) of Chapter 1, each element of the cone in M is the supremum of a set C that is majorized in E and consists of elements of the cone majorized by multiples of y. Since f is a positive linear functional and $f(y) = 0$, it follows that f vanishes on any set C of this sort. Moreover, if $D(C)$ denotes the set of all suprema of finite subsets of C, then the filter of sections of $D(C)$ converges to sup (C) for the order topology $\mathfrak{T}_0$ since E is minimal (see (1.26) of Chapter 4). Since f is continuous for $\mathfrak{T}_0$, we have $f\big(\sup (C)\big) = 0$. Therefore, f vanishes on M, which completes the proof of (c).

To prove (d), suppose that x_0 is a weak order unit, then the band M in E^{++} generated by x_0 obviously contains E. Also, the linear hull M_0 of the order interval $[\theta, x_0]$ in E^{++} is dense in M for $\sigma(M, E^+)$ (see the proof of (c)). But M_0 is contained in E since E is a full subset of E^{++}; consequently, M_0 is a dense linear subspace of $E(\mathfrak{T}_0)$. In view of the fact that $\mathfrak{T}$ is coarser than $\mathfrak{T}_0$, it follows that M_0 is dense in $E(\mathfrak{T})$; that is, x_0 is a quasi-interior point of K.

The following result relates the concepts introduced in (4.1) to the stronger notions of order unit and interior point.

4.3 Proposition. If x_0 is an order unit in an ordered topological vector space $E(\mathfrak{T})$, then x_0 is a quasi-interior point of K, a nonsupport point of K, and a weak order unit. Moreover, if K has a nonempty interior, the concepts of interior point, order unit, quasi-interior point and nonsupport point all coincide.

Proof. The first assertion is obvious. To prove the second assertion of the proposition, it is only necessary to show that each nonsupport point x_0 of K is an interior point of K. Hence, suppose that x_0 is not an interior point of K. Then, since the interior of K is a convex body, there is a nonzero, continuous linear functional on $E(\mathfrak{T})$ such that $f(x) \geq 0$ for all $x \in K$ and $f(x_0) = 0$. But this contradicts the fact that x_0 is a nonsupport point of K; hence, x_0 must be an interior point of K.

4.4   Examples.   a. If λ is a sequence space equipped with its weak topology $\sigma(\lambda, \lambda^\times)$ and the order determined by the cone K of all elements in λ with non-negative components, and if $x \in K$, the following statements are equivalent:

(1) x is a quasi-interior point of K.
(2) x is a nonsupport point of K.
(3) x is a weak order unit.
(4) $x_n > 0$ for all n.

In fact, (4.2) shows that (1) implies (2). If x is a nonsupport point of K, suppose that $x_n = 0$ for some n. Then, the linear functional on λ determined by the element $e^{(n)} \in \lambda^\times$ (where $e^{(n)} = (\delta_{nk} : k = 1, 2, \ldots)$) yields a hyperplane of support to K passing through x. Therefore $x_n > 0$ for all n; consequently, x is a weak order unit. If x is a weak order unit, then, for each integer n, there is a nonzero element $z^{(n)}$ in K such that $z^{(n)} \leq e^{(n)}$ and $z^{(n)} \leq x$. It follows that $x_n > 0$ for all n. Finally, if x is an element of λ such that $x_n > 0$ for all n, then the linear hull of $[\theta, x]$ contains φ, and φ is dense in λ for $\sigma(\lambda, \lambda^\times)$. Therefore, x is a quasi-interior point of K.

b.   In the sequence space ℓ^∞ of bounded sequences of real numbers ordered as in (a) and equipped with the norm

$$\|x\| = \sup_n \{|x_n|\}$$

the cone K has a nonempty interior. Therefore, by (4.3), the following statements concerning an element $x \in K$ are equivalent:

(1) x is a quasi-interior point of K.
(2) x is a nonsupport point of K.
(3) $\inf_n \{x_n\} > 0$.

Consequently, there are weak order units in ℓ^∞ that are not quasi-interior points or nonsupport points of K.

c. Suppose that (S, Σ, μ) is a σ-finite measure space and that $L^p(S, \Sigma, \mu)$ $(p \geq 1)$ is ordered by the cone K of functions in L^p that are non-negative μ-almost everywhere on S. If $L^p(S, \Sigma, \mu)$ is equipped with the norm

$$\|f\| = \left(\int_S |f|^p \, d\mu \right)^{1/p}$$

and if $f \in K$, the following assertions about f are equivalent:

(1) f is a quasi-interior point of K.
(2) f is a nonsupport point of K.
(3) f is a weak order unit.
(4) $f(t) > 0$ for almost all $t \in S$.

In fact, the equivalence of (1), (2), (3) is an immediate consequence of (4.2) since $L^1(S, \Sigma, \mu)$ is a lattice ideal in its order bidual by IV. 8.16 of Dunford-Schwartz [1] and (4.12) of Chapter 1.

If f satisfies (4) and if g is a function in K that is strictly positive on a set A of positive measure, define $B = \{t \in S : f(t) \leq 0\}$; then, $\mu(B) = 0$ and f and g are strictly positive on $A - B$. Therefore, $\inf \{f, g\} \neq \theta$, that is, f is a weak order unit in $L^p(S, \Sigma, \mu)$. On the other hand, if f is a weak order unit, then f cannot vanish on a set of finite positive measure. Consequently, f satisfies (4).

4.5 Proposition. The set K_q of quasi-interior points of the cone in an ordered topological vector space $E(\mathfrak{T})$ is either empty or dense in the cone K of $E(\mathfrak{T})$.

Proof. Suppose that $K_q \neq \phi$ and that $f \in E'$ has the property that $f(x) \geq 0$ for all $x \in K_q$. If $f \notin K'$, then there is an $x_0 \in \overline{K}$ such that $f(x_0) < 0$ $\big($see (1.19) of Chapter 2$\big)$. If $x \in K_q$, there is a $\mu_x > 0$ such that $f(x_0 + \mu_x x) < 0$ since f is continuous. But this contradicts the fact that $f(x) \geq 0$ for all $x \in K_q$ since $K + K_q \subset K_q$. Therefore, $f \in K'$; that is, the polars of K and K_q coincide. The conclusion now follows from the Bipolar Theorem.

4.6 Proposition. If $E(\mathfrak{T})$ is a separable, metrizable locally convex space ordered by a complete cone K such that $K - K$ is dense in

$E(\mathfrak{T})$, then K has quasi-interior points. If $E(\mathfrak{T})$ is also normable, the dual cone K' for K contains a quasi-interior point for $\sigma(E', E)$.

Proof. Choose an increasing sequence $\{p_n\}$ of seminorms generating the topology $\mathfrak{T}$ and a sequence $\{x_n\}$ that is dense in K. The sequence $\{z_k\}$ defined by

$$z_k = \sum_{n=1}^{k} \frac{1}{2^n} \frac{x_n}{p_n(x_n)}$$

is easily seen to be a Cauchy sequence in K. Since K is complete, the sequence $\{z_k\}$ converges to some element $z_0 \in K$. The linear hull of $[\theta, z_0]$ contains x_n for each n; consequently, z_0 is a quasi-interior point of K since $K - K$ is dense in $E(\mathfrak{T})$.

In addition, if $E(\mathfrak{T})$ is normable and if B is the unit ball in $E'(\beta(E', E))$, then $K' \cap B$ is separable for $\sigma(E', E)$. Moreover, $K' - K'$ is $\sigma(E', E)$-dense in E' by (1.19) of Chapter 2. Consequently, a construction similar to that used in the first part of the proof yields the conclusion that K' contains quasi-interior points for $\sigma(E', E)$.

In Section 3 of Chapter 1, we introduced the notion of a base for a cone and studied some of the basic algebraic features of these sets. We shall now resume this study briefly to consider some of the topological features of bases for cones. (2.13) of Chapter 2 is an example of an interesting consequence of a compactness restriction on the base for a cone. The following result provides a topological description of the class of ordered locally convex spaces for which the cone has a compact base.

4.7 Proposition. Suppose that $E(\mathfrak{T})$ is a locally convex space ordered by a closed cone K. K has a compact base if and only if K equipped with the induced topology has a neighborhood basis of θ consisting of compact sets.

Proof. If K has a compact base B, choose a continuous linear functional f on $E(\mathfrak{T})$ such that the hyperplane $H = \{x \in E : f(x) = 1\}$ separates B and $\{\theta\}$ and such that $\theta \notin H$. If $V_n = \left\{x \in E : f(x) \le \frac{1}{n}\right\}$ $(n = 1, 2, \ldots)$, then V_n is a closed neighborhood of θ in $E(\mathfrak{T})$.

Moreover, if B_n is the convex hull of $\left\{ \{\theta\} \cup \dfrac{1}{n} B \right\}$, then B_n is compact and $V_n \cap K = V_n \cap B_n$ for each positive integer n. Consequently, there is a neighborhood basis of θ in K consisting of compact sets.

On the other hand, suppose that V is a convex neighborhood of θ in $E(\mathfrak{X})$ such that $V \cap K$ is compact. Define D to be the boundary of $V \cap K$, then the closed convex hull C of D is a compact convex set. Consequently, all of the extreme points of C are in D; in particular, $\theta \notin C$. It follows that there is a continuous linear functional f on $E(\mathfrak{X})$ such that $H = \{x \in E : f(x) - 1\}$ separates C and $\{\theta\}$. Therefore, $B = \{x \in K : f(x) = 1\}$ is a compact base for K.

4.8 Proposition. Suppose that E is a regularly ordered vector space and that K is the positive cone in E. If E contains an order unit e, the dual cone K^* for K in E^b has a $\sigma(E^b, E)$-compact base.

Proof. The set $B = \{f \in K^* : f(e) = 1\}$ is clearly a base for K^*. Moreover, since $[-e, e]$ is a neighborhood of θ for the order topology on E, B is an equicontinuous set in E^b. Consequently, B is compact for $\sigma(E^b, E)$.

4.9 Notes. Freudenthal [1] first introduced the concept of a weak order unit in connection with his work concerning the integral representation of elements of a σ-order complete vector lattice. (Also, see Birkhoff [2].) His paper also includes the result corresponding to (4.6) for weak order units in Banach lattices. Kakutani [2] used weak order units (under the name of F-units) in his work on the representation of L-spaces. Klee [3] studied nonsupport points for convex sets, and he established an analog to (4.6) for these points.

The notion of a quasi-interior point was introduced independently by Fullerton [1] and Schaefer [4], and various parts of (4.2) and (4.3) were established in these papers. Quasi-interior points have played a basic role in the development of the spectral theory of positive linear operators. Schaefer [6] uses these points to define a class of positive linear operators that he calls the quasi-interior operators. Then, in [7], he shows that the spectrum of a quasi-interior operator has cyclic properties analogous to the irreducible non-negative matrix operators considered in the classical Perron-Froebenius Theorem in matrix theory.

Proposition (4.7) was established by Klee [3]. A number of further topological properties of bases can be found in Edwards [1] and Ellis [1], [3].

Other papers related to the subject matter of this section: Brainerd [1], Fullerton-Braunschweiger [1].

Appendix

===

Summary of Locally Convex Space Theory

For the convenience of the reader, we shall now summarize the definitions, notations, and some of the results from locally convex space theory that have been employed in the main body of the text. Further information concerning results stated here can be found, for example, in Bourbaki [1], Kelley-Namioka [1], Köthe [1], Robertson-Robertson [1], and Schaefer [1].

A **topological vector space** $E(\mathfrak{T})$ is a vector space E equipped with a topology $\mathfrak{T}$ for which the operations of addition and scalar multiplication in E are jointly continuous. If $E(\mathfrak{T})$ is a topological vector space, the mappings $\psi_{x_0} : E(\mathfrak{T}) \to E(\mathfrak{T})$ and $\varphi_{\lambda_0} : E(\mathfrak{T}) \to E(\mathfrak{T})$ defined for $x \in E$ by

$$\psi_{x_0}(x) = x_0 + x \qquad \varphi_{\lambda_0}(x) = \lambda_0 x$$

are homeomorphisms for each x_0 in E and each nonzero scalar λ_0. Therefore, the neighborhood system of x_0 is given by the class $\{\psi_{x_0}(W) : W \in \mathscr{W}\}$ where $\mathscr{W}$ is the neighborhood system of the zero element θ in $E(\mathfrak{T})$.

A **neighborhood basis** of a point x_0 in a topological space is a family $\mathscr{W}$ of neighborhoods of x_0 with the property that each neighborhood of x_0 contains a set in $\mathscr{W}$. If $E(\mathfrak{T})$ is a topological vector space, there is a neighborhood basis $\mathscr{W}$ of θ in $E(\mathfrak{T})$ such that

(1)   Given W_1, W_2 in $\mathscr{W}$, there is a W_3 in $\mathscr{W}$ such that W_3 is contained in $W_1 \cap W_2$.

(2)   If $W_1 \in \mathscr{W}$, there is a $W_2 \in \mathscr{W}$ such that $W_2 + W_2 \subset W_1$.

(3)   Each $W \in \mathscr{W}$ is **circled**, that is, if $x \in W$ and $|\lambda| \leq 1$, then $\lambda x \in W$.

(4)   Each $W \in \mathscr{W}$ is **radial**, that is, for each $x \in E$, there is a scalar $\lambda_x > 0$ such that $\lambda x \in W$ for all $|\lambda| \leq \lambda_x$.

Conversely, if $\mathscr{W}$ is any class of subsets of a vector space E satisfying (1)–(4), there is a unique topology $\mathfrak{T}$ on E such that $E(\mathfrak{T})$ is a topological vector space and $\mathscr{W}$ is a neighborhood basis of θ for $\mathfrak{T}$. Two topological vector spaces $E_1(\mathfrak{T}_1)$ and $E_2(\mathfrak{T}_2)$ are **isomorphic** if there is a linear homeomorphism of $E_1(\mathfrak{T}_1)$ onto $E_2(\mathfrak{T}_2)$. If A, B are subsets of a vector space E, then A **absorbs** B if there is a constant $\lambda_0 > 0$ such that $\lambda B \subset A$ for all scalars λ such that $|\lambda| \leq \lambda_0$. A subset A of E is **radial at** x_0 if $A - x_0$ absorbs each point of E. A subset B of a topological vector space $E(\mathfrak{T})$ is $\mathfrak{T}$-**bounded** (or **bounded**) if B is absorbed by each neighborhood of θ in $E(\mathfrak{T})$. B is bounded in $E(\mathfrak{T})$ if and only if $\{\lambda_n x_n\}$ converges to θ for $\mathfrak{T}$ whenever $\{x_n\} \subset B$ and $\{\lambda_n\}$ decreases to 0. A subset B of $E(\mathfrak{T})$ is **precompact** if the closure of B in the completion of $E(\mathfrak{T})$ is compact. Every precompact set is bounded and every Cauchy sequence is precompact.

If $E(\mathfrak{T})$ is a topological vector space and M is a linear subspace of $E(\mathfrak{T})$, then M is a topological vector space for the topology induced by $\mathfrak{T}$. Also, the quotient vector space E/M is a topological vector space for the topology on E/M determined by the neighborhood basis $\{\varphi(V) : V \in \mathscr{W}\}$ of the zero element, where φ is the canonical map of E onto E/M and $\mathscr{W}$ is a neighborhood basis of θ in $E(\mathfrak{T})$. We

shall refer to the topologies just mentioned as the **subspace topology**
on M and the **quotient topology** on E/M. The quotient topology on
E/M is a Hausdorff topology if and only if M is a closed linear subspace of $E(\mathfrak{T})$.

If the vector space E is a Hausdorff topological vector space for each
of the topologies $\mathfrak{T}_1$ and $\mathfrak{T}_2$, if $\mathfrak{T}_1$ is finer than $\mathfrak{T}_2$, and if there is a
neighborhood basis of θ for $\mathfrak{T}_1$ consisting of sets that are closed for $\mathfrak{T}_2$,
then each complete subset of $E(\mathfrak{T}_2)$ is complete in $E(\mathfrak{T}_1)$. Therefore,
if E is a Hausdorff topological vector space for both $\mathfrak{T}_1$ and $\mathfrak{T}_2$, if $\mathfrak{T}_1$
is finer than $\mathfrak{T}_2$, and if there is a neighborhood basis of θ for $\mathfrak{T}_1$
consisting of sets that are complete for $\mathfrak{T}_2$, then $E(\mathfrak{T}_1)$ is complete
(see, for example, pp. 11–12 in Chapter I of Bourbaki [1]).

If $\{E_\alpha(\mathfrak{T}_\alpha) : \alpha \in A\}$ is a family of topological vector spaces and if $\mathscr{U}_\alpha$
is a neighborhood basis of θ in $E_\alpha(\mathfrak{T}_\alpha)$ for each $\alpha \in A$, the class $\mathscr{U}$ of
all subsets V of the product space $E = \prod_{\alpha \in A} E_\alpha$ of the form $W = \prod_{\alpha \in A} W_\alpha$
$\left(\text{where } W_\alpha = E_\alpha \text{ for all } \alpha \in A \text{ except for a finite set } \{\alpha_1, \ldots, \alpha_n\} \subset A\right.$
and $\left. W_{\alpha_i} \in \mathscr{U}_{\alpha_i} (i = 1, 2, \ldots, n)\right)$ is a neighborhood basis of θ in E
for the **product topology** on E. The **topological direct sum topology** on
the linear subspace $F = \bigoplus_{\alpha \in A} E_\alpha$ of E is defined by the neighborhood

basis $\mathscr{W}$ of θ in F consisting of all sets of the form $\left(\prod_{\alpha \in A} V_\alpha\right) \cap F$
where $V_\alpha \in \mathscr{U}_\alpha$ for each $\alpha \in A$. The space $E = \prod_{\alpha \in A} E_\alpha$ (resp. $F = \bigoplus_{\alpha \in A} E_\alpha$)
equipped with the product topology (resp. the topological direct sum
topology) is a topological vector space called the **topological product**
(resp. **topological direct sum**) of the family $\{E_\alpha(\mathfrak{T}_\alpha) : \alpha \in A\}$.

If $E(\mathfrak{T})$ is a topological vector space, and if E^* is the **algebraic dual**
of E, that is, E^* is the collection of all linear functionals on E, the
linear subspace E' of E^* consisting of all continuous linear func-
tionals on $E(\mathfrak{T})$ is called the **dual** of $E(\mathfrak{T})$. If M is a linear subspace of
a topological vector space $E(\mathfrak{T})$, if $M \neq E$, and if M is not properly
contained in a proper linear subspace of E, then M is a **maximal
linear subspace** of E. If M is a maximal linear subspace of E and
$x_0 \in E$, the linear manifold $H = x_0 + M$ is a **hyperplane** in E (through
x_0). H is a hyperplane in E if and only if there is a nonzero linear functional $f \in E^*$ and a real number α such that $H = \{x \in E : f(x) = \alpha\}$.

H is closed if and only if $f \in E'$. If $H = \{x \in E : f(x) = \alpha\}$ is a closed hyperplane in $E(\mathfrak{T})$, the sets $S_1 = \{x \in E : f(x) > \alpha\}$, $S_2 = \{x \in E : f(x) < \alpha\}$ (resp. $\bar{S}_1 = \{x \in E : f(x) \geq \alpha\}$, $\bar{S}_2 = \{x \in E : f(x) \leq \alpha\}$) are called the **open semispaces** (resp. **closed semispaces**) determined by H. A hyperplane H **supports** a convex set A at $x_0 \in A$ if $x_0 \in H$ and A lies in one of the closed semispaces determined by H.

A Hausdorff topological vector space $E(\mathfrak{T})$ is metrizable if and only if it has a countable neighborhood basis of θ for $\mathfrak{T}$. A criterion for metrizability and normability of topological vector spaces is provided by Kolmogorov's Theorem: If $E(\mathfrak{T})$ is a Hausdorff topological vector space that contains a bounded (resp. bounded, convex) neighborhood of θ, then $E(\mathfrak{T})$ is metrizable (resp. normable). One form of the Open Mapping Theorem asserts that if T is a continuous mapping on a complete metrizable topological vector space $E(\mathfrak{T})$ with its range of second category in a Hausdorff topological vector space $F(\mathfrak{O})$, then T maps E onto F and T maps open sets in $E(\mathfrak{T})$ onto open sets in $F(\mathfrak{O})$. In particular, every one-to-one, continuous linear mapping of a complete metrizable topological vector space $E(\mathfrak{T})$ onto a Hausdorff topological vector space $F(\mathfrak{O})$ of second category is necessarily an isomorphism.

Proposition (Klee [4]). If $E(\mathfrak{T})$ is a metrizable topological vector, space ordered by a complete cone K and if $\mathscr{W} = \{W_n : n = 1, 2, \dots \}$ is a countable neighborhood basis of θ for $\mathfrak{T}$ consisting of closed, circled sets such that $W_{n+1} + W_{n+1} \subset W_n$, then the class

$$\mathscr{U} = \{V_n = (W_n \cap K - W_n \cap K) : n = 1, 2, \dots \}$$

is a neighborhood basis for a topology $\mathfrak{T}_K$ on the linear hull $E_K = K - K$ of K that is finer than the topology induced by $\mathfrak{T}$; moreover, $E_K(\mathfrak{T}_K)$ is a complete metrizable topological vector space. If $E(\mathfrak{T})$ is of second category and if K is a generating cone in E, then $\mathfrak{T}_K = \mathfrak{T}$.

Proof. It is clear that $\mathscr{U}$ is a neighborhood basis of θ in E_K for a metrizable topology $\mathfrak{T}_K$ on E_K finer than the topology induced by $\mathfrak{T}$; moreover, $V_{n+1} + V_{n+1} \subset V_n$ for each positive integer n. Suppose that $\{z_n\}$ is a Cauchy sequence in $E_K(\mathfrak{T}_K)$, then, without loss in generality, we can assume that $z_{n+1} - z_n \in V_n$ for each positive integer n. By definition of V_n, we can write

$$z_{n+1} - z_n = x_n - y_n; \quad x_n \in W_n \cap K, \, y_n \in W_n \cap K$$

for each positive integer n. The sequences

$$\left\{ \sum_{k=1}^{n} x_k : n = 1, 2, \ldots \right\}, \qquad \left\{ \sum_{k=1}^{n} y_k : n = 1, 2, \ldots \right\}$$

are Cauchy sequences in K for the uniform structure associated with $\mathfrak{T}$ since, for example,

$$\sum_{k=n+1}^{n+p} x_k \in W_{n+1} + \cdots + W_{n+p} \subset W_n \qquad n, p = 1, 2, \ldots$$

Let x and y denote the respective $\mathfrak{T}$-limits in K for these Cauchy sequences, then x and y are also the $\mathfrak{T}_K$-limits of these sequences by definition of $\mathfrak{T}_K$. Therefore, the sequence $\{z_n\}$ converges for $\mathfrak{T}_K$ to the limit $z_1 + x - y$, that is, $E_K(\mathfrak{T}_K)$ is complete.

If K is generating, then $E_K = E$ and the identity mapping of $E(\mathfrak{T}_K)$ onto $E(\mathfrak{T})$ is continuous. Therefore, by the Open Mapping Theorem, the identity mapping is an isomorphism, that is, $\mathfrak{T}_K = \mathfrak{T}$ which completes the proof of the proposition.

If there is a neighborhood basis of θ in a topological vector space $E(\mathfrak{T})$ consisting of convex, circled sets, then $\mathfrak{T}$ is a **locally convex topology**. A topology $\mathfrak{T}$ on a vector space E is a locally convex topology if and only if there is a family $\{p_\alpha : \alpha \in A\}$ of functionals p_α defined on E with values in the non-negative real numbers such that:

a. For each $\alpha \in A$, p_α is a **seminorm**, that is $p_\alpha(x + y) \leq p_\alpha(x) + p_\alpha(y)$; $p_\alpha(\lambda x) = |\lambda| p_\alpha(x)$ for all x, y in E and all λ.

If, for each positive integer n, the set $V_{\alpha n}$ is defined by $V_{\alpha n} = \left\{ x \in E : p_\alpha(x) \leq \dfrac{1}{n} \right\}$,

b. the class $\mathscr{W}$ of all intersections of finite subclasses of the class

$$\mathscr{U} = \{ W_{\alpha n} : \alpha \in A, n = 1, 2, \ldots \}$$

is a neighborhood basis of θ in $E(\mathfrak{T})$.

In this case, we say that the locally convex topology $\mathfrak{T}$ is **generated** by the family $\{p_\alpha : \alpha \in A\}$ of seminorms on E. The set $V_{\alpha 1}$ is called the **gauge set** of the seminorm p_α. If V is a convex, radial, circled set in a vector space E, then the functional p_V defined on E by

$$p_V(x) = \inf \{\lambda > 0 : x \in \lambda V\}$$

is a seminorm called the **Minkowski functional** of V.

If $\mathfrak{T}$ is a Hausdorff locally convex topology on E, then $E(\mathfrak{T})$ is a **locally convex space**. In this case, the dual E' of E separates points of E, that is, if $\theta \neq x \in E$, there is an $f \in E'$ such that $f(x) \neq 0$.

A locally convex space $E(\mathfrak{T})$ is **bornological** if every convex, circled set that absorbs each bounded set in $E(\mathfrak{T})$ is a neighborhood of θ. A locally convex space $E(\mathfrak{T})$ is bornological if and only if every linear mapping of $E(\mathfrak{T})$ into a locally convex space $F(\mathfrak{D})$ that maps each $\mathfrak{T}$-bounded set into an $\mathfrak{D}$-bounded set is continuous. Every metrizable locally convex space, in particular, every normed space, is bornological. A locally convex space $E(\mathfrak{T})$ is a **barreled space** if each closed, convex, circled, radial subset of $E(\mathfrak{T})$ is a neighborhood of θ. If $E(\mathfrak{T})$ is a locally convex space of second category, in particular, if $E(\mathfrak{T})$ is a complete metrizable locally convex space, then $E(\mathfrak{T})$ is a barreled space. A locally convex space $E(\mathfrak{T})$ is **quasicomplete** if every closed bounded subset of $E(\mathfrak{T})$ is complete. Each complete locally convex space is quasicomplete, and each quasicomplete locally convex space is sequentially complete. If $E(\mathfrak{T})$ is a quasicomplete, bornological space, then $E(\mathfrak{T})$ is a barreled space.

Every linear subspace of a locally convex space is a locally convex space. If $E(\mathfrak{T})$ is a locally convex space and M is a closed subspace of $E(\mathfrak{T})$, then the quotient space E/M is a locally convex space for the quotient topology. The product (resp. topological direct sum) of any family of locally convex spaces is a locally convex space. An interesting topology on the direct sum of a family $\{E_\alpha(\mathfrak{T}_\alpha) : \alpha \in I\}$ of locally convex spaces that may be distinct from the topological direct sum topology is the so-called **locally convex direct sum topology**. This topology is defined to be the finest locally convex topology $\mathfrak{T}$ on $E = \bigoplus_{\alpha \in I} E_\alpha$ for which all of the canonical embedding mappings

$f_\alpha : E_\alpha(\mathfrak{T}_\alpha) \to E(\mathfrak{T})$ ($\alpha \in I$) are continuous. If $\mathscr{W}_\alpha$ is a neighborhood basis of θ in $E_\alpha(\mathfrak{T}_\alpha)$ consisting of convex, circled sets, then a neighborhood basis of θ in E for the locally convex direct sum topology is given by the class of all sets of the form:

$$V = \text{convex circled hull} \left\{ \bigcup_{\alpha \in I} f_\alpha(V_\alpha) \right\}$$

where $V_\alpha \in \mathscr{W}_\alpha$. The locally convex direct sum topology is finer than the topological direct sum topology in general, but these two topologies coincide for countable families of locally convex spaces.

Suppose that $\{E_\alpha(\mathfrak{T}_\alpha) : \alpha \in I\}$ is an indexed family of locally convex spaces such that, if $\alpha \in I, \beta \in I, \alpha \le \beta$, there is a continuous linear mapping $f_{\alpha\beta}$ of $E_\beta(\mathfrak{T}_\beta)$ into $E_\alpha(\mathfrak{T}_\alpha)$. Define E to be the (closed) linear subspace of $\prod_{\alpha \in I} E_\alpha(\mathfrak{T}_\alpha)$ consisting of all elements $x = (x_\alpha : \alpha \in I)$ $\in \prod_{\alpha \in I} E_\alpha$ such that $f_{\alpha\beta}(x_\beta) = x_\alpha$ whenever α, β are in I and $\alpha \le \beta$. If E is equipped with the topology $\mathfrak{T}$ induced by the product topology, then $E(\mathfrak{T})$ is the **projective limit** of the family $\{E_\alpha(\mathfrak{T}_\alpha) : \alpha \in I\}$ of locally convex spaces with respect to the family $\{f_{\alpha\beta} : \alpha \in I, \beta \in I, \alpha \le \beta\}$ of linear mappings. If f_α is the linear mapping of E into E_α that is defined at $x = (x_\alpha : \alpha \in I) \in E$ by $f_\alpha(x) = x_\alpha$, then $\mathfrak{T}$ is the coarsest locally convex topology on E for which each $f_\alpha(\alpha \in I)$ is continuous, that is, $\mathfrak{T}$ is the **projective topology** on E with respect to the family $\{E_\alpha(\mathfrak{T}_\alpha) : \alpha \in I\}$ of locally convex spaces and the family $\{f_\alpha : \alpha \in I\}$ of linear mappings. Since E is a closed subspace of $\prod_{\alpha \in I} E_\alpha(\mathfrak{T}_\alpha)$, $E(\mathfrak{T})$ is complete (resp. quasicomplete) if each $E_\alpha(\mathfrak{T}_\alpha)(\alpha \in I)$ is complete (resp. quasicomplete).

Dually, suppose that $\{E_\alpha(\mathfrak{T}_\alpha) : \alpha \in I\}$ is an indexed family of locally convex spaces such that, if $\alpha \in I, \beta \in I, \alpha \le \beta$, there is a continuous linear mapping $f_{\alpha\beta}$ of $E_\alpha(\mathfrak{T}_\alpha)$ into $E_\beta(\mathfrak{T}_\beta)$. Define E to be the quotient space of the locally convex direct sum $\bigoplus_{\alpha \in I} E_\alpha(\mathfrak{T}_\alpha)$ with respect to the linear subspace M spanned by the ranges of the linear mappings $\{f_\alpha - f_\beta \circ f_{\alpha\beta} : \alpha \in I, \beta \in I, \alpha \le \beta\}$ (where f_α denotes the canonical embedding of E_α into $\bigoplus_{\alpha \in I} E_\alpha$ for each $\alpha \in I$). If M is closed, the vector space E equipped with the quotient topology is called the **inductive limit** of the family $\{E_\alpha(\mathfrak{T}_\alpha) : \alpha \in I\}$ of locally convex spaces with respect to linear mappings $\{f_{\alpha\beta} : \alpha \in I, \beta \in I, \alpha \leq \beta\}$.

A particularly important special case of the preceding construction concerns the situation in which the family $\{E_\alpha : \alpha \in I\}$ is a family of linear subspaces of a vector space E such that $E = \bigcup_{\alpha \in I} E_\alpha$ and $E_\alpha \subset E_\beta$ whenever $\alpha \leq \beta$ for α, β in I. In this case, if each $E_\alpha(\mathfrak{T}_\alpha)$ is a locally convex space, the requirement that the canonical embedding mapping $f_{\alpha\beta} : E_\alpha(\mathfrak{T}_\alpha) \to E_\beta(\mathfrak{T}_\beta)$ be continuous is equivalent to the assumption that $\mathfrak{T}_\beta$ induces a topology on E_α that is coarser than the topology $\mathfrak{T}_\alpha$. Moreover, if g_α denotes the canonical embedding mapping of E_α into E and if $\mathfrak{T}$ is the finest locally convex topology on E for which each $g_\alpha : E_\alpha(\mathfrak{T}_\alpha) \to E(\mathfrak{T})$ is continuous (that is, $\mathfrak{T}$ is the **inductive topology** on E with respect to the family $\{E_\alpha(\mathfrak{T}_\alpha) : \alpha \in I\}$ of linear subspaces of E), then $\mathfrak{T}$ coincides with the topology on the inductive limit of $\{E_\alpha(\mathfrak{T}_\alpha) : \alpha \in I\}$ with respect to the family $\{f_{\alpha\beta} : \alpha \in I, \beta \in I, \alpha \leq \beta\}$ of linear mappings, provided $\mathfrak{T}$ is a Hausdorff topology. A linear mapping T of $E(\mathfrak{T})$ into a locally convex space $F(\mathfrak{D})$ is continuous if and only if the restriction of T to each $E_\alpha(\mathfrak{T}_\alpha)(\alpha \in I)$ is continuous.

A **sublinear functional** on a vector space E is a real-valued function p defined on E such that $p(x + y) \leq p(x) + p(y)$ and $p(\lambda x) = \lambda p(x)$ for all x, y in E and all $\lambda \geq 0$. The Hahn-Banach Theorem asserts that if p is a sublinear functional on a real vector space E and if f is a linear functional defined on a linear subspace M of E such that $f(x) \leq p(x)$ for all $x \in M$, then there is an extension $\hat{f}$ of f defined on E such that $\hat{f}(x) \leq p(x)$ for all $x \in E$. This result implies the following " geometric form " of the Hahn-Banach Theorem: If A is a convex open set in a topological vector space $E(\mathfrak{T})$ and if M is a linear manifold in E (that is, M is a translate of a linear subspace of E) such that $M \cap A = \phi$, then there is a closed hyperplane H in $E(\mathfrak{T})$ such that $H \supset M$ and $H \cap A = \phi$. This result in turn can be used to establish the following separation theorems: If A, B are disjoint, nonempty, convex sets in a topological vector space $E(\mathfrak{T})$ and if A is an open set, then there is a closed hyperplane H that **separates** A and B, that is, there exist a real number α and a nonzero, continuous linear functional f such that $H = \{x \in E : f(x) = \alpha\}$ and $f(a) \geq \alpha$ for all $a \in A$ while $f(b) \leq \alpha$ for all $b \in B$. Moreover, if B is also open, the hyperplane H **strictly separates** A and B, that is, $f(a) > \alpha$ for all $a \in A$ while $f(b) < \alpha$ for all $b \in B$. If A and B are disjoint, nonempty, convex subsets of a locally convex space $E(\mathfrak{T})$, if A is compact, and if B is closed, then there is a closed hyperplane H strictly separating A and B.

An element x_0 of a convex set A is an **extreme point** of A if there do not exist y, z in A such that $x_0 = \frac{1}{2}y + \frac{1}{2}z$. The Krein-Milman Theorem asserts that each compact, convex set A in a locally convex space $E(\mathfrak{T})$ coincides with the closed, convex hull of the set Ext (A) of extreme points of A. Moreover, if $S \subset A$, then the closure of S contains Ext (A) if and only if sup $\{f(x) : x \in S\} = $ sup $\{f(x) : x \in A\}$ for each $f \in E'$. A "converse" to the Krein-Milman Theorem is also valid: Suppose that $E(\mathfrak{T})$ is a locally convex space and that K is a compact subset of $E(\mathfrak{T})$ whose closed convex hull C is compact, then every extreme point of C is in K.

Suppose that $F(\mathfrak{O})$ is a topological vector space and that $\mathfrak{S}$ is a class of subsets of a vector space E such that, if $S_1 \in \mathfrak{S}, S_2 \in \mathfrak{S}$, there is an $S_3 \in \mathfrak{S}$ such that $S_3 \supset S_1 \cup S_2$. For each $x \in E$, define F_x to be the vector space F, then $F^E = \prod_{x \in E} F_x$ is the vector space of all mappings of E into F. If $\mathcal{W}$ is a neighborhood basis of θ in $F(\mathfrak{O})$, if $V \in \mathcal{W}$, and if $S \in \mathfrak{S}$, let $N_0(S, V)$ be the subset of F^E defined by

$$N_0(S, V) = \{T \in F^E : T(S) \subset V\};$$

then the class $\{N_0(S, V) : S \in \mathfrak{S}, V \in \mathcal{W}\}$ is a neighborhood basis of θ in F^E for the **topology** $\mathfrak{T}_{\mathfrak{S}}$ **of uniform convergence on the sets in** $\mathfrak{S}$ or, more briefly, the $\mathfrak{S}$**-topology**. Though F^E is a topological group for the $\mathfrak{S}$-topology, it is not a topological vector space in general. If G is a linear subspace of F^E, then G is a topological vector space for the topology induced by the $\mathfrak{S}$-topology if and only if $T(S)$ is a bounded set in $F(\mathfrak{O})$ for all $T \in G, S \in \mathfrak{S}$. In particular, if G is the subspace $\mathcal{L}(E, F)$ of F^E consisting of all continuous linear mappings of a topological vector space $E(\mathfrak{T})$ into $F(\mathfrak{O})$, and if $\mathfrak{S}$ is a class of

$\mathfrak{X}$-bounded subsets of $E(\mathfrak{X})$, then $\mathscr{L}(E, F)$ is a topological vector space for the $\mathfrak{S}$-topology. A neighborhood basis $\mathscr{W}_{\mathfrak{S}}$ of θ for the $\mathfrak{S}$-topology on $\mathscr{L}(E, F)$ is given by the class of sets

$$N(S, V) = \{T \in \mathscr{L}(E, F) : T(S) \subset V\} \qquad (S \in \mathfrak{S}; V \in \mathscr{W})$$

If V is convex, then $N(S, V)$ is convex for each $S \in \mathfrak{S}$; hence, if $\mathfrak{S}$ is a class of bounded subsets of $E(\mathfrak{X})$, the $\mathfrak{S}$-topology on $\mathscr{L}(E, F)$ is a locally convex topology if the topology $\mathfrak{O}$ on F is a locally convex topology. Also, if $F(\mathfrak{O})$ is a Hausdorff topological vector space and if the linear hull of $\left(\bigcup_{S \in \mathfrak{S}} S \right)$ is dense in $E(\mathfrak{X})$, then the $\mathfrak{S}$-topology on $\mathscr{L}(E, F)$ is a Hausdorff topology. It is sometimes possible to enlarge the class $\mathfrak{S}$ without altering the corresponding $\mathfrak{S}$-topology. In fact, if $\overline{\mathfrak{S}}$ is the class of all subsets of multiples of the closed, convex, circled hulls of unions of finite subclasses of $\mathfrak{S}$, then the $\overline{\mathfrak{S}}$-topology coincides with the $\mathfrak{S}$-topology. $\overline{\mathfrak{S}}$ is called the **saturated hull** of the class $\mathfrak{S}$; if $\mathfrak{S} = \overline{\mathfrak{S}}$, then $\mathfrak{S}$ is said to be **saturated**.

The space $\mathscr{L}(E, F)$ equipped with the $\mathfrak{S}$-topology will be denoted by $\mathscr{L}_{\mathfrak{S}}(E, F)$. If $\mathfrak{S}$ is the class of all bounded subsets of $E(\mathfrak{X})$ (resp. if $\mathfrak{S}$ is the class of all finite subsets of E), the corresponding $\mathfrak{S}$-topology is called the **topology of bounded convergence** (resp. the **topology of pointwise convergence**) on $\mathscr{L}(E, F)$.

A subset $\mathscr{B}$ of $\mathscr{L}_{\mathfrak{S}}(E, F)$ is bounded if and only if $\bigcup_{T \in \mathscr{B}} T(S)$ is bounded in $F(\mathfrak{O})$ for each $S \in \mathfrak{S}$. A subset $\mathscr{B}$ of $\mathscr{L}(E, F)$ is bounded for the topology of pointwise convergence if and only if it is bounded for the $\mathfrak{S}$-topology corresponding to the class $\mathfrak{S}$ of all complete, bounded, convex, circled subsets of $E(\mathfrak{X})$. In particular, the following Principle of Uniform Boundedness is valid: If $E(\mathfrak{X})$, $F(\mathfrak{O})$ are locally convex spaces and if $E(\mathfrak{X})$ is quasicomplete, then the bounded subsets of $\mathscr{L}(E, F)$ are the same for all $\mathfrak{S}$-topologies determined by a class $\mathfrak{S}$ of bounded subsets of $E(\mathfrak{X})$ for which $E = \cup \{S : S \in \mathfrak{S}\}$. A subset $\mathscr{H}$ of $\mathscr{L}(E, F)$ is **equicontinuous** if, for each neighborhood W of θ in $F(\mathfrak{O})$, there is a neighborhood V of θ in $E(\mathfrak{X})$ such that $\bigcup_{T \in \mathscr{H}} T(V) \subset W$. If $\mathscr{H}$ is an equicontinuous subset of $\mathscr{L}(E, F)$, then $\mathscr{H}$ is bounded for each $\mathfrak{S}$-topology on $\mathscr{L}(E, F)$. On the other hand, if

$E(\mathfrak{T})$ is a barreled space and $F(\mathfrak{D})$ is a locally convex space, every subset of $\mathscr{L}(E, F)$ that is bounded for the topology of pointwise convergence is equicontinuous. Under the same assumptions on $E(\mathfrak{T})$ and $F(\mathfrak{D})$, this result yields the following form of the Banach-Steinhaus Theorem: If $\{T_\alpha : \alpha \in I\}$ is a net in $\mathscr{L}(E, F)$ such that some section of $\{T_\alpha : \alpha \in I\}$ is bounded for the topology of pointwise convergence, and if, for each $x \in E$, the net $\{T_\alpha x : \alpha \in I\}$ converges to an element $y(x) \in F(\mathfrak{D})$, then the mapping $T_0 : E \to F$ defined for each $x \in E$ by $T_0 x = y(x)$ belongs to $\mathscr{L}(E, F)$ and $\{T_\alpha : \alpha \in I\}$ converges to T_0 for the topology of uniform convergence on all precompact subsets of $E(\mathfrak{T})$.

If E, F are vector spaces over the real field and if $(x, y) \to \langle x, y \rangle$ is a real-valued bilinear functional defined on $E \times F$ such that

(1) $\langle x_0, y \rangle = 0$ for all $y \in F$ implies $x_0 = \theta$,
(2) $\langle x, y_0 \rangle = 0$ for all $x \in E$ implies $y_0 = \theta$,

then E and F are **in duality** with respect to the bilinear functional, and we refer to the triple $\{E, F, (x, y) \to \langle x, y \rangle\}$ as a **dual system** $\langle E, F \rangle$ (with respect to the bilinear functional $(x, y) \to \langle x, y \rangle$). If $\langle E, F \rangle$ is a dual system with respect to the bilinear functional $(x, y) \to \langle x, y \rangle$, then the real-valued functions g_x and f_y defined by

$$f_y(x) = \langle x, y \rangle \qquad g_x(y) = \langle x, y \rangle$$

are linear functionals on E and F, respectively. Thus, E may be identified with a linear subspace of the algebraic dual F^* of F, and F may be regarded as a linear subspace of E^*. The **weak topology** $\sigma(E, F)$ on E (with respect to F) is the coarsest locally convex topology on E for which each $f_y(y \in F)$ is continuous. $\sigma(E, F)$ is the topology of pointwise convergence on $\mathscr{L}(F, R)$, and $\sigma(E, F)$ is generated by the family $\{p_y : y \in F\}$ of seminorms defined for each $x \in E$ by

$$p_y(x) = |\langle x, y \rangle|$$

If E is equipped with $\sigma(E, F)$, the dual space can be identified with F. The weak topology $\sigma(F, E)$ on F with respect to E is defined in a similar way.

If $\langle E, F \rangle$ is a dual system and if A is a subset of E, the **polar** A° (resp. the **absolute polar** A_{ab}°) of A is the subset of F defined by $A^\circ = \{y \in F : \langle x, y \rangle \leq 1 \text{ for all } x \in A\}$ (resp. $A_{ab}^\circ = \{y \in F : |\langle x, y \rangle| \leq 1 \text{ for all } x \in A\}$). The polar and absolute polar of a subset of F is defined in a similar way. The absolute polar of a set A coincides with the polar of the circled hull of A. The Bipolar Theorem asserts that the polar $(A^\circ)^\circ$ of the polar A° of a subset A of E coincides with the $\sigma(E, F)$-closed, convex, hull of $(A \cup \{\theta\})$. Note that a neighborhood basis of θ for $\sigma(E, F)$ is provided by the class of the absolute polars of all finite subsets of F.

If $\mathfrak{S}$ is the class of all $\sigma(F, E)$-bounded subsets of F, the class of polars of all sets in $\mathfrak{S}$ is a neighborhood basis of θ in E for a locally convex topology $\beta(E, F)$ called the **strong topology** on E with respect to F. $\beta(E, F)$ is the topology of bounded convergence on $\mathscr{L}(F, R)$ when F is equipped with its weak topology $\sigma(F, E)$. A locally convex space $E(\mathfrak{T})$ is barreled if and only if $\mathfrak{T} = \beta(E, E')$.

If $\langle E, F \rangle$ is a dual system and $\mathfrak{T}$ is a Hausdorff locally convex topology on E, then $\mathfrak{T}$ is **consistent** with this dual system if F can be identified with $E(\mathfrak{T})'$ through the bilinear functional defining the duality between E and F. The class of all bounded subsets of E is the same for any topology consistent with the dual system $\langle E, F \rangle$. The Mackey-Arens Theorem asserts that a Hausdorff locally convex topology $\mathfrak{T}$ on E is consistent with the dual system $\langle E, F \rangle$ if and only if $\mathfrak{T}$ is the $\mathfrak{S}$-topology corresponding to a class $\mathfrak{S}$ of convex, circled $\sigma(F, E)$-compact subsets of F such that $F = \cup\{S : S \in \mathfrak{S}\}$. The finest consistent topology is called the **Mackey topology** $\tau(E, F)$ on E with respect to F. In particular, if $E(\mathfrak{T})$ is a locally convex space, then $\mathfrak{T}$ is the $\mathfrak{S}$-topology corresponding to the class of all equicontinuous subsets of F.

If $E(\mathfrak{T})$ is a locally convex space and E' is the dual of E, then E' equipped with $\beta(E', E)$ is called the **strong dual** of E, while E' equipped with $\sigma(E', E)$ is the **weak dual** of E. Every equicontinuous subset of the weak dual of a locally convex space E is relatively compact. (This result implies the classical Alaoglu Theorem for normed spaces.) The weak dual of a barreled space is quasicomplete.

The dual of the strong dual of E is called the **bi-dual** E'' of E. E can be canonically identified with a linear subspace of E''; in fact, the mapping $J : E \to E''$ defined for $x \in E$ by

$$Jx(x') = x'(x) \qquad x' \in E'$$

is a one-to-one linear mapping of E into E''. If J maps E onto E'', then $E(\mathfrak{T})$ is **semireflexive**. A locally convex space $E(\mathfrak{T})$ is semireflexive if and only if every $\sigma(E, E')$-bounded subset of E is $\sigma(E, E')$-relatively compact. A semireflexive space $E(\mathfrak{T})$ is **reflexive** if $\mathfrak{T} = \beta(E, E')$.

If $E(\mathfrak{T})$ and $F(\mathfrak{O})$ are locally convex spaces and if $T \in \mathcal{L}(E, F)$, then T is **compact** if T maps some neighborhood of θ in $E(\mathfrak{T})$ into a relatively compact set. If $F(\mathfrak{O})$ is quasicomplete and $T \in \mathcal{L}(E, F)$, then T is **nuclear** if T can be written in the form

$$Tx = \sum_{n=1}^{\infty} \lambda_n f_n(x) y_n \qquad (x \in E)$$

where $\{f_n\}$ is an equicontinuous subset of E', $\{y_n\}$ is a bounded sequence in $F(\mathfrak{O})$, and $\sum_{n=1}^{\infty} |\lambda_n| < +\infty$. Every nuclear mapping is compact. A locally convex space $E(\mathfrak{T})$ is **nuclear** if every continuous linear mapping of $E(\mathfrak{T})$ into any Banach space is nuclear. Every quasicomplete nuclear space is semireflexive.

Suppose that $\langle E_1, F_1 \rangle$ and $\langle E_2, F_2 \rangle$ are dual systems and that T is a linear mapping of E_1 into E_2. The linear mapping T^* of the algebraic dual E_2^* into the algebraic dual E_1^* defined at each $y^* \in E_2^*$ by

$$T^*y^*(x) = y^*(Tx) \qquad (x \in E_1)$$

is called the **algebraic adjoint** of T. T is continuous for $\sigma(E_1, F_1)$ and $\sigma(E_2, F_2)$ if and only if $T^*(F_2) \subset F_1$. If T is continuous for $\sigma(E_1, F_1)$ and $\sigma(E_2, F_2)$, the restriction T' of T^* to F_2 is the **adjoint** of T. T' is continuous for $\sigma(F_2, E_2)$ and $\sigma(F_1, E_1)$, and the adjoint of T' is T. The adjoint T' of T satisfies the following basic equation:

$$\langle Tx, y' \rangle = \langle x, T'y' \rangle \qquad (x \in E_1, y' \in E_2')$$

Consequently, if A, B are subsets of E_1, E_2 respectively, then $T(A) \subset B$ implies $T'(B^\circ) \subset A^\circ$; moreover, if A, B are weakly closed convex sets containing θ, then $T'(B^\circ) \subset A^\circ$ implies $T(A) \subset B$.

If $E(\mathfrak{T})$ and $F(\mathfrak{O})$ are locally convex spaces and if T is a linear mapping of $E(\mathfrak{T})$ into $F(\mathfrak{O})$, then:

a. The continuity of T for $\mathfrak{T}$ and $\mathfrak{O}$ implies the continuity of T for $\sigma(E, E')$ and $\sigma(F, F')$; the converse is also true if $\mathfrak{T} = \tau(E, E')$.

b. The continuity of T for $\sigma(E, E')$ and $\sigma(F, F')$ is equivalent to the continuity of T for $\tau(E, E')$ and $\tau(F, F')$. Moreover, the continuity of T for $\sigma(E, E')$ and $\sigma(F, F')$ implies the continuity of the adjoint T' for $\beta(F', F)$ and $\beta(E', E)$.

Bibliography

Amemiya, I.
1. A generalization of Riesz-Fischer's theorem, *J. Math. Soc. Japan*, **5**, 353–354 (1953).
2. On ordered topological linear spaces, *Proc. Inter. Symp. Linear Spaces, Israel Acad. Sci. and Hum.*, Jerusalem (1961).
3. On the unconditional convergence in semi-ordered linear spaces, *J. Fac. Sci. Hokkaido Univ.*, **13**, 54–59 (1956).

Amemiya, I. and Mori, T.
1. Topological structures in ordered linear spaces, *J. Math. Soc. Japan*, **9**, 131–142 (1957).

Ando, T.
1. On fundamental properties of a Banach space with a cone, *Pacific J. Math.*, **12**, 1163–1169 (1962).
2. Positive linear operators in semi-ordered linear spaces, *J. Fac. Sci. Hokkaido Univ.*, **13**, 214–228 (1957).

Aubert, K. E.
1. Convex ideals in ordered group algebras and the uniqueness of the Haar measure, *Math. Scand.*, **6**, 181–188 (1958).

Bauer, H.
1. Sur le prolongement des formes linéaires positives dans un espace vectoriel ordonné, *C. R. Acad. Sci.* (Paris), **244**, 289–292 (1957).

2. Eine Rieszsche Bandzerlegung im Räume der Bewertungen eines Verbandes, *Bayer. Akad. Wiss. München, Math. Nat. Kl.*, 1953, 89–117 (1954).
3. Über die Fortsetzung positiver Linearformen, *Bayer. Akad. Wiss. München, Math. Nat. Kl.*, 1957, 177–190 (1958).

Birkhoff, G.
1. On the structure of abstract algebras, *Proc. Camb. Phil. Soc.*, **31**, 433–454 (1935).
2. Lattice theory, revised edition, *Amer. Math. Soc. Coll. Pub.*, **25**, New York (1948).

Bishop, E. and de Leeuw, K.
1. The representation of linear functionals by measures on sets of extreme points, *Ann. Inst. Fourier* (Grenoble), **9**, 305–331 (1959).

Bonsall, F. F.
1. Extreme maximal ideals of a partially ordered vector space, *Proc. Amer. Math. Soc.*, **7**, 831–837 (1956).
2. Sublinear functionals and ideals in partially ordered vector spaces, *Proc. London Math. Soc.*, **4**, 402–418 (1954).
3. The decomposition of continuous linear functionals into nonnegative components, *Proc. Univ. Durham Phil. Soc.*, **13**, 6–11 (1957).
4. Endomorphisms of a partially ordered vector space without order unit, *J. London Math. Soc.*, **30**, 144–153 (1955).
5. Regular ideals of partially ordered vector spaces, *Proc. London Math. Soc.*, **6**, 626–640 (1956).

Bonsall, F. F. and Reuter, G. E. H.
1. A fixed point theorem for transition operators in an *L*-space, *Quart. J. Math.*, **7**, 244–248 (1956).

Bourbaki, N.
1. Espaces vectoriels topologiques, *Elém. de Math., Livre 5, Act. Sci. et Ind.*, No. 1189, 1229, *Hermann et Cie*, Paris (1953, 1955).
2. Intégration, *Elém. de Math., Livre 6, Act. Sci. et Ind.*, No. 1175, *Hermann et Cie*, Paris (1952).

Brainerd, B.
1. On the embedding of a vector lattice in a vector lattice with a weak unit, *Akad van Wet. Amsterdam, Series A*, **63**, 25–31 (1960); **64**, 318 (1961).

Braunschweiger, C. C.
1. A geometric construction of *L*-spaces, *Duke Math. J.*, **23**, 271–280 (1956).
2. Interior-like elements of the positive cone in L^p, *Arch. der Math.*, **17**, 459–461 (1966).
3. A geometric construction of the *M*-space conjugate to an *L*-space, *Proc. Amer. Math. Soc.*, **10**, 77–82 (1959).

Choquet, G.
1. Existance et unicité des representations intégrales dans les cones convexes, *C. R. Acad. Sci.* (Paris), **243**, 555–557, 699–702, 736–737 (1956).

Clarkson, J. A.
1. A characterization of *C*-spaces, *Ann. of Math.*, **48**, 845–850 (1947).

Cogburn, R. G.
1. Conditional probability operators, *Ann. Math. Stat.*, **33**, 634–658 (1962).

Cooke, R. G.
1. *Infinite matrices and sequence spaces*, Macmillan, London (1950).
2. *Linear operators*, Macmillan, London (1953).

Cunningham, F.
1. *L*-structure in *L*-spaces, *Trans. Amer. Math. Soc.*, **95**, 274–299 (1960).

Curtis, P. C.
1. Order and commutativity in Banach algebras, *Proc. Amer. Math. Soc.*, **9**, 643–646 (1958).

Day, M. M.
1. The spaces L^p with $0 < p < 1$, *Bull. Amer. Math. Soc.*, **46**, 816–823 (1940).
2. Normed linear spaces, *Ergeb. der Math.*, *Heft*, **21**, *Springer-Verlag*, Berlin-Göttingen-Heidelberg (1958).

de Leeuw, K. (see Bishop, E. and de Leeuw, K.)

DeMarr, R. E.
1. Order convergence in linear topological spaces, *Pacific J. Math.*, **14**, 17–20 (1964).
2. Partially ordered linear spaces and locally convex linear topological spaces, *Illinois J. Math.*, **8**, 601–606 (1964).

Dieudonné, J.
1. Sur les espaces de Köthe, *J. Analyse Math.*, **1**, 81–115 (1951).

Dilworth, R. P.
1. The normal completion of the lattice of continuous functions, *Trans. Amer. Math. Soc.*, **68**, 427–438 (1950).

Dixmier, J.
1. Sur un théorèm de Banach, *Duke Math. J.*, **15**, 1057–1071 (1948).

Dunford, N. and Schwartz, J.
1. *Linear operators*, Part 1, Interscience, New York (1958).

Edwards, D. A.
1. On the homeomorphic affine embedding of a locally compact cone into a Banach dual space endowed with the vague topology, *Proc. London Math. Soc.*, **14**, 399–414 (1964).

Edwards, R. E.
1. *Functional analysis*, Holt, Rinehart and Winston, New York (1965).

Ellis, A. J.
1. The duality of partially ordered normed linear spaces, *J. London Math. Soc.*, **39**, 730–744 (1964).
2. Perfect order ideals, *J. London Math. Soc.*, **40**, 288–294 (1965).
3. Linear operators in partially ordered normed vector spaces, *J. London Math. Soc.*, **41**, 323–332 (1966).

Fan, K.
1. On systems of linear inequalities and related systems, *Ann. of Math. Studies*, No. 38, 99–156, Princeton Univ. Press, Princeton, N. J. (1956).

Freudenthal, H.
1. Teilweise geordnete Moduln, *Proc. Akad. Wet. Amsterdam*, **39**, 641–651 (1936).

Fukamiya, M., Misonou, Y. and Takeda, Z.
1. On order and commutativity of B^*-algebras, *Tohoku Math. J.*, **6**, 89–93 (1954).

Fullerton, R. E.
1. Quasi-interior points of cones in a linear space, *ASTIA Doc.*, No. AD–120406 (1957).
2. A characterization of L-spaces, *Fund. Math.*, **38**, 127–136 (1951).

Fullerton, R. E. and Braunschweiger, C. C.
1. Quasi-interior points and the extension of linear functionals, *Math. Ann.*, **162**, 214–224 (1966).

Geba, K. and Semadeni, Z.
1. On the *M*-subspaces of the Banach spaces of continuous functions, *Zeszyty Nauk, Univ. Mickiewicza*, **25**, 53–68 (1960).

Gillman, L. and Jerison, M.
1. *Rings of continuous functions*, Van Nostrand, Princeton (1960).

Goffman, C.
1. Completeness in topological vector lattices, *Amer. Math. Monthly*, **66**, 87–92 (1959).
2. Compatible seminorms in a vector lattice, *Proc. Nat. Acad. Sci. U.S.A.*, **42**, 536–538 (1956).

Gordon, H.
1. Topologies and projections on Riesz spaces, *Trans. Amer. Math. Soc.*, **94**, 529–551 (1960).
2. Relative uniform convergence, *Math. Ann.*, **153**, 418–427 (1964).
3. Decomposition of linear functionals on Riesz spaces, *Duke Math. J.*, **27**, 597–606 (1960).
4. Measures defined by abstract L_p-spaces, *Pacific J. Math.*, **10**, 557–562 (1960).

Gordon, H. and Lorch, E. R.
1. The projection of a linear functional on the manifold of integrals, *Canadian J. Math.*, **9**, 465–474 (1957).

Grosberg, J. (see Krein, M. G. and Grosberg, J.)

Halperin, I. and Luxemburg, W. A. J.
1. The Riesz-Fischer theorem for function spaces and vector lattices, *Trans. Royal Soc. Canada*, **50**, 33–39 (1956).

Hardy, G. H., Littlewood, J. E., and Polya, G.
1. *Inequalities*, Camb. Univ. Press (1934).

Heider, L. J.
1. *T*-sets and abstract *L*-spaces, *Pacific J. Math.*, **7**, 1611–1618 (1957).
2. Lattice ordering on Banach spaces, *Proc. Amer. Math. Soc.*, **3**, 833–838 (1952).

Hustad, O.
1. Linear inequalities and positive extension of linear functionals, *Math. Scand.*, **8**, 333–338 (1960).
2. On positive and continuous extension of positive functionals defined over dense subspaces, *Math. Scand.*, **7**, 392–404 (1959).
3. Extension of positive linear functionals, *Math. Scand.*, **11**, 63–78 (1962).

Ito, T.
1. Remarks on completeness of the continuous function lattice, *J. Fac. Sci. Hokkaido Univ.*, **17**, 149–151 (1963).

Jerison, M. (see Gillman, L. and Jerison, M.)

Johnson, D. G. and Mack, J. E.
1. The Dedekind completion of $C(X)$ (to appear in *Pacific J. Math.*).

Kadison, R. V.
1. A representation theory for commutative topological algebra, *Amer. Math. Soc. Memoir*, No. 7, Providence (1951).
2. Order properties of bounded, self-adjoint operators, *Proc. Amer. Math. Soc.*, **2**, 505–510 (1951).

Kakutani, S.
1. Concrete representations of abstract M-spaces, *Ann. of Math.*, **42**, 994–1024 (1941).
2. Concrete representations of abstract L-spaces and the mean ergodic theorem, *Ann. of Math.*, **42**, 523–537 (1941).

Kantorovitch, L.
1. Sur les espaces semiordonnes linéaires et leurs applications a la théorie des opérations linéaires. *Doklady Akad. Nauk. SSSR*, **4**, 13–16 (1935).
2. Linear halbgeordnete Räume, *Mat. Sbornik*, **2**, 121–168 (1937).
3. Linear operations in semiordered spaces, *Math. Sbornik*, **7**, 209–280 (1940).
4. Sur la théorie générale des opérations dans les espaces semi-ordonnes, *Doklady Akad. Nauk. SSSR*, **11**, 283–286 (1936).

Kantorovitch, L., Vulih, B., and Pinsker, A.
1. Functional analysis in partially ordered spaces. *Indat. Tehn-Teor. Lit.*, Moscow-Leningrad (1950) (in Russian).

Kaplan, S.
1. On the second dual of the space of continuous functions, *Trans. Amer. Math. Soc.*, **86**, 70–90 (1957).
2. The second dual of the space of continuous functions. II, *Trans. Amer. Math. Soc.*, **93**, 329–350 (1959).
3. The second dual of the space of continuous functions. III, *Trans. Amer. Math. Soc.*, **101**, 34–51 (1961).

Karlin, S.
1. Positive operators, *J. of Math. and Mech.*, **8**, 907–937 (1959).

Kawai, I.
1. Locally convex lattices, *J. Math. Soc. Japan*, **9**, 281–314 (1957).

Kelley, J. L., Namioka, I. and co-authors
1. *Linear topological spaces*, Van Nostrand, Princeton (1963).

Kendall, D. G.
1. Simplexes and vector lattices, *J. London Math. Soc.*, **37**, 365–371 (1962).

Kist, J.
1. Locally *o*-convex spaces, *Duke Math. J.*, **25**, 569–582 (1958).
2. Indecomposable maximal ideals of a partially ordered vector space, *J. London Math. Soc.*, **36**, 436–438 (1961).

Klee, V. L.
1. Iteration of the "lin" operation for convex sets, *Math. Scand.*, **4**, 231–238 (1956).
2. Some new results on smoothness and rotundity in normed linear spaces, *Math. Ann.*, **139**, 51–63 (1959).
3. Convex sets in linear spaces, *Duke Math., J.*, **18**, 443–466 (1951).
4. Boundedness and continuity of linear functionals, *Duke Math. J.*, **22**, 263–269 (1955).

Komura, Y.
1. Some examples on linear topological spaces, *Math. Ann.*, **153**, 150–162 (1964).

Komura, Y. and Koshi, S.
1. Nuclear vector lattices, *Math. Ann.*, **163**, 105–110 (1966).

Koshi, S. (see Komura, Y. and Koshi, S.)

Köthe, G.
1. Topologische lineare Räume I, *Springer-Verlag*, Berlin-Göttingen-Heidelberg (1960).

Köthe, G. and Toeplitz, O.
1. Lineare Räume mit unendlichvielen Koordinaten und Ringe unendlicher Matrizen, *J. Reine Angew. Math.*, 171, 193–226 (1934).

Krein, M. G.
1. Propriétés fondamentales des ensembles coniques normaux dans l'espace de Banach, *Doklady Akad. Nauk. SSSR*, 28, 13–17 (1940).

Krein, M. G. and Grosberg, J.
1. Sur la decomposition des fonctionelles en composantes positives, *Doklady Akad. Nauk. SSSR*, 25, 723–726 (1939).

Krein, M. G. and Rutman, M.
1. Linear operators leaving invariant a cone in a Banach space, *Uspehi Mat. Nauk. SSSR*, 3, 3–95 (1948); also, *Amer. Math. Soc. Translation*, No. 26 (1950).

Krengel, U.
1. Über den Absolutbetrag stetiger linearer Operatoren und seine Anwendung auf ergodische Zerlegungen, *Math. Scand.*, 13, 151–187 (1963).
2. Remark on the modulus of compact operators. *Bull. Amer. Math. Soc.*, 72, 132–133 (1966).

Kuller, R. G.
1. Locally convex topological vector lattices and their representations, *Mich. Math. J.*, 5, 83–90 (1958).

Littlewood, J. E. (see Hardy, G. E., Littlewood, J. E., and Polya, G.)

Lorch, E. R. (see Gordon, H. and Lorch, E. R.)

Lorentz, G.
1. Über die Grenzwerte in Verbanden, *Math. Zeit.*, 51, 404–422 (1948).

Mack, J. (also see Johnson, D. G. and Mack, J.)
1. The order dual of the space of Radon measures, *Trans. Amer. Math. Soc.*, 113, 219–239 (1964).

Maltese, G.
1. Convex ideals and positive multiplicative forms in partially ordered algebras, *Math. Scand.*, **9**, 372–382 (1961).

Mazur, S. and Orlicz, W.
1. Sur les espaces métriques lineaires. II, *Studia Math.*, **13**, 137–179 (1953).

Moore, E. H.
1. On the foundations of a theory of linear integral equations, *Bull. Amer. Math. Soc.*, **18**, 334–362 (1912).

Mori, T. (see Amemiya, I. and Mori, T.)

Mullins, C. W.
1. Order continuous mappings on general Köthe spaces, *Dissertation*, Univ. of Illinois (1966).

Nachbin, L.
1. *Topology and order*, Van Nostrand, Princeton (1965).

Nakamuro, M.
1. Notes on Banach spaces. IX, *Tohoko Math. J.* **1**, 100–108 (1949).

Nakano, H.
1. Über das System aller stetigen Funktionen auf einem Topologischen Räum, *Proc. Imp. Acad.* (*Tokyo*), **17**, 308–310 (1941).
2. Modulared semiordered linear spaces, *Maruzen*, Tokyo (1950).
3. Linear topologies on semiordered linear spaces, *J. Fac. Sci. Hokkaido Univ.*, **12**, 87–104 (1953).
4. Modern spectral theory, *Maruzen*, Tokyo (1950).
5. Semiordered linear spaces, *Japan Soc. Prom. Sci.*, Tokyo (1955).

Nakano, K. and Shimogaki, T.
1. A note on the cut extension of *C*-spaces, *Proc. Japan Acad.*, **38**, 473–477 (1962).

Namioka, I. (also see Kelley, J. L. and Namioka, I.)
1. Partially ordered linear topological spaces, *Amer. Math. Soc. Memoir*, No. 24, Providence (1957).

Nef, W.
1. Über monotone Linearformen die im Lebesgueschen Sinne stetig sind, *Arch. Math.*, **8**, 334–335 (1957).
2. Monotone Linearformen auf teilgeordneten Vektorräume, *Monatsh. Math.*, **60**, 190–197 (1956).
3. Über die Fortsetzung monotoner Linearformen, *Math. Zeit.*, **66**, 129–142 (1956).

Orihara, M.
1. On regular vector lattices, *Proc. Imp. Acad.* (*Tokyo*), **18**, 525–529 (1942).

Orlicz, W. (see Mazur, S. and Orlicz, W.)

Peressini, A. L.
1. On topologies in ordered vector spaces, *Math. Ann.*, **144**, 199–223 (1961).
2. A note on abstract *M*-spaces, *Illinois J. Math.*, **7**, 118–120 (1963).
3. Concerning the order structure of Köthe sequence spaces, *Mich. Math. J.*, **10**, 409–415 (1963).
4. Concerning the order structure of Köthe sequence spaces. II, *Mich. Math. J.*, **11**, 357–364 (1964).

Peressini, A. L. and Sherbert, D. R.
1. Order properties of linear mappings on sequence spaces, *Math. Ann.*, **165**, 318–332 (1966).

Phelps, R. R.
1. *Lectures on Choquet's theorem*, Van Nostrand, Princeton (1966).

Pietsch, A.
1. Nukleare lokalkonvexe Räume, *Akademie-Verlag*, Berlin (1965).
2. Absolute Summierbarkeit in Vektorverbanden, *Math. Nachr.*, **26**, 15–23 (1963).

Pinsker, A. (see Kantorovitch, L., Vulih, B. and Pinsker, A.)

Polya, G. (see Hardy, G. H., Littlewood, J. E., and Polya, G.)

Ptak, V.
1. On a theorem of Mazur and Orlicz, *Studia Math.*, **15**, 365–366 (1956).

Reuter, G. E. H. (see Bonsall, F. F. and Reuter, G. E. H.)

Riedl, J.
1. Partially ordered locally convex vector spaces and extensions of positive continuous linear mappings, *Math, Ann.*, **157**, 95–124 (1964).

Riesz, F.
1. Sur la decomposition des opérations linéaires, *Atti. del Congresso Bologna*, **3**, 143–148 (1928).
2. Sur quelques notions fondamentales dans la theorie générale des opérations linéaires, *Ann. of Math.*, **41**, 174–206 (1940).

Roberts, G. T.
1. Order continuous measures, *Proc. Camb. Phil. Soc.*, **60**, 205–207 (1964).
2. Topologies in vector lattices, *Proc. Camb. Phil. Soc.*, **48**, 533–546 (1952).

Robertson, A. P. and Robertson, W. J.
1. *Topological vector spaces*, Cambridge Univ. Press (1964).

Rota, G. C.
1. An "alterneirende Verfahren" for general positive operators, *Bull. Amer. Math. Soc.*, **68**, 95–102 (1962).

Schaefer, H. H.
1. *Topological vector spaces*, Macmillan, New York (1966).
2. Halbgeordnete lokalkonvexe Vektorräume, *Math. Ann.*, **135**, 115–141 (1958).
3. Halbgeordnete lokalkonvexe Vektorräume. II, *Math. Ann.*, **138**, 259–286 (1959).
4. Halbgeordnete lokalkonvexe Vektorräume. III, *Math. Ann.*, **141**, 113–142 (1960).
5. On the completeness of topological vector lattices, *Mich. Math. J.*, **7**, 303–309 (1960).
6. Some spectral properties of positive linear operators, *Pacific J. Math.*, **10**, 1009–1019 (1960).
7. Spektraleigenschaften positiver Operatoren, *Math. Zeit.*, **82**, 303–313 (1963).
8. On the singularities of an analytic function with values in a Banach space, *Arch. Math.*, **11**, 40–43 (1960).

Semadeni, Z. (see Geba, K. and Semadeni, Z.)

Sherbert, D. R. (see Peressini, A. L. and Sherbert, D. R.)

Sherman, S.
1. Order in operator algebras, *Amer. J. Math.*, **73**, 227–232 (1951).

Shimogaki, T. (see Nakano, K. and Shimogaki, T.)

Silverman, R. J.
1. Means on semi-groups and the Hahn-Banach extension property, *Trans. Amer. Math. Soc.*, **83**, 222–237 (1956).
2. Invariant means and cones with vector interiors, *Trans. Amer. Math. Soc.*, **88**, 75–79 and 327–330 (1958).

Stone, M. H.
1. Boundedness properties in function lattices, *Canadian Math. J.*, **1**, 176–186 (1949).
2. A general theory of spectra. II, *Proc. Nat. Acad. Sci. U.S.A.*, **27**, 83–87 (1941).

Swong, K.
1. A representation theory of continuous linear maps, *Math. Ann.*, **155**, 270–291 (1964).

Toeplitz, O. (also see Köthe, G. and Toeplitz, O.)
1. Die linearen vollkommenen Räume der Funktionentheorie, *Comm. Math. Helv.*, **23**, 222–242 (1949).

Topping, D. M.
1. Vector lattices of self-adjoint operators, *Trans. Amer. Math, Soc.*, **115**, 14–30 (1965).

Tsuji, K.
1. W^*-algebras and abstract L-spaces, *Bull. Kyushu Inst. Tech.* (*Math., Nat. Sci.*), **3**, 11–13 (1957).

Veksler, A. I.
1. Linear structures with a sufficient set of maximal l-ideals, *Doklady Akad. Nauk. SSSR*, **150**, 715–718 (1964).

Vladimirov, D. A.
1. On the completeness of a partially ordered space, *Uspehi Mat. Nauk*, **15**, 165–172 (1960).

Vulih, B. (see Kantorovitch, L., Vulih, B. and Pinsker, A.)

Weston, J. D.
1. Convergence of monotonic sequences in vector spaces, *J. London Math. Soc.*, **32**, 476–477 (1957).
2. A topological characterization of *L*-spaces, *J. London Math. Soc.*, **32**, 473–476 (1957).
3. Relations between order and topology in vector spaces, *Quart. J. Math.*, **10**, 1–8 (1959).
4. The decomposition of a continuous linear functional into nonnegative components, *Math. Scand.*, **5**, 54–56 (1957).

Yamamuro, S.
1. Monotone completeness of semi-ordered linear spaces, *Pacific J. Math.*, **7**, 1715–1725 (1957).

Yosida, K.
1. Functional Analysis, *Springer-Verlag*, Berlin-Göttingen-Heidelberg (1965).

Yosida, K. and Hewitt, E.
1. Finitely additive measures, *Trans. Amer. Math. Soc.*, **72**, 46–66 (1952).

Zeller, K.
1. Theorie der Limitierungsverfahren, *Ergeb. der. Math.*, *Springer-Verlag*, Berlin-Göttingen-Heidelberg (1958).

Glossary and Index
of Special Symbols

219

Index

221